Cells Tissues Organs

in vivo, in vitro

Founded 1945 as 'Acta Anatomica' by R. Chambers, G. Glimstedt, T. Peterfi and G. Wolf-Heidegger
Continued 1962–1974 by E.A. Boyden, 1955–1980 by A. Delmas, 1972–1980 by F. Walberg, 1945–1980 by G. Wolf-Heidegger, 1981–1988 by R. O'Rahilly, Davis, Calif., 1989–1990 by G.E. Goslow, Jr., Providence, R.I., 1981–1992 by W. Lierse, Hamburg, since 1992 by H.-W. Denker, Essen, and A.W. English, Atlanta, Ga., continued 1999 as 'Cells Tissues Organs' by H.-W. Denker, Essen, and A.W. English, Atlanta, Ga.

KARGER

Printed in Switzerland on acid-free and non-aging paper (ISO 9706) by Reinhardt Druck, Basel

Appears monthly: 2 volumes per year (12 issues)

Guidelines for Authors

Cells
Tissues
Organs

Aims and Scope

Cells Tissues Organs is an international forum for communication among scientists interested in current research on functional morphology and morphogenesis at all levels of organization, from subcellular to macroscopy, with emphasis on humans and higher vertebrates. The journal offers rapid exchange of novel and significant information gained from experimental and theoretical investigations on all aspects that are pertinent to the formation and transformation of biological structure.

Topics of special interest include

Developmental and reproductive biology, cell biology, tissue engineering, artificial organs, in vitro systems and transplantation. Papers highlighting the links between structural and functional aspects are preferred.

Types of Papers

The journal publishes: (1) Original papers on experimental research. (2) Theoretical contributions. These will appear in the section 'Hypotheses and Concepts' and may include provocative hypotheses, provided that they are innovative, well founded and show promise for new avenues of research. (3) Reviews. Suggestions concerning reviews on current topics of high interest are welcome.

All manuscripts must be accompanied by a cover letter signed by all authors. Assurance should be given that the manuscript is not under simultaneous consideration by any other publication. Reported studies using animal and human subjects must have been approved by the appropriate institutional review boards.

Research on Human Pluripotent Stem Cells

Research involving human embryonic stem cells or embryonic germ cells must comply with the ISSCR 'Guidelines for the Conduct of Human Embryonic Stem Cell Research' **http://www.isscr.org/guidelines/ISSCRhESCguidelines2006.pdf** or an equivalent set of guidelines or applicable regulations. Confirmation of this should be included in the manuscript as well as in the cover letter.

Submission

Manuscripts to *Cells Tissues Organs* can now be submitted online! Detailed online submission instructions with a link to the submission website can be found at **www.karger.com/cto**. Before submitting your manuscript, you are encouraged to review the detailed guidelines at **www.karger.com/cto_guidelines** for specific directions as how to get a manuscript ready for submission. Should you have any problems with your submission or feel the need to submit the paper in a non-electronic form, please contact the editorial office:

S. Karger AG
Editorial Office 'Cells Tissues Organs'
Beatrice Brogli
Tel. +41 61 306 13 58
Fax +41 61 306 14 34
E-Mail cto@karger.ch

Mailing address for courier deliveries only:
Allschwilerstr. 10
CH–4055 Basel (Switzerland)

Conditions

All manuscripts are subject to peer review. Names, postal and e-mail addresses of four experts in the appropriate area of research should accompany each manuscript. At the Editors' discretion scientist(s) selected from this list may be invited to act as referee(s). Referees suggested should not be from the same institution as the author. Submission of an article for publication implies the transfer of the copyright from the author to the publisher upon acceptance. Accepted papers become the permanent property of *Cells Tissues Organs* and may not be reproduced by any means, in whole or in part, without the written consent of the publisher. It is the author's responsibility to obtain permission to reproduce illustrations, tables, etc. from other publications.

Format and Arrangement

Manuscripts should be written in English and be as concise as possible.

Title page: The first page of each paper should indicate the title, the authors' names, the institute where the work was conducted, and a short title for use as running head.
NB: Authors wishing to preserve the phonetic meaning of diacritics (PubMed reduces diacritics to their root characters) must spell their names accordingly when submitting manuscripts (e.g. Müller should be Mueller).

Full address: The exact postal address of the corresponding author complete with postal code must be given at the bottom of the title page. Please also supply phone and fax numbers, as well as e-mail address.

Key words: For indexing purposes provide a list of up to 5 key words.

Abstract: Each paper needs an abstract of a maximum of 250 words summarizing the essential new information communicated.

Subheadings: Introduction; Materials and Methods; Results; Discussion.

List of Abbreviations: Provide a list of the abbreviations used in your paper. Please list them on a separate page of the manuscript. The list will be printed as a footnote at the bottom of the first page of your article.

Footnotes: With the exception of the list of abbreviations, footnotes should be avoided. When essential, they are numbered consecutively and typed at the foot of the appropriate page.

Nomenclature: The nomenclature used should conform, wherever possible, to the current edition of the Nomina Anatomica (Terminologia Anatomica), Nomina Anatomica Veterinaria, or to the Nomina Anatomica Avium.

Tables and illustrations: Tables and illustrations (both numbered in Arabic numerals) should be prepared as separate files. Tables require a heading and figures a legend, prepared on a separate page. Please only use scale bars to indicate magnifications of the illustrations. Due to technical reasons, figures with a screen background should not be submitted. When possible, group several illustrations on one block for reproduction (max. size 180 × 223 mm) or provide crop marks. Each illustration must be labelled with its number and the author's name. B/w half-tone and color illustrations must have a final resolution of 300 dpi after scaling (final size), line drawings one of 800–1200 dpi. Figure files must not be embedded in a document file but submitted separately (see detailed instructions at **www.karger.com/cto**).

Color illustrations: During the review process, the decision will be made as to which color illustrations of a manuscript can be reproduced *free of charge*. Authors will be informed of this at the time of acceptance of their paper. Otherwise, these illustrations will be reproduced at the author's expense. Up to 6 color illustrations per page can be integrated into the text at the special price of CHF 800.– per page.

References: References in the text should be made by author's name followed by the year of publication, arranged chronologically, then alphabetically. When there are more than two authors, use the first author's name and et al. When references are made to more than one paper by the same author, published in the same year, designate them as a, b, c, etc. The list of references should include only those publications which are cited in the text. Material submitted for publication but not yet accepted may be cited in the text as 'unpublished data' but must not be included in the reference list. In the list of references, arrange references alphabetically listing all authors, then year of publication. Preferably, please cite all authors. Abbreviate journal names according to Index Medicus.

Examples
(a) Papers published in periodicals: Robinson, C.M., D. O'Dee, T. Hamilton, G.J. Nau (2010) Cytokines involved in interferon-γ production by human macrophages. J Innate Immun *2*: 56–65.
(b) Papers published only with DOI numbers: Konstantinou, G.N., P.J. Bousquet, T. Zuberbier, N.G. Papadopoulos: The longest wheal diameter is the optimal measurement for the evaluation of skin prick tests. Int Arch Allergy Immunol DOI: 10.1159/000250443.
(c) Monographs: Matthews, D.E., V.T. Farewell (2007) Using and Understanding Medical Statistics, ed 4, revised. Basel, Karger.
(d) Chapters published in edited books: Li, L., V. Boussiotis (2009) Control and regulation of peripheral tolerance in allergic infl ammatory disease: therapeutic consequences; in Blaser, K. (ed): T Cell Regulation in Allergy, Asthma and Atopic Skin Diseases. Chem Immunol. Basel, Karger, vol 94, pp 178–188.

Further details: Authors may consult the 'Guide to Writing Articles in English' by R. O'Rahilly (Acta Anat *131:* 1–2, 1988).

Digital Object Identifier (DOI)

S. Karger Publishers supports DOIs as unique identifiers for articles. A DOI number will be printed on the title page of each article. DOIs can be useful in the future for identifying and citing articles published online without volume or issue information. More information can be found at www.doi.org.

Author's Choice™

Karger's Author's Choice service broadens the reach of your article and gives all users worldwide free and full access for reading, downloading and printing at

KARGER

Fax +41 61 306 12 34
E-Mail karger@karger.ch
www.karger.com

The Guidelines for Authors are available at:
www.karger.com/cto_Guidelines

www.Karger.com. The option is available for a one-time fee of CHF 3000.–, which is a permissible cost in grant allocation. More information can be found at www.karger.com/authors_choice.

NIH-Funded Research

The U.S. National Institutes of Health (NIH) mandates under the NIH Public Access Policy that final, peer-reviewed manuscripts appear in its digital database within 12 months of the official publication date. As a service to authors, Karger submits the final version of your article on your behalf to PubMed Central. For those selecting our premium Author's Choice service, we will send your article immediately upon publishing, accelerating the accessibility of your work without the usual embargo. More details on NIH's Public Access Policy is available at http://publicaccess.nih.gov/FAQ.htm#a1

Self-Archiving

Karger permits authors to archive their pre-prints (i.e. pre-refereeing) or post-prints (i.e. final draft post-refereeing) on their personal or institution's servers, provided the following conditions are met: Articles may not be used for commercial purposes, must be linked to the publisher's version, and must acknowledge the publisher's copyright. Authors selecting Karger's Author's Choice feature, however, are also permitted to archive the final, published version of their article, which includes copyediting and design improvements as well as citation links.

Proofs

Unless indicated otherwise, proofs are sent to the corresponding author and should be returned with the least possible delay. Alterations made in proofs, other than the correction of printer's errors, are charged to the author.

E-pub First

All articles are published electronically ahead of print with a DOI number and are supplemented later with the definite reference of the printed version. The articles become available immediately after the authors' approval to publication, with the added advantage of being citable much earlier than in print. Authors can influence the time of appearance by promptly returning the proofs.

Reprints

Order forms and a price list are sent with the proofs. Orders submitted after the issue is printed are subject to considerably higher prices.

KARGER

Fax +41 61 306 12 34
E-Mail karger@karger.ch
www.karger.com

The Guidelines for Authors are available at: www.karger.com/cto_Guidelines

General Information

Cells Tissues Organs

ISSN Print Edition: 1422–6405
ISSN Online Edition: 1422–6421

Journal Homepage: www.karger.com/cto

Publication Data: 'Cells Tissues Organs' is published 12 times a year. Volumes 193–194, each with 6 issues, appear in 2011.

Subscription Rates: Subscriptions run for a full calendar year. Prices are given per year.

Personal subscription:

Print or Online	**Print+Online combined**
CHF 422.65	CHF 518.65
EUR 313.10	EUR 385.10
USD 394.90	USD 484.90

postage and handling (added to print and print+online)
CHF 78.60 Europe, CHF 117.– Overseas
EUR 58.80
USD 109.20

Institutional subscription:

Print or Online	**Print+Online combined**
CHF 3842.–	CHF 4226.–
EUR 2846.–	EUR 3130.–
USD 3590.00	USD 3950.00

postage and handling (added to print and print+online)
CHF 98.40 Europe, CHF 146.40 Overseas
EUR 73.20
USD 136.80

Airmail surcharge: CHF 99.60 / USD 93.60

Back Volumes and Single Issues: Information on availability and prices of single print issues and print or electronic back volumes can be obtained from Customer Service at *service@karger.ch.*

Bibliographic Indices: This journal is regularly listed in bibliographic services, including *Current Contents®* and PubMed/MEDLINE.

Photocopying: This journal has been registered with the Copyright Clearance Center (CCC), as indicated by the code appearing on the first page of each article. For readers in the US, this code signals consent for copying of articles for personal or internal use, or for the personal or internal use of specific clients, provided that the stated fee is paid per copy directly to
Copyright Clearance Center Inc.
222 Rosewood Drive
Danvers, MA 01923 (USA)
A copy of the first page of the article must accompany payment. Consent does not extend to copying for general distribution, for promotion, for creating new works, or for resale. In these cases, specific written permission must be obtained from the copyright owner,
S. Karger AG, P.O. Box
CH–4009 Basel (Switzerland).

Subscription Orders:
Orders can be placed at agencies, bookstores, directly with the Publisher

S. Karger AG
Medical and Scientific Publishers
P.O. Box
CH–4009 Basel
Switzerland
(for courier services only:
Allschwilerstrasse 10
CH–4055 Basel)
Tel. +41 61 306 11 11
Fax +41 61 306 12 34
E-Mail karger@karger.ch
www.karger.com

or further Karger offices or representatives:

France:
Librairie Medi-Sciences Sarl
36, bd de Latour-Maubourg
75007 Paris
France
Tél. +33 1 45 51 42 58
Fax +33 1 45 56 07 80
E-Mail librairie@medi-sciences.fr
www.medi-sciences.fr

Germany:
S. Karger GmbH
Postfach
79095 Freiburg
Deutschland
(Hausadresse: Wilhelmstrasse 20 A
79098 Freiburg)
Tel. +49 761 45 20 70
Fax +49 761 45 20 714
E-Post information@karger.de
www.karger.de

India, Bangladesh, Sri Lanka:
Medscience India
Plot No. 17, Yusuf Sarai Market
B.L. Glass Building, 2nd Floor
Sri Aurobindo Marg
New Delhi 110 016
India
Tel. +91 11 46029 633
Fax +91 11 46029 634
Cell phone +91 98 91052 128
E-Mail medsci.india@gmail.com

Japan:
Karger Japan, Inc.
Yushima S Bld. 3F
4-2-3, Yushima, Bunkyo-ku
Tokyo 113-0034
Japan
Tel. +81 3 3815 1800
Fax +81 3 3815 1802
E-Mail publisher@karger.jp

China, Taiwan and Malaysia:
Karger China
Suite 409, Apollo Building
1440 Central Yan An Road
Shanghai 200040
China
Tel. +86 21 6133 1861
Fax +86 21 6133 1862
E-Mail karger.ray@gmail.com

South America and Central America:
Cranbury International LLC
7 Clarendon Ave., Suite 2
Montpelier, VT 05602
USA
Tel. +1 802 223 6565
Fax +1 802 223 6824
E-Mail
eatkin@cranburyinternational.com
www.cranburyinternational.com

United Kingdom, Ireland:
S. Karger AG
c/o London Liaison Office
4 Rickett Street
London SW6 1RU
United Kingdom
Tel. +44 20 7386 0500
Fax +44 20 7610 3337
E-Mail uk@karger.ch

USA:
S. Karger Publishers, Inc.
26 West Avon Road
P.O. Box 529
Unionville, CT 06085
USA
Toll free: +1 800 828 5479
Tel. +1 860 675 7834
Fax +1 860 675 7302
E-Mail karger@snet.net

Change of Address:
Both old and new address should be sent to the subscription source.

KARGER

Fax +41 61 306 12 34
E-Mail karger@karger.ch
www.karger.com

The Journal Home Page is available at:
www.karger.com/cto

Cells
Tissues
Organs

Epithelial-Mesenchymal Transitions: New Advances in Development, Fibrosis and Cancer

Guest Editors
Erik W. Thompson, Melbourne
Donald F. Newgreen, Melbourne
Pierre Savagner, Montpellier
Raymond B. Runyan, Tucson, Ariz.

39 figures, 17 in color, and 9 tables, 2011

KARGER Basel · Freiburg · Paris · London · New York · Bangalore · Bangkok · Shanghai · Singapore · Tokyo · Sydney

S. Karger
Medical and Scientific Publishers
Basel • Freiburg • Paris • London •
New York • Bangalore • Bangkok •
Shanghai • Singapore • Tokyo • Sydney

Printed in Switzerland
on acid-free and non-aging paper (ISO 9706) by
Reinhardt Druck, Basel
ISBN 978–3–8055–9621–3
e-ISBN 978–3–8055–9622–0

KARGER

Fax +41 61 306 12 34
E-Mail karger@karger.ch
www.karger.com

Vol. 193, No. 1–2, 2011

Cells Tissues Organs

A Selection of Papers from the International EMT Meeting, September 23–26, 2009, Tucson, Ariz., USA

Contents

KARGER

Fax +41 61 306 12 34
E-Mail karger@karger.ch
www.karger.com

Access to full text and tables of contents, including tentative ones for forthcoming issues:
www.karger.com/cto_issues

Preface

Cells
Tissues
Organs

Cells Tissues Organs 2011;193:4–7
DOI: 10.1159/000321662

Published online: November 8, 2010

Out of the Desert: The 4th TEMTIA Meeting on New Advances in Development, Fibrosis and Cancer

Erik W. Thompson[a] Raymond Runyan[c] Pierre Savagner[d] Donald F. Newgreen[b]

[a]Invasion and Metastasis Unit, St. Vincent's Institute and University of Melbourne, Department of Surgery, St. Vincent's Hospital, Melbourne, Vic., and [b]Embryology Laboratory, Murdoch Children's Research Institute, Royal Children's Hospital, Parkville, Vic., Australia; [c]Department of Cell Biology and Anatomy, University of Arizona, Tucson, Ariz., USA; [d]Génotypes et Phénotypes Tumoraux, Centre de Recherche en Cancérologie, CRLC Val d'Aurelle-Paul Lamarque, 1EMI229 Institut National de la Santé et de la Recherche Médicale, Montpellier, France

Epithelial mesenchymal transition (EMT) is a basic cellular process by which epithelial cells change their phenotype and become invasive cells within a three-dimensional setting. The embryo uses EMT to form three-dimensional tissues from sheets of cells while the majority of EMT in the adult produces pathologies. Examples of EMT in the embryo include gastrulation, neural crest cell formation, heart valve and fibroblast formation and breakdown of the mullerian duct in the reproductive system. In pathology, kidney/liver fibrosis and cancer progression/metastasis have been shown to invoke EMT mechanisms.

Though the process of EMT was first discussed in the late 1970s and early 1980s in the context of developmental biology, it was not widely appreciated until the middle 1990s and the field became much more topical as it was discovered by cancer biologists. The first papers on experimental analysis of EMT [Greenburg and Hay, 1982; Newgreen and Gibbins, 1982; Runyan and Markwald, 1983] all had a developmental focus looking at lens, neural crest and heart development, respectively. Some earlier work did not adopt the same title but was EMT nonetheless, for example in the neural crest field what we now refer to as EMT was mostly called 'migration onset' or 'delamination' in the 1970s and 1980s [Newgreen and Gibbins, 1982]. The EMT concept was extended quite early to reproductive biology, specifically to trophoblast invasiveness and endometrial receptivity at embryo implantation [Denker, 1986; Denker, 1990]. By 1992, there were still fewer than 75 papers in this area, but, notably, effects of extracellular matrix and growth factors on EMT in cancer cell lines were examined [Tucker et al., 1990; Valles et al., 1990]. Studies on EMT in cancer continued to accumulate throughout the 1990s and showed a surge with the finding of common transcriptional regulators of EMT in development and cancer [Cano et al., 2000].

More recently, there has been a surge in interest in this area as pathologists have related wound healing and fibrosis of the heart, liver and kidney to EMT, and the EMT phenotype has been linked to cancer stem cells. If the current rate is maintained, there will be approximately 855 articles in 2010 on EMT listed on ISI Web of Science using a search for 'epithelial* AND mesenchymal*' AND 'transition OR transformation', where the total is currently 629 (out of 3,477 primary papers returned by the search for all years). Among all EMT papers identified, 27% have been published since the start of 2009, consistent with the

KARGER
Fax +41 61 306 12 34
E-Mail karger@karger.ch
www.karger.com

1422–6405/11/1932–0004$38.00/0

Accessible online at:
www.karger.com/cto

Prof. Erik Thompson
St. Vincent's Institute and University of Melbourne, Department of Surgery
Room 210, Clinical Sciences Building, St. Vincent's Hospital
29 Regent Street, Fitzroy, Melbourne, VIC 3065 (Australia)
Tel. +61 3 9288 2569, Fax +61 3 9416 2676, E-Mail rik@svi.edu.au

exponential increase in this field in recent years. Only 9.5% of those are attributable to *development* – the oldest area of EMT research. In contrast, the areas of *cancer* and *organ fibrosis* are the hottest areas, each with approximately one third of the total output published in this recent period. The category of *cell biology*, which includes *biochemistry and molecular biology* and focuses on mechanisms of EMT rather than the cell source, has also increased in this later period, accounting for some 25% of publications. Categories are as identified in the Web of Science database. These data confirm a translational shift towards the more disease-related EMT and the underlying mechanisms that will underpin therapeutic advances, and reflect the number of researchers in these fields relative to the 'traditional' EMT area of developmental biology.

The 1st International EMT Meeting was organized in Port Douglas, Qld., Australia, in 2003. This 'Boden Conference on Epithelial-Mesenchymal Transitions' was held on October 5–8, 2003, at Port Douglas. The meeting was convened locally by Don Newgreen, Erik Thompson and Guy Lyons, and had an international committee chaired by Prof. Elizabeth Hay (USA) including Mina Bissell (USA), Suresh Mohla (USA), Shoukat Dedhar (Canada), Masatoshi Takeishi (Japan), Hans-Werner Denker (Germany) and Jean-Paul Thiery (France). This meeting grew out of the landmark collection of EMT reviews assembled as special editions to *Acta Anatomica (Basel)*, now *Cells Tissues Organs*, in 1995 and 1996, and was expressly designed to bring together development, cancer and fibrosis communities in a way that had never been done before, and yet was so clearly needed. The principal supporters of the conference were the Boden Foundation, Australia, and the National Institutes of Health (NIH), USA. *Cells Tissues Organs* devoted another special issue to papers originating from that conference (volume 179, issues 1–2). The Second International EMT meeting was organized in Vancouver, B.C., Canada, in 2005, by Shoukat Dedhar and Raghu Kalluri, and the international program committee comprising Elizabeth Hay (USA), Mina Bissell (USA), Kohei Miyazono (Japan), Suresh Mohla (USA), Don Newgreen (Australia), Pierre Savagner (France), Jean-Paul Thiery (France), Erik Thompson (Australia) and Robert Weinberg (USA). The meeting was made possible with generous support from the Canadian Institutes for Health Research and the National Cancer Institute of Canada and an NIH conference grant. Papers arising from that meeting are found in volume 185 (2007) of *Cells Tissues Organs*.

The 3rd TEMTIA Meeting was organized in Krakow, Poland, in 2007. It was convened by Pierre Savagner, Aristidis Moustakas, Antonio Garcia de Herreros and Amparo Cano as an EMBO Workshop, co-sponsored by TEMTIA and the Marie-Curie Epiplastcarcinoma EU-RTN network, and was supported by OSI Pharmaceuticals, the Ludwig Institute for Cancer Research (Uppsala, Sweden), Merck Serono, Landes Biosciences and S. Karger AG. The International Program Committee included Shoukat Dedhar (Canada), Raghu Kalluri (USA), Suresh Mohla (USA), Don Newgreen (Australia), Angela Nieto (Spain), Ray Runyan (USA) and Kristin Verschueren (Belgium). This meeting introduced the Elizabeth D. Hay Lecture to honor a pioneering scientist in the field of EMT, who sadly passed away in 2007 [Trelstad, 2004; Watt, 2004; Svoboda and Gordon, 2008] (see also http://www.nlm.nih.gov/changingthefaceofmedicine/physicians/biography_141.html). The Inaugural Betty D. Hay Lecture was presented by preeminent EMT researcher Jean-Paul Thiery, A*STAR, Singapore (EMT in Neural Crest and Cancer), at the Krakow meeting. As an EMBO workshop, a meeting report was published in *EMBO Reports* [Acloque et al., 2008], and *Developmental Dynamics* published a special issue on EMT in honor of Dr. Hay including [Svoboda and Gordon, 2008].

This 5th Special Edition of *Cells Tissues Organs* on Epithelial-Mesenchymal Transitions arises from the 4th International Conference on EMT, which was convened by Ray Runyan and Parker Antin on the 23rd–26th of September in 2009 in Tucson, Ariz., USA. An international program committee comprising S. Dedhar (Canada), D. Newgreen (Australia), P. Savagner (France), E. Thompson (Australia) and A. Moustakas (Sweden) created a dynamic program straddling the themes of physiological EMT (embryological development and placentation); pathological EMT (carcinoma progression, metastasis, fibrosis and wound healing); functional aspects of EMT (modulation of cell-cell adhesion, induction of cell motility and control of cell differentiation); commonality of EMT pathways; modulation of EMT; posttranscriptional regulation of EMT, and directions and issues in EMT research. Selected articles from these areas were solicited from speakers at the meeting for this special issue. As suggested in our title, the Tucson conference and this special issue celebrated the further emergence of EMT research into the mainstream of biomedical research, with landmark discoveries into important roles of EMT in the pathology of fibrosis and the manifestations of therapeutic resistance and metastatic competence in malignancy.

The articles of this special issue of *Cells Tissues Organs* are arranged in a continuum starting with articles focused on signaling pathways and regulatory mechanisms, with important new advances in TGF-β_1 signaling in carcinoma-associated EMT, such as the unexpected role of c-Abl in repressing TGF-β_1-induced EMT in carcinoma [Allington and Schiemann, 2011]; the interplay between the non-Smad PI3 kinase-Akt-mTOR axis and EMT-associated invasion in response to TGF-β [Lamouille and Derynck, 2011], and the complex stage-dependent opposing roles for Smad3 in the generation of myofibroblasts in organ fibrosis [Masszi and Kapus, 2011]. This is followed by a comprehensive review of the growth factor pathways regulating either EMT or MET with known relevance to metastasis, again with emphasis on their interdependence and interaction [Said and Williams, 2011]. Developmental scenarios/regulators are represented by work on dystrogylcan in chick gastrulation [Nakaya et al., 2011] and periostin in palate fusion [Kitase et al., 2011]; fibrotic kidney disease with angiotensin II downstream of the intrarenal renin-angiotensin system, which operates both through and independent of TGF-β_1 [Burns and Thomas, 2011], and carcinoma progression with articles on the E-cadherin repressor interactome in breast cancer systems [Hugo et al., 2011] and cooperation in EMT-regulating signals between oncostatin M, hepatocyte growth factor and TGF-β in carcinoma EMT, arising from a survey of some 60 growth factors/cytokines in 30 cell lines [Argast et al., 2011]. These articles capture the current flavor of complexity surrounding EMT regulation, with a large number of regulatory pathways across the different models. Emphasis on regulatory hierarchies and cross modulation are a constant theme, as are the cellular manifestations that underpin the role of EMT in disease.

The success of this 4th meeting hosted by TEMTIA – the EMT International Association (http://www.mtci.com.au/temtia.html or <http://www.emtmeeting.org>), is testament to the continued recognition of EMT as an important process in many disciplines. Indeed, the growing acceptance and interest in EMT has seen a proliferation of EMT meetings, including an American Association for Cancer Research Special Conference on EMT (Arlington, Va., USA, March 2010) and a Keystone Symposium on Epithelial Plasticity and Epithelial to Mesenchymal Transition (January 21–26, 2011, Vancouver, B.C., Canada). The 5th International Epithelial Mesenchymal Transition Meeting (TEMTIA V) is set for Biopolis, Singapore, October 10–13, 2011, and will be co-convened by Jean-Paul Thiery and Erik Thompson, with an International Committee comprising Shoukat Dedhar (Canada), David Epstein (USA), Raghu Kalluri (USA), Don Newgreen (Australia), Angela Nieto (Spain), Raymond Runyan (Spain), Pierre Savagner (France), Guojun Sheng (Japan), Bob Weinberg (USA), Alice Wong (Hong Kong), and Hongquan Zhang (China). The TEMTIA IV conference in Tucson would not have been possible without the generous support of an NIH (USA) R13 Conference grant representing numerous Institutes [NIHLB (primary sponsor), NCI, NICHD, NIDCR; NIH 1R13HL97541-1], OSI Pharmaceuticals, R&D Systems, the American Association of Anatomists and Procter & Gamble Global Biotechnology.

References

Acloque, H., J.P. Thiery, M.A. Nieto (2008) The physiology and pathology of the EMT. Meeting on the epithelial-mesenchymal transition. EMBO Rep *9:* 322–326.

Allington, T.M., W.P. Schiemann (2011) The cain and Abl of epithelial-mesenchymal transition and transforming growth factor-β in mammary epithelial cells. Cells Tissues Organs *193:* 98–113.

Argast, G.M., P.M. Iain, J.M. O'Connor, D.M. Shaaban, D.M. Epstein, J.A. Pachter, J.L. Kan (2011) Cooperative signaling between oncostatin M, hepatocyte growth factor and transforming growth factor-β enhances epithelial to mesenchymal transition in lung and pancreatic tumor models. Cells Tissues Organs *193:* 114–132.

Burns, W.C., M.C. Thomas (2011) Angiotensin II and its role in tubular epithelial to mesenchymal transition associated with chronic kidney disease. Cells Tissues Organs *193:* 74–84.

Cano, A., M.A. Perez-Moreno, I. Rodrigo, A. Locascio, M.J. Blanco, M.G. del Barrio, F. Portillo, M.A. Nieto (2000) The transcription factor snail controls epithelial-mesenchymal transitions by repressing E-cadherin expression. Nat Cell Biol *2:* 76–83.

Denker, H.-W. (1986) Epithel-Epithel-Interaktionen bei der Embryo-Implantation: Ansätze zur Lösung eines zellbiologischen Paradoxons. Anat Anz 160(Suppl): 93–114.

Denker, H.-W. (1990) Trophoblast-endometrial interactions at embryo implantation: A cell biological paradox, in Denker, H.-W., J.D. Aplin (eds): Trophoblast Invasion and Endometrial Receptivity. Novel Aspects of the Cell Biology of Embryo Implantation. Trophoblast Res, New York, Plenum Medical Book Company, vol 4, pp 3–29.

Greenburg, G., E.D. Hay (1982) Epithelia suspended in collagen gels can lose polarity and express characteristics of migrating mesenchymal cells. J Cell Biol *95:* 333–339.

Hugo, H.J., M.I. Kokkinos, T. Blick, M.L. Ackland, E.W. Thompson, D.F. Newgreen (2011) Defining the E-cadherin repressor interactome in epithelial-mesenchymal transition: The PMC42 model as a case study. Cells Tissues Organs *193:* 23–40.

Kitase, Y., K. Yamashiro, K. Fu, J.M. Richman, C.F. Shuler (2011) Spatiotemporal localization of periostin and its potential role in epithelial-mesenchymal transition during palatal fusion. Cells Tissues Organs *193:* 53–63.
Lamouille, S., R. Derynck (2011) Emergence of the phosphoinositide 3-kinase-akt-mammalian target of rapamycin axis in transforming growth factor-β-induced epithelial-mesenchymal transition. Cells Tissues Organs *193:* 8–22.
Masszi, A., A. Kapus (2011) Smaddening complexity: The role of Smad3 in epithelial-myofibroblast Transition. Cells Tissues Organs *193:* 41–52.
Nakaya, Y., E.W. Sukowati, C. Alev, F. Nakazawa, G. Sheng (2011) Involvement of dystroglycan in epithelial-mesenchymal transition during chick gastrulation. Cells Tissues Organs *193:* 64–73.
Newgreen, D.F., I.L. Gibbins (1982) Factors controlling the time of onset of the migration of neural crest cells in the fowl embryo. Cell Tissue Res *224:* 145–160.
Runyan, R.B., R.R. Markwald (1983) Invasion of mesenchyme into three-dimensional collagen gels: a regional and temporal analysis of interaction in embryonic heart tissue. Dev Biol *95:* 108–114.
Said, N.A., E.D. Williams (2011) Growth factors in induction of epithelial-mesenchymal transition and metastasis. Cells Tissues Organs *193:* 85–97.
Svoboda, K.H., M. Gordon (2008) A tribute to Elizabeth D. Hay, 1927–2007. Dev Dyn *237:* 2605–2606.
Trelstad, R.L. (2004) The extracellular matrix in development and regeneration. An interview with Elizabeth D. Hay. Int J Dev Biol *48:* 687–694.
Tucker, G.C., B. Boyer, J. Gavrilovic, H. Emonard, J.P. Thiery (1990) Collagen-mediated dispersion of NBT-II rat bladder carcinoma cells. Cancer Res *50:* 129–137.
Valles, A.M., B. Boyer, J. Badet, G.C. Tucker, D. Barritault, J.P. Thiery (1990) Acidic fibroblast growth factor is a modulator of epithelial plasticity in a rat bladder carcinoma cell line. Proc Natl Acad Sci USA *87:* 1124–1128.
Watt, F. (2004) Women in cell science – Elizabeth Hay. J Cell Sci *117:* 4617–4618.

Editorial Note

With this volume, *Cells Tissues Organs* continues a series of Special Topic Issues on EMT. This journal has pioneered publishing on EMT under its previous name *Acta Anatomica,* i.e. at a time when EMT/MET was still considered a quite new and debated concept. The editors are happy to see the high degree of recognition that this concept has received in the meantime and that it has much stimulated research, in particular in the areas of developmental and tumor biology. *Cells Tissues Organs* plans to maintain one of its focuses on this exciting and rapidly expanding field of research.

H.-W. Denker, Essen

Previous Special Topic Issues on EMT:

- Acta Anatomica Vol. 154, No. 1, 1995: Epithelial-Mesenchymal Transitions. Part I.
  Guest Editor: D.F. Newgreen, Melbourne
- Acta Anatomica Vol. 156, No. 3, 1996: Epithelial-Mesenchymal Transitions. Part II.
  Guest Editor: D.F. Newgreen, Melbourne
- Cells Tissues Organs Vol. 179, No. 1–2, 2005: Recent Progress in Epithelial-Mesenchymal Transitions. Development – Cancer – Pathology.
  Guest Editors: D.F. Newgreen and E.W. Thompson, Melbourne
- Cells Tissues Organs Vol. 185, No. 1–3, 2007: Advances in Epithelial-Mesenchymal Transitions.
  Guest Editors: E.W. Thompson and D.F. Newgreen, Melbourne

Cells
Tissues
Organs

Cells Tissues Organs 2011;193:8–22
DOI: 10.1159/000320172

Published online: November 2, 2010

Emergence of the Phosphoinositide 3-Kinase-Akt-Mammalian Target of Rapamycin Axis in Transforming Growth Factor-β-Induced Epithelial-Mesenchymal Transition

Samy Lamouille Rik Derynck

Departments of Cell and Tissue Biology, and Anatomy, Programs in Cell Biology and Developmental Biology, University of California, San Francisco, Calif., USA

Key Words
Cell invasion · Epithelial-mesenchymal transition · Metastasis · Smad signaling

Abstract
During development and in pathological contexts such as fibrosis and cancer progression, epithelial cells can initiate a complex transcriptional reprogramming, accompanied by dramatic morphological changes, in a process named 'epithelial-mesenchymal transition' (EMT). In this transition, epithelial cells lose their epithelial characteristics to acquire mesenchymal properties and increased motile and invasive behavior. Transforming growth factor-β (TGF-β) has emerged as a major inducer of EMT through activation of downstream signaling pathways, including Smad and non-Smad signaling pathways. Among the non-Smad pathways, increasing evidence is emerging that the phosphoinositide 3-kinase-Akt-mammalian target of rapamycin axis plays a major role in TGF-β-induced EMT, notably through the regulation of translation and cell invasion. Pharmacological inhibitors of the phosphoinositide 3-kinase-Akt-mammalian target of rapamycin pathway may therefore represent an opportunity to selectively target essential aspects of TGF-β-induced EMT and provide an approach to prevent cancer cell dissemination toward metastasis, without the need to fully inactivate TGF-β signaling.

Definition of Epithelial-Mesenchymal Transition

During development, in response to injury, inflammation and pathological conditions, epithelial cells show a remarkable differentiation plasticity. A manifestation of this plasticity is the process that has been named 'epithelial to mesenchymal transformation' or 'transdifferentiation', but is now more commonly referred to as 'epithelial-mesenchymal transition' (EMT). In EMT, the loss of epithelial characteristics, such as intercellular contacts and cell polarity, is complemented by the acquisition of mesenchymal characteristics and increased cell motility and invasion (fig. 1). This transition involves a complex transcriptional reprogramming and non-transcriptional signaling events that contribute to major changes in cell morphology and behavior. Depending on the physiological and tissue contexts, cells that have undergone EMT can revert to reacquire their epithelial characteristics, thus leading to a mesenchymal-epithelial transition [Kalluri and Weinberg, 2009]. Over the last 15 years, transforming growth factor-β (TGF-β) has been shown to function as a potent inducer of EMT, with its signaling pathways intimately involved in the activation and progression of EMT [Moustakas and Heldin, 2007; Miyazono, 2009; Xu et al., 2009].

KARGER

Fax +41 61 306 12 34
E-Mail karger@karger.ch
www.karger.com

Accessible online at:
www.karger.com/cto

Dr. Rik Derynck
Department of Cell and Tissue Biology, University of California at San Francisco
513 Parnassus Avenue, Room HSW-613
San Francisco, CA 94143-0512 (USA)
Tel. +1 415 476 7322, Fax +1 415 502 7338, E-Mail rik.derynck@ucsf.edu

Abbreviations used in this paper

ATF3	activating transcription factor 3	PDK1	3-phosphoinositide-dependent kinase 1
bHLH	basic helix-loop-helix	PI3	phosphoinositide 3
CAR	coxsackie and adenovirus receptor	PIP3	phosphatidylinositol (3,4,5)-triphosphate
4E-BP1	eIF4E-binding protein	Protor	protein observed with Rictor
eIF4E	eukaryotic translation initiation factor 4E	PTEN	phosphatase and tensin homolog
EMT	epithelial-mesenchymal transition	Raptor	regulatory associated protein of mammalian target of rapamycin
Erk	extracellular-regulated kinase	Rheb	ras homolog enriched in brain
Grb2	growth factor receptor-bound protein 2	Rictor	rapamycin-insensitive companion of mammalian target of rapamycin
GSK-3β	glycogen synthase kinase-3β	ROCK	rho-associated coiled-coil containing protein kinase
HMGA2	high-mobility group A2	ShcA	src homology 2 domain containing transforming protein A
Id	inhibitor of DNA binding	Sos	son of sevenless
JNK	c-Jun N-terminal kinase	TAK1	transforming growth factor-β-activated kinase 1
MAP	mitogen-activated protein	TGF-β	transforming growth factor-β
MEK	mitogen-activated protein kinase/Erk kinase	TRAF6	tumor necrosis factor receptor-associated factor 6
mLST8	mammalian lethal with SEC13 protein 8	TSC	tuberous sclerosis complex
mSin1	mammalian stress-activated protein kinase-interacting protein 1	TβRI	transforming growth factor-β type I receptor
mTOR	mammalian target of rapamycin	TβRII	transforming growth factor-β type II receptor
mTORC1	mammalian target of rapamycin complex 1	ZEB	zinc finger E-box binding homeobox
mTORC2	mammalian target of rapamycin complex 2		
NMuMG	normal murine mammary gland cell		

Three types of EMT with distinct functional consequences have been distinguished, depending on the developmental and physiological context [Kalluri and Weinberg, 2009]. Type 1 EMT is linked to developmental processes. During vertebrate embryonic development, EMT occurs in a precise and programmed spatiotemporal manner, starting as early as gastrulation, when it mediates the formation of the mesoderm. EMT is also a key process in the delamination of neural crest cells that disperse to give rise to a variety of cell types, including osteoblasts, chondrocytes and muscle cells. At later stages, an EMT-like process allows endothelial cells to transition into mesenchymal cells, e.g. in heart development. EMT is also involved in the fusion of the palatal shelves and in Müllerian duct regression [Acloque et al., 2009; Thiery et al., 2009]. The 2 other types of EMT are not involved in normal development, but occur in response to injury or inflammation and are at the basis of pathological processes. Type 2 EMT occurs in wound healing, tissue repair and regeneration and is also associated with inflammation-induced fibrosis. Such fibrosis involves a mesenchymal conversion of epithelial cells in addition to an infiltration and proliferation of fibroblasts [Iwano et al., 2002; Kalluri and Neilson, 2003]. Finally, during tumor progression, carcinoma cells can escape the environment of the primary tumor by initiating an EMT process, resulting in motility and invasive behavior which potentially leads to metastasis at distant sites. Once in the new loci, these cancer cells can then revert through mesenchymal-epithelial transition to form metastatic carcinomas. The EMT associated with cancer invasion and progression has been classified as type 3 EMT [Thiery and Sleeman, 2006; Kalluri and Weinberg, 2009; Klymkowsky and Savagner, 2009].

Molecular Events during EMT

The transition from an epithelial to a mesenchymal phenotype involves dramatic changes in gene expression, as well as in cell morphology and behavior (fig. 1). An early step in EMT is the dissolution of epithelial cell junction complexes that mediate cell-cell adhesion. These specialized junction complexes consist of transmembrane molecules that, through interactions with adaptor proteins beneath the plasma membrane, interact with the actin cytoskeleton, intermediate filaments or microtubules. Among these complexes, tight junctions contain occludin and claudins that bind zonula occludens proteins, adherens junctions are characterized by E-cadherin that binds to β- or p120-catenin, gap junctions contain connexins, and desmosomes consist of desmosal cadherins that bind proteins in the submembranous plaque. The rapid delocalization of these junctional pro-

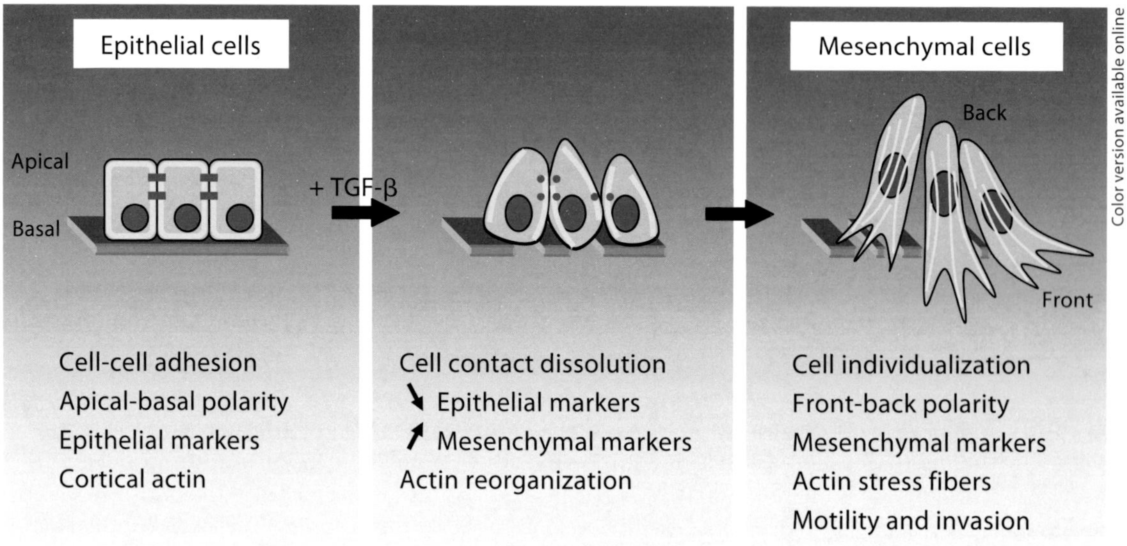

Fig. 1. TGF-β-induced EMT. Disassembly of epithelial cell-cell contacts (red in the online version) and loss of cell polarity are the first steps in TGF-β-induced EMT. The expression of epithelial marker genes is repressed concomitantly with increased expression of mesenchymal markers. In addition, cortical actin (yellow in the online version) reorganizes into stress fibers. TGF-β-induced EMT is accompanied by increased motility and invasive behavior, in part mediated by the expression of metalloproteinases and matrix protein turnover.

teins and the downregulation of their expression represent early steps in EMT that lead to the individualization of the cells [Thiery and Sleeman, 2006; Xu et al., 2009]. Concomitantly, the cells lose their apical-basal polarity and epithelial cell architecture. Two polarity complexes, one composed of Par3 and Par6, and the other one comprising Crumbs-3, localize predominantly to tight junctions and are disrupted when the tight junctions are disassembled [Moreno-Bueno et al., 2008]. Accompanying the disassembly of the junction complexes, the cortical actin cytoskeleton is reorganized through the activities of Rho-like GTPases (Rho, Rac and Cdc42) into stress fibers extending within lamellipodia and filopodia. In these stress fiber-enriched protrusions, actin can dynamically polymerize and depolymerize allowing for enhanced cell motility [Zavadil and Böttinger, 2005; Yilmaz and Christofori, 2009].

Since many of the junction complex proteins characterize epithelial cells, the dissolution of the junctions results in a loss of many epithelial marker proteins. Among them, decrease in E-cadherin expression has become a major indication of loss of epithelial characteristics. Further, the expression of other epithelial proteins, such as epithelial-specific cytokeratins, is also downregulated. In EMT, the loss of epithelial markers is accompanied by an induction of the expression of mesenchymal proteins, such as vimentin. In addition, expression of N-cadherin, a mesenchymal protein that promotes migration and invasion, increases while the expression of E-cadherin decreases. EMT is also marked by increased expression of matrix metalloproteinases, which degrade extracellular matrix, and extracellular matrix proteins such as fibronectin, collagens or laminin [Zavadil and Böttinger, 2005; Zeisberg and Neilson, 2009]. Together, loss of epithelial protein expression, changes in cell shape and expression of mesenchymal proteins result in a motile cell behavior that allows invasion into surrounding tissues with increased extracellular matrix turnover.

The complex changes in gene expression that are at the basis of EMT result largely from the actions of 3 families of transcription factors, i.e. the Snail, ZEB and basic helix-loop-helix (bHLH) families, whose expression and activities are induced upon initiation of EMT [Peinado et al., 2007]. The Snail (Snail1, Snail2 and Snail3) and ZEB (ZEB1 and ZEB2) proteins represent 2 classes of zinc finger transcription factors whose expression increases during EMT and which bind E-box elements in regulatory promoter sequences. Snail1 and Snail2 can recruit corepressors such as histone deacetylases or C-terminal binding proteins, and in this way transcriptionally repress the expression of target genes, such as the gene encoding E-cadherin [Batlle et al., 2000; Cano et al., 2000; Barrallo-

Gimeno and Nieto, 2005]. Similarly, the ZEB transcription factors also have the ability to recruit corepressors, such as C-terminal binding protein, and repress E-cadherin transcription [Comijn et al., 2001; Eger et al., 2005]. Together, Snail and ZEB proteins repress the expression of a number of genes encoding tight junction, adherens junction, desmosome and polarity complex proteins. Besides repressing the expression of epithelial markers, these transcription factors also participate in the increased expression of proteins that characterize the mesenchymal phenotype, such as fibronectin, vitronectin, collagen, N-cadherin and matrix metalloproteinases [Peinado et al., 2007]. bHLH transcription factors also play a role in the progression of EMT. Among these, Twist1 and Twist2 dimerize with another type of bHLH proteins, i.e. E-proteins. These heterodimers then bind to DNA and repress the expression of some epithelial genes such as the gene encoding E-cadherin, while activating the expression of some mesenchymal genes [Perez-Moreno et al., 2001; Yang et al., 2004]. Since inhibitor of DNA binding (Id) proteins inhibit the dimerization and function of Twist transcription factors through dominant negative interference, induction of EMT is accompanied by downregulation of Id protein expression [Ruzinova and Benezra, 2003; Perk et al., 2005]. Interestingly, Snail proteins orchestrate the induction of EMT by increasing the expression of ZEB and bHLH factors [Peinado et al., 2007]. A further level of control in the regulation of this transcription network is exerted by microRNAs. Indeed, members of the miR-200 family act as essential regulators of EMT. They were shown to target and repress the expression of ZEB1 and ZEB2, and, accordingly, their expression is downregulated in cells that undergo EMT, thus leading to a decrease in E-cadherin expression [Gregory et al., 2008].

Recent insights have revealed that signaling pathways, including those initiated by TGF-β, regulate the expression and activities of these transcription factors [Moustakas and Heldin, 2007; Xu et al., 2009]. The orchestration of these transcription pathways, in combination with non-transcription signaling responses, allows TGF-β to act as a potent inducer of EMT. Dissecting the mechanisms of the EMT response to TGF-β provides a paradigm for the cellular basis of epithelial plasticity.

TGF-β, a Major Inducer of EMT

A variety of studies have implicated TGF-β as an inducer or essential mediator of EMT in embryonic development, fibrosis and tumorigenesis. For example, during cardiac development, TGF-β_1 and TGF-β_2 are expressed in the atrioventricular canal and outflow tract tissue at the onset of EMT, permitting the formation of the heart valves [Nakajima et al., 2000]. TGF-β_2 null mice present severe cardiac defects with abnormalities in these regions, and inhibition of TGF-β_2 blocks EMT in mouse heart explant cultures [Azhar et al., 2003; Mercado-Pimentel and Runyan, 2007]. As another example, TGF-β_3 expression is essential for palatal development and fusion. It is expressed at the site and time of fusion of the palatal shelves, when the epithelial cells undergo EMT, and targeted inactivation of the gene encoding TGF-β_3 results in a cleft palate that correlates with the absence of EMT [Pelton et al., 1990; Nawshad et al., 2004].

Consistent with its ability to induce a strong fibrotic response when injected subcutaneously, TGF-β acts as a mediator of pathological fibrosis in a variety of tissues including the kidney, liver, lung and heart. While this response involves the attraction and proliferation of fibroblasts in response to TGF-β, increasing evidence is emerging that TGF-β is also involved in EMT leading to fibrosis. Accordingly, in mouse models and human patients, TGF-β_1 expression is increased in chronic kidney disease prior to fibrosis [Schnaper et al., 2003]. Patients with liver disease progressing to hepatic fibrosis also show increased TGF-β_1 expression in biliary epithelial cells, and increased TGF-β_1 expression occurs in a mouse model of induced liver fibrosis, while blocking TGF-β_1 signaling demonstrated significant antifibrotic effect in the liver [Gressner et al., 2002; Meindl-Beinker and Dooley, 2008]. Fibroblasts isolated from patients with pulmonary fibrosis show increased secretion of TGF-β resulting in hyperactive TGF-β signaling [Willis and Borok, 2007]. Further, lineage-tracing experiments in mouse models illustrate a role of EMT of alveolar epithelial cells in lung fibrosis. In the adult heart, an endothelial to mesenchymal transition process occurs in cardiac fibrosis. This process is controlled by TGF-β, and progression of cardiac fibrosis is inhibited in transgenic mice with impaired TGF-β signaling [Zeisberg et al., 2007]. These in vivo observations are complemented by cell culture experiments showing that TGF-β induces EMT in renal tubular epithelial cells, hepatic stellate cells and alveolar epithelial cells, as well as initiating endothelial to mesenchymal transition in endothelial cells [Gressner et al., 2002; Zeisberg et al., 2003; Willis and Borok, 2007; Zeisberg et al., 2007].

TGF-β-induced EMT may also play an important role in carcinoma progression. EMT is thought to be a prerequisite for the invasive behavior of carcinoma cells, leading to dissemination and metastasis [Thiery, 2003; Thiery and Sleeman, 2006; Kalluri and Weinberg, 2009]. Such a role for TGF-β is consistent with the increased production and activation of TGF-β by cancer cells and has been well validated by cell culture and mouse model studies [Bierie and Moses, 2006a]. In addition, in vivo studies confirmed a correlation between the conversion of squamous into more invasive spindle cell carcinomas and the expression of activated TGF-β_1 [Cui et al., 1996; Portella et al., 1998; Akhurst, 2008]. Moreover, the increase in TGF-β expression and/or activity provides an advantage for tumor progression not only by inducing EMT, but also by creating an immunosuppressive environment and initiating angiogenesis [Padua and Massagué, 2009]. How important EMT, and more specifically TGF-β-induced EMT, is in human carcinoma progression, invasion and metastasis remains unclear. Nevertheless, research on the molecular mechanisms and the role of TGF-β in EMT and cancer progression has been greatly aided by the characterization of cell culture models for TGF-β-induced EMT. Among these, the normal murine mammary gland (NMuMG) epithelial cell line is perhaps the best studied cell system. In these cells, addition of TGF-β induces an EMT program in cell culture that is completed in 36 h [Miettinen et al., 1994].

Other members of the TGF-β family are also involved in regulating EMT events during development and in cancer, although the knowledge of their roles is currently poorly developed. Bone morphogenetic proteins are involved in EMT processes during gastrulation, neural crest delamination and atrioventricular cushion patterning [Kishigami and Mishina, 2005; Ma et al., 2005; Acloque et al., 2009], and the anti-Müllerian hormone is required for the second phase of Müllerian duct regression [Klattig and Englert, 2007]. In the pathological context, bone morphogenetic proteins have been linked to EMT and invasiveness of several types of cancer cells [Theriault et al., 2007; Gordon et al., 2009], while in other cases, they promote or may be involved in mesenchymal-epithelial transition [Zeisberg et al., 2005].

Discussion of the role of these members of the TGF-β family in EMT is beyond the scope of this overview.

TGF-β-Induced Smad Signaling in EMT

TGF-β signals through a heterotetrameric complex of two TGF-β type II (TβRII) and two TGF-β type I (TβRI) transmembrane dual specificity kinase receptors. Upon TGF-β binding to the receptors, TβRII activates TβRI, which in turn phosphorylates and activates the intracellular mediators Smad2 and Smad3. Once activated, Smad2 and/or Smad3 dissociate from the receptor complex and combine with the common Smad, Smad4, to form trimeric complexes of Smad proteins. These translocate to the nucleus where they cooperate with other transcription factors, coactivators or corepressors, to regulate gene transcription (fig. 2). The inhibitory Smad6 and Smad7 block the activation of Smad2 and Smad3 by preventing their interaction with TβRI. They do not serve as transcription activators, yet may function as transcription repressors [Shi and Massagué, 2003; Feng and Derynck, 2005]. Consistent with the role of TGF-β as inducer of EMT, these receptors and Smads were shown to play a role in EMT.

Expression of a cytoplasmically truncated TβRII has been shown to block TGF-β-induced EMT in normal and cancer epithelial cells through dominant negative interference both in vitro and in vivo [Oft et al., 1998; Portella et al., 1998; Han et al., 2005]. In NMuMG cells, expression of a cytoplasmically truncated TβRI similarly inhibits TGF-β-induced EMT, whereas a constitutively active mutant of TβRI induces EMT in the absence of added TGF-β [Piek et al., 1999; Valcourt et al., 2005]. Similar to the effect of the dominant negative form of TβRI, a pharmacological inhibitor that represses the kinase activity of TβRI prevents TGF-β-induced EMT [Kondo et al., 2004; Lamouille and Derynck, 2007]. Downstream of the receptors, the Smad effectors mediate gene expression responses that are required for the induction of EMT upon TGF-β stimulation [Akhurst, 2008]. Indeed, expression of Smad2, Smad3 and Smad4 mutants that can interfere with Smad function, or downregulation of Smad4 expression using RNA interference, was also shown to inhibit the conversion from an epithelial to a mesenchymal phenotype [Valcourt et al., 2005; Deckers et al., 2006]. However, in some cell contexts, Smad2 was reported to act as an antagonist in TGF-β-induced EMT. For example, Smad2-deficient keratinocytes undergo EMT and promote skin tumor formation through enhanced activities of Smad3 and Smad4 [Hoot et al., 2008; see also Masszi and Kapus, 2011, this issue]. Finally, increased expression of the inhibitory Smad7 represses TGF-β-induced EMT in various epithelial cells [Valcourt et al., 2005; Zavadil and Böttinger, 2005].

The induction of EMT in response to TGF-β has been attributed in part to the Smad transcription complexes that regulate transcription of essential genes involved in this process. Notably, TGF-β signaling directly activates the expression of Snail proteins through Smads. Smad3

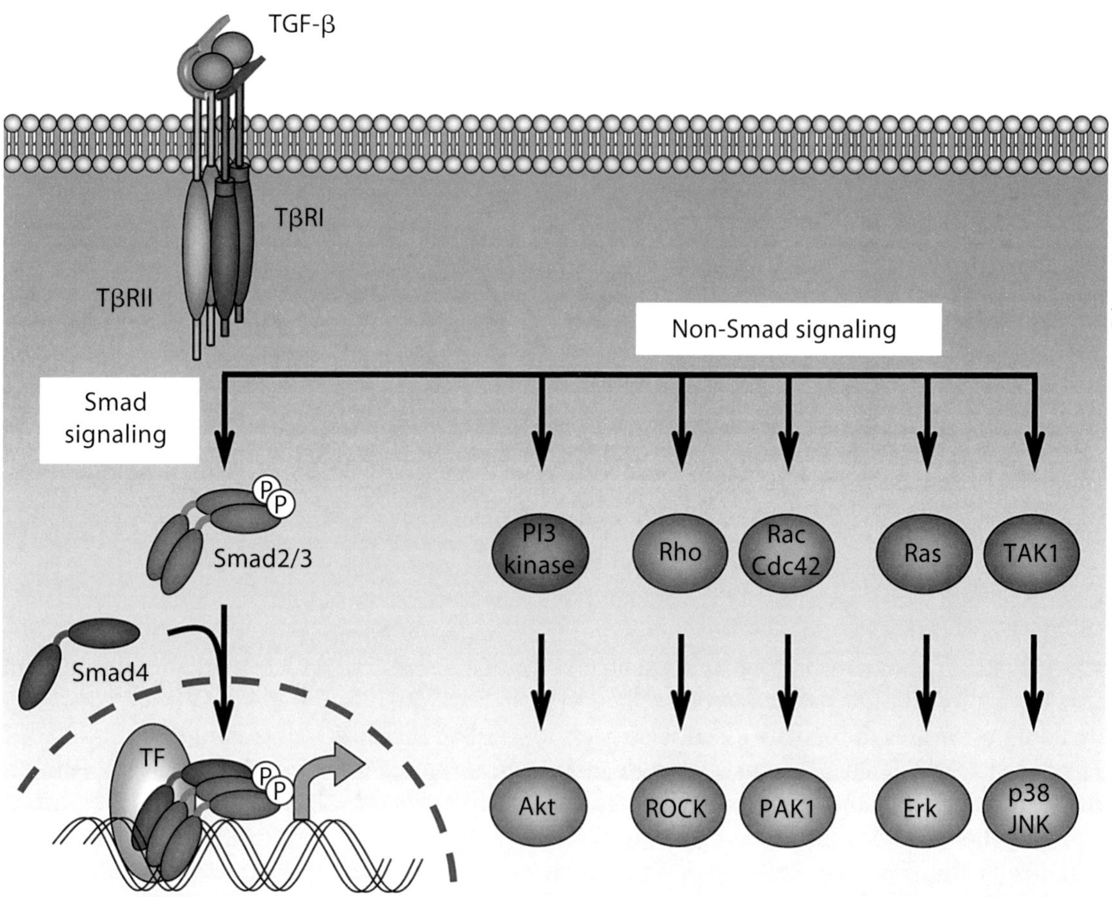

Color version available online

Fig. 2. Smad and non-Smad signaling in TGF-β-induced EMT. TGF-β initiates signaling through 2 pairs of dual specificity kinase receptors that activate the intracellular signal transducers Smad2 and Smad3 through direct C-terminal phosphorylation. Following activation, Smad2 and Smad3 combine with Smad4, and these trimeric complexes then translocate into the nucleus and regulate transcription of target genes through interaction with DNA-binding transcription factors (TF), coactivators and corepressors. In addition, TGF-β initiates non-Smad signaling pathways such as PI3 kinase-Akt, Rho-like GTPases and MAP kinase pathways. Both Smad and non-Smad signaling pathways are involved in TGF-β-induced EMT responses.

binds to regulatory promoter sequences of the gene encoding Snail1 and activates its transcription [Cho et al., 2007; Hoot et al., 2008]. In addition, Smad3 and Smad4 form a complex with Snail1 that binds to E-box and Smad-binding elements in the promoters of the genes encoding E-cadherin, occludin and the tight junction-associated cell adhesion molecule CAR, consequently repressing their transcription [Vincent et al., 2009]. In cells induced to undergo EMT, TGF-β also activates the expression of ZEB transcription factors through upregulation of the expression of the transcription factor Ets1, which then may cooperate with the bHLH transcription factor E47 [Shirakihara et al., 2007]. Moreover, the expression of the miR-200 microRNAs is downregulated in TGF-β-induced EMT, resulting in an increase in translation of the ZEB1 and ZEB2 mRNAs [Gregory et al., 2008]. In addition, expression of ZEB1 and ZEB2 directly represses the transcription of the miR-200 family through binding to ZEB-type E-box motifs in a compact region of the miR-200 family promoter [Bracken et al., 2008; Burk et al., 2008]. TGF-β signaling also regulates the activities of the bHLH family of transcription factors during EMT by repressing the expression of Id factors. In the case of Id1, a complex formed by Smad3, Smad4 and the transcription repressor ATF3, binds sequences in the Id1 promoter and represses its transcription [Kang et al., 2003]. The decrease in expression of Id factors then increases activity of E-proteins and Twist, resulting in transcriptional repression of the E-cadherin gene. Finally, the transcription factor HMGA2, whose expression increases during TGF-β-induced EMT through a Smad3/Smad4-dependent mechanism, has also emerged as an essential mediator in TGF-β-induced EMT by enhancing the expression of Snail and Twist proteins, and by repressing the expression of Id2 [Thuault et al., 2006].

Non-Smad Signaling in TGF-β-Induced EMT

In addition to Smad signaling, which directly targets transcriptional regulation, TGF-β initiates non-Smad signaling pathways (fig. 2) [Derynck and Zhang, 2003; Moustakas and Heldin, 2005]. These pathways include the 3 mitogen-activated protein (MAP) kinase pathways that lead to activation of extracellular-regulated kinase (Erk), p38 and JNK. However, these pathways are generally more prominently activated by tyrosine kinase receptors, principally in response to growth factor stimulation. Activation of these pathways complements the Smad signaling responses to regulate essential aspects of TGF-β-induced EMT, such as cytoskeleton reorganization, and cell migration and invasion. Their synergy with TGF-β/Smad signaling in inducing EMT has been well illustrated through the cooperation of tyrosine kinase receptor activation with TGF-β signaling. For example, epidermal growth factor stimulates Ras and Erk MAP kinase signaling, which enhances TGF-β-induced EMT responses such as repression of E-cadherin expression and activation of Snail2, N-cadherin and matrix metalloproteinase expression [Grande et al., 2002; Schmidt et al., 2005; Uttamsingh et al., 2008]. Accordingly, pharmacological inhibition of MEK proteins, which activate Erk MAP kinase, prevents the EMT process induced by TGF-β [Xie et al., 2004]. Chemical inhibitors of p38 MAP kinase or JNK MAP kinase, and antisense oligonucleotides targeting JNK, have also been reported to block TGF-β-induced EMT as observed with morphological changes and epithelial versus mesenchymal marker regulation [Bakin et al., 2002; Yu et al., 2002; Santibanez, 2006; Alcorn et al., 2008].

TGF-β activates the Ras-Raf-MEK-Erk MAP kinase pathway through the association of ShcA with the TGF-β receptor complex and direct serine and threonine phosphorylation of ShcA by TβRI in response to TGF-β. The phosphorylated tyrosines on ShcA provide a docking site for the recruitment of Grb2 and Sos, and this complex initiates Ras activation leading to Erk MAP kinase signaling cascade [Lee et al., 2007]. TGF-β has been shown to induce p38 and JNK MAP kinase signaling through activation of TAK1 by the ubiquitin ligase TRAF6 that interacts with the TGF-β receptor complex [Sorrentino et al., 2008; Yamashita et al., 2008]. The recent characterization of how these MAP kinase pathways are activated in response to TGF-β should enable a dissection of their relative contributions to TGF-β-induced EMT.

TGF-β also regulates the activity of the small GTPase proteins Rho, Rac and Cdc42, which function as key signaling mediators in the reorganization of the actin cytoskeleton and the formation of lamellipodia and filopodia, actin protrusions that are required for cell migration [Bhowmick et al., 2001; Zavadil and Böttinger, 2005; Yilmaz and Christofori, 2009]. The mechanisms underlying regulation of the small GTPases by TGF-β receptor activation remain poorly characterized. In the early stage of TGF-β-induced EMT, the polarity molecule Par6 interacts at tight junctions with TβRI, and the phosphorylation of TβRI by TβRII recruits the E3 ubiquitin ligase Smurf1 which mediates the ubiquitination and consequently the degradation of RhoA during tight junction disruption [Ozdamar et al., 2005]. In addition, the microRNA miR-155 that targets RhoA expression is upregulated in TGF-β-induced EMT [Kong et al., 2008]. However, during EMT, TGF-β also activates RhoA and its downstream targets rho-associated coiled-coil containing protein kinase (ROCK) and LIM kinase, mediators of actin stress fiber formation [Vardouli et al., 2005; Pellegrin and Mellor, 2007]. Indeed, antisense oligonucleotides that downregulate the expression of ROCK or LIM kinase, and pharmacological inhibition of ROCK, inhibit the actin reorganization that accompanies TGF-β-induced EMT [Bhowmick et al., 2001; Tavares et al., 2006; Cho and Yoo, 2007].

Finally, TGF-β induces Akt activation through phosphoinositide 3 (PI3) kinase during EMT [Bakin et al., 2000; Lamouille and Derynck, 2007]. Once activated, Akt initiates signaling pathways such as the mammalian target of rapamycin (mTOR) pathway, that play roles in cell survival, growth, migration and invasion. The essential role of TGF-β-induced PI3 kinase-Akt-mTOR signaling in the context of EMT is discussed in the remainder of this review.

The TGF-β-PI3 Kinase-Akt-mTOR Axis in EMT

A variety of tyrosine kinase receptors for growth factors, such as epidermal growth factor, fibroblast growth factor, insulin-like growth factor-1 and insulin, activate signaling through the PI3 kinase-Akt pathway. Moreover, activation of PI3 kinase and Akt signaling has been detected in cells undergoing EMT [Larue and Bellacosa, 2005]. We and others have observed that TGF-β induces the PI3 kinase-Akt pathway in various cell types, including cells that undergo TGF-β-induced EMT [Bakin et al., 2000; Lee et al., 2004; Lien et al., 2006; Rodriguez-Barbero et al., 2006; Lamouille and Derynck, 2007; Lin et al., 2007; Yeh et al., 2008]. These observations raise the question as to what role the activation of PI3 kinase-Akt signaling plays in TGF-β-induced EMT.

Activation of PI3 kinase results in the generation of phosphatidylinositol (3,4,5)-triphosphate (PIP3), which provides a phospholipid binding site for proteins that contain a pleckstrin homology domain, such as Akt. Once Akt is recruited to the plasma membrane, it is fully activated upon phosphorylation on a threonine by the kinase PDK1, and on a serine principally by mTOR in mTOR complex 2 (mTORC2). In some cell models, Akt may also be activated by integrin-linked kinase, a cytoplasmic kinase that relays signals between integrins and the actin cytoskeleton, and integrin-linked kinase function may be required for EMT [McDonald et al., 2008]. The 3 Akt kinases in mammalian cells (Akt1, Akt2 and Akt3) can phosphorylate a range of proteins that regulate physiological processes such as cell survival, growth, metabolism and migration. However, these Akt proteins display distinct functions, based on gene targeting studies [Gonzalez and McGraw, 2009]. In cell culture, downregulation of Akt2 expression blocks the phenotypical changes and cell migration increase that accompany insulin-like growth factor-1-dependent EMT, while downregulating Akt1 expression enhances this effect [Irie et al., 2005]. In the same epithelial cell model, decreased Akt1 expression promotes TGF-β-induced EMT through a decrease in abundance of the miR-200 family [Iliopoulos et al., 2009]. Interestingly, TGF-β_2 selectively activates Akt2 but not Akt1 in NMuMG cells [Chaudhury et al., 2010]. However, the role of Akt in EMT, cell migration and invasion may differ depending on the TGF-β isoform and cell model used.

A downstream target of Akt proteins is glycogen synthase kinase-3β (GSK-3β), a kinase that binds to and phosphorylates Snail1, resulting in enhanced cytoplasmic retention and degradation of Snail1. Phosphorylation of GSK-3β by Akt results in its ubiquitination and degradation, leading to increased accumulation of Snail1 in the nucleus and repression of E-cadherin expression, consequently inducing EMT [Zhou et al., 2004; Bachelder et al., 2005]. In addition, Akt induces transcription of the Snail1 gene, through nuclear factor-κB activation, in squamous cell carcinoma lines that undergo EMT [Julien et al., 2007]. The nuclear factor-κB pathway can also promote EMT, invasion and metastasis in murine mammary cells transformed with H-Ras. Interestingly, interference with nuclear factor-κB activity in this cell model prevents TGF-β-induced EMT [Huber et al., 2004]. Akt also phosphorylates TSC2 in the TSC2-TSC1 complex, thus inhibiting its function as GTPase-activating protein toward the small GTPase protein Rheb. As a result, accumulation of Rheb-GTP activates the kinase mTOR in a complex called 'mTOR complex 1' (mTORC1) [Laplante and Sabatini, 2009]. Two major kinase targets of mTORC1 have been characterized: S6 kinases and 4E-BP1. The phosphorylation of S6 kinases 1 and 2 by mTORC1 regulates translation initiation and ribosome biogenesis, notably through activation of downstream targets such as the ribosomal protein S6 [Hay and Sonenberg, 2004; Holz et al., 2005]. Phosphorylation of 4E-BP1 by mTORC1 releases the eukaryotic translation initiation factor eIF4E from its interaction with 4E-BP1, thus initiating cap-dependent translation of mRNAs, such as the mRNA for cyclin D1, which is involved in cell cycle progression and proliferation [Hay and Sonenberg, 2004; Robert and Pelletier, 2009]. Therefore, activation of mTORC1 results in enhanced protein synthesis and, consequently, increased cell size. mTORC1 is activated not only in response to growth factors, but also responds to nutrients, amino acids and stress signals [Laplante and Sabatini, 2009].

Besides mTORC1 that comprises mTOR, mLST8 and Raptor, mTOR can also form a complex with mLST8, Rictor, mSin1 and Protor. The biology of this second complex named 'mTORC2' is less characterized when compared with mTORC1 [Laplante and Sabatini, 2009]. As mentioned already, mTORC2 mediates Akt phosphorylation, contributing to its full activation [Sarbassov et al., 2005]. It also phosphorylates protein kinase Cα and is believed to regulate the cytoskeletal organization by regulating Rho and Rac activities [Jacinto et al., 2004; Sarbassov et al., 2004]. Rapamycin acts as a specific inhibitor of mTORC1 activity and interferes with the recruitment and activation of mTORC1 targets, possibly by destabilizing the interaction of Raptor with mTOR. Rapamycin does not inhibit the activity of mTORC2, although prolonged rapamycin exposure can decrease mTORC2 activity by destabilizing the assembly of the regulatory components of this complex [Guertin and Sabatini, 2007].

We and others observed that TGF-β induces increases in cell size and protein content in various cell types, including epithelial cells that undergo EMT in response to

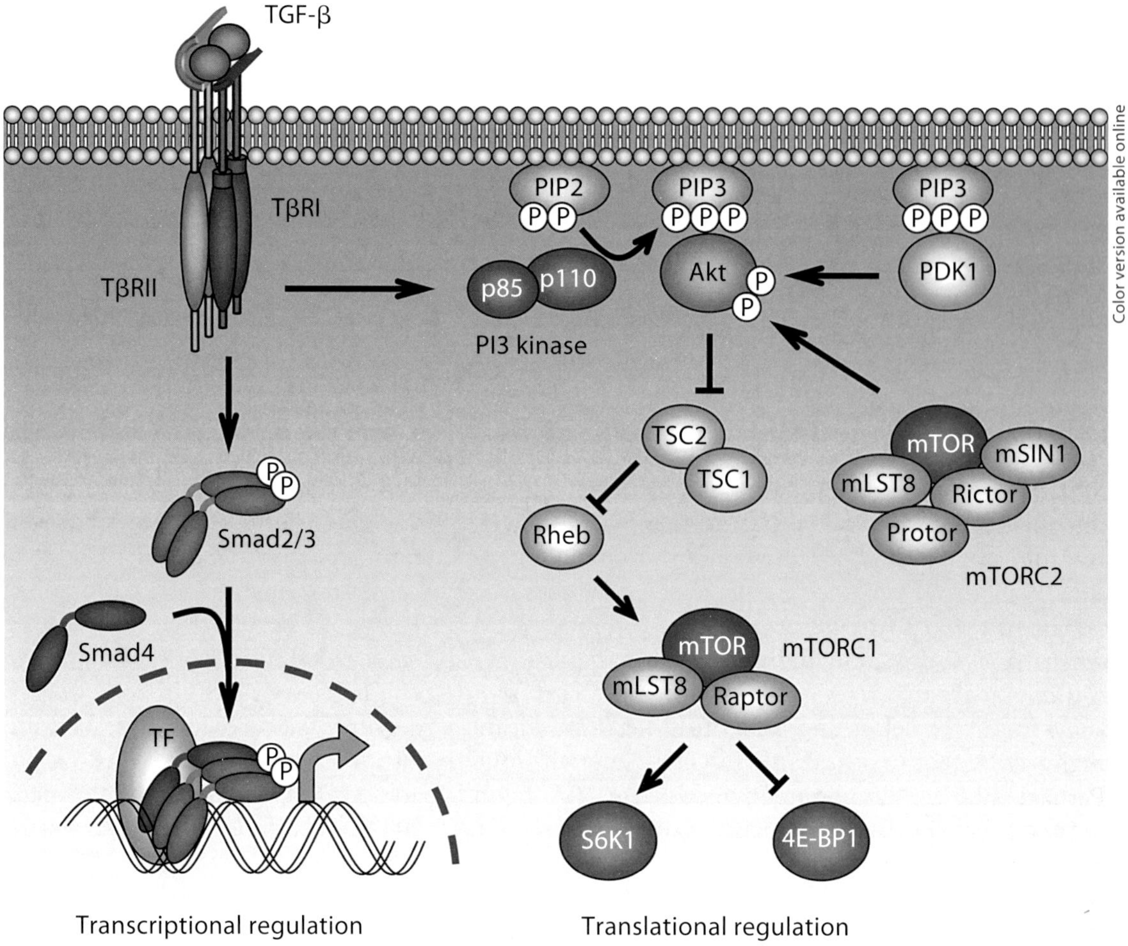

Color version available online

Fig. 3. PI3 kinase-Akt-mTOR signaling in TGF-β-induced EMT. During EMT, TGF-β activates mTORC1 in a PI3 kinase-Akt-dependent manner. This results in increases in protein synthesis, via phosphorylation of mTORC1 targets such as S6 kinase 1 (S6K1) and 4E-BP1, cell size, motility and invasion. This translational regulation complements the Smad-dependent transcriptional regulation. mTORC2 phosphorylates Akt, thus contributing to its activation, but its exact role in TGF-β-induced EMT remains to be discovered.

TGF-β [Lamouille and Derynck, 2007; Das et al., 2008; Wu and Derynck, 2009]. These increases were apparent in 2 models of TGF-β-induced EMT, the murine mammary gland NMuMG cells and the human HaCaT keratinocytes. In these cells, we also detected a TGF-β-induced activation of mTOR resulting in phosphorylation of the 2 targets of mTORC1, S6 kinase 1 and 4E-BP1, through the activation of PI3 kinase and Akt (fig. 3) [Lamouille and Derynck, 2007]. How TGF-β signaling links to activation of PI3 kinase is as yet unclear, although PI3 kinase has been found in association with the activated TGF-β receptor complex [Yi et al., 2005]. The increases in cell size and protein content in response to TGF-β are mediated by the activation of mTORC1, and accordingly, rapamycin inhibits the TGF-β-induced cell size and the protein content increases [Lamouille and Derynck, 2007]. The activation of S6 kinase 1 and 4E-BP1 is most likely responsible for the increased protein synthesis that occurs during TGF-β-induced EMT. These observations demonstrate that TGF-β regulates translation via PI3 kinase, Akt and mTORC1 during EMT. The activation of this translation pathway complements the transcriptional regulation through Smad signaling (fig. 3). Whereas the activation of translation by mTORC1 in response to TGF-β may complement the increased Smad-mediated transcriptional responses, it may also allow for selective translational control of target genes that potentially play a role in the phenotype and behavior of cells that have undergone EMT. Interestingly, increased S6 kinase 1 activity enhances EMT and invasion in human ovarian cancer cells through induction of Snail1 expression at the transcriptional level, but the mechanism of such regulation remains unclear [Pon et al., 2008].

To further define the role of the activation of mTORC1 in TGF-β-induced EMT, we treated NMuMG and HaCaT cells with TGF-β to induce EMT, in the presence of rapamycin. While the cells did not increase in size and protein content, the inhibition of mTORC1 did not block the morphological changes associated with EMT. Accordingly, similar to cells in the absence of rapamycin, TGF-β induced cell shape changes, accompanied with cytoskeletal reorganization, dissolution of the junctions with delocalization of E-cadherin and zona occludens-1, and induction of mesenchymal markers such as fibronectin and N-cadherin. Besides the morphological and gene expression changes, EMT is accompanied by a change in cell behavior, specifically migration and invasion. However, when mTORC1 activity is blocked using rapamycin in cell culture, the cells that have undergone EMT do not show the increases in migration and invasion that normally accompany EMT [Lamouille and Derynck, 2007]. Perhaps the increased protein synthesis that follows mTORC1 activation may participate in the enhanced expression of specific proteins that act directly or indirectly in cell migration and invasion, such as matrix metalloproteinases. Therefore, activation of mTORC1 downstream of PI3 kinase-Akt and in response to TGF-β contributes to EMT in 2 ways. While it mediates the increase in protein synthesis and cell size during EMT, mTORC1 activity is also essential for the increased motility and invasion of cells that have undergone EMT. Since increased invasion plays a key role in cancer progression toward metastasis, these results highlight a role for Akt-mTOR signaling in cancer progression, independent of cell proliferation regulation. Therefore, rapamycin analogs or other inhibitors of mTOR activity may aid in preventing invasion, cancer progression and metastasis. In line with our observations, rapamycin has been found to inhibit the downregulation of E-cadherin expression in mesothelial cells that undergo TGF-β-induced EMT [Aguilera et al., 2005], and to block motility in some other cell models [Liu et al., 2006; Gulati et al., 2009]. On the other hand, the rapamycin-insensitive mTORC2 is believed to play a role in cytoskeleton arrangement through the regulation of Rho, Rac and protein kinase Cα activities [Jacinto et al., 2004; Sarbassov et al., 2004]. Therefore, it is conceivable that this complex could be involved in the process of actin cytoskeleton reorganization that occurs during TGF-β-induced EMT. Interestingly, decreased activity of mTORC2 inhibits the migratory behavior of breast cancer cells [Qiao et al., 2007]. Additional studies will be needed to decipher a possible implication of mTORC2 in EMT and the mechanisms that regulate its activation.

TGF-β Signaling and the PI3 Kinase-Akt-mTOR Pathway in Cancer

In epithelial cells, TGF-β signaling leads to inhibition of cell proliferation, which serves as an autocrine tumor suppressor function, while other signaling responses can promote the transition toward carcinoma cells and aid in cancer progression. An early event in the transition from epithelial to carcinoma cells is the inactivation of the tumor suppressor effect of TGF-β [Bierie and Moses, 2006b; Nguyen and Massagué, 2007]. Mutations in TβRII and TβRI receptors, as well as in TGF-β Smads, have been observed in carcinomas and inactivate the growth inhibitory activity of TGF-β. In addition, alterations in downstream components of Smad signaling have been shown to result in a similar effect without inactivating other TGF-β responses that are beneficial to the tumor cells [Bierie and Moses, 2006a]. As cancer cells often have increased expression and activation of TGF-β, the autocrine responses of carcinoma cells to TGF-β, in particular the loss of the epithelial phenotype and induction of EMT, are thought to play an important role in driving the invasive behavior of carcinoma cells and progression toward metastasis [Derynck et al., 2001; Nguyen and Massagué, 2007]. Accordingly, expression of dominant negative TβRII receptor in metastatic cell lines inhibits EMT in vitro and in vivo [Oft et al., 1998; Portella et al., 1998; Han et al., 2005]. Therefore, TGF-β-induced EMT correlates with tumor metastasis through an increase in cell-invasive characteristics.

The complexity of the TGF-β signaling responses, and the dual nature of their effects on epithelial cancer cells, i.e. tumor suppression versus cancer progression, has made the development of anti-cancer approaches based on inhibition of TGF-β signaling challenging. Nevertheless, TβRI kinase inhibitors, neutralizing TGF-β antibodies and the dimerized TβRII extracellular domain fused to human IgG Fc domain, are being evaluated in preclinical and clinical trials as inhibitors of cancer progression [Bonafoux and Lee, 2009]. Rather than developing approaches to block all TGF-β signaling and cellular responses, it is preferable to selectively target the TGF-β-induced promotion of invasion and metastasis of cancer cells, thereby avoiding an inactivation of the tumor suppression function of TGF-β. Our insights into the role of Akt-mTOR signaling in TGF-β-induced EMT, and in particular invasion, may provide a basis for such a targeted approach.

Deregulation and increased activities of PI3 kinase and Akt have been linked to tumorigenesis and cancer progression. The gene encoding the catalytic subunit p110α of PI3 kinase is frequently mutated in human tumors, resulting in increased PIP3 production and, consequently, increased Akt signaling. Mutations in the gene encoding the PI3 kinase regulatory subunit p85α have also been identified, and these lead to constitutive PI3 kinase activity [Liu et al., 2009]. Moreover, amplification of Akt genes or overexpression of Akt has been observed in a range of human tumors and is generally associated with poor prognosis. Recently, mutations in the pleckstrin homology domain of Akt1 that lead to growth factor-independent anchoring to the plasma membrane and increased Akt1 phosphorylation have been identified in several cancers [Gonzalez and McGraw, 2009]. Finally, loss of the tumor suppressor PTEN, a phosphatase that antagonizes PI3 kinase activity by dephosphorylating PIP3, is commonly observed in cancer progression [Liu et al., 2009]. These and many other findings link an increase in PI3 kinase and Akt signaling to tumorigenesis and to increased cell survival and decreased apoptosis.

Increased and deregulated mTORC1 and mTORC2 activities have also been observed in tumors and linked to cancer progression. In a tightly controlled manner, mTORC1 regulates the synthesis of proteins involved in cell cycle progression, apoptosis, invasion and angiogenesis. A deregulation of mTORC1-dependent translation initiation consequently allows for enhanced tumor growth and metastasis. Accordingly, increased levels and phosphorylation of downstream targets of mTORC1 have been correlated with tumor aggressiveness in various human malignancies [Guertin and Sabatini, 2007]. In addition, mTORC2 phosphorylates Akt, and this phosphorylation, together with the phosphorylation of Akt by PDK1, results in full Akt activation [Sarbassov et al., 2005]. Although the mechanism of mTORC2 activation requires further characterization, the elevated Akt phosphorylation observed in various human tumors may be explained by a hyperactivation of mTORC2. It has recently been shown that mTORC2 is required for tumor initiation in a model of prostate cancer cells in PTEN-deficient mouse [Guertin et al., 2009].

Because of the frequently observed deregulation in PI3 kinase-Akt-mTOR signaling in human cancers, and its link to increased cell proliferation and survival, the PI3 kinase-Akt-mTOR pathway has been extensively targeted in the development of cancer therapies. Wortmannin and LY294002 represented a first generation of PI3 kinase inhibitors, but their lack of selectivity and high toxicity made these drugs unsuitable for the treatment of cancers. Recently, more isoform-specific chemical inhibitors of PI3 kinase have been developed, with some also targeting the mTOR kinase. For example, PI-103 inhibits the activities of p110α and mTOR, and its use for cancer therapy is being explored [Liu et al., 2009]. With its central role, Akt is also considered an attractive therapeutic target. Accordingly, several Akt inhibitors are currently in clinical trials for cancer treatment. They comprise lipid-based phosphatidylinositol analogs that prevent the localization of Akt to the plasma membrane, ATP-competitive kinase inhibitors and allosteric inhibitors [Liu et al., 2009]. Rapamycin is a natural inhibitor of mTORC1 but its poor solubility led pharmaceutical companies to develop analogs with improved pharmacokinetic properties, some of which are already in clinical use [Guertin and Sabatini, 2009]. Whereas rapamycin inhibits the activity of mTORC1, it does not block the activities of mTORC2, although prolonged exposure to rapamycin can affect the assembly of mTORC2 components [Guertin and Sabatini, 2007]. However, mTORC2 activity has been shown to be enhanced following inhibition of mTORC1, as observed by Akt hyperphosphorylation following rapamycin treatment in several cell models. Therefore, it may be imperative to also target mTORC2. Consequently, pharmacological kinase inhibitors of mTOR that inhibit both mTORC1 and mTORC2 have recently been developed and are clinically evaluated as therapy to cancer progression [Guertin and Sabatini, 2009].

Conclusions and Perspectives

The realization that TGF-β activates signaling through the PI3 kinase-Akt-mTOR axis and that this pathway is required for EMT and invasion now opens several opportunities, yet also leads to new questions. Our current data suggest that, in TGF-β-induced EMT, activation of mTOR signaling is required for motility and invasion, raising the possibility that inhibition of mTOR activity may prevent cancer dissemination. While such an approach may not block the cell morphological changes of

EMT, inhibiting the invasion process at the very basis of cancer progression may represent an avenue of selectively inhibiting the cancer-promoting effects of TGF-β without the concern of relieving the tumor suppressor activity of TGF-β. The current findings also raise a number of new questions about the molecular mechanisms and functions associated with TGF-β-induced PI3 kinase-Akt-mTOR signaling. How activation of the TGF-β receptor complex leads to activation of PI3 kinase-Akt-mTOR signaling is currently unclear, nor do we know which PI3 kinase or Akt proteins are involved. Inhibition of mTORC1 represents an attractive approach for the prevention of EMT-associated cell motility and invasion, and in uncovering novel effectors of this process which lie under mTORC1 selective translational regulation. Such a strategy should provide insight into the link between TGF-β-induced EMT and the mechanisms underlying cancer progression.

Acknowledgments

We are grateful to J. Smyth and J. Xu for their critical review of the manuscript. This research was supported by grants RO1-CA136690 and PO1-HL60231 (project III) to R. Derynck, a postdoctoral fellowship grant (grant 5566-07) from the Leukemia and Lymphoma Society and a scientist development grant (grant 09SDG2280008) from the American Heart Association to S. Lamouille.

References

Acloque, H., M.S. Adams, K. Fishwick, M. Bronner-Fraser, M.A. Nieto (2009) Epithelial-mesenchymal transitions: the importance of changing cell state in development and disease. J Clin Invest *119:* 1438–1449.

Aguilera, A., L.S. Aroeira, M. Ramirez-Huesca, M.L. Perez-Lozano, A. Cirugeda, M.A. Bajo, G. Del Peso, A. Valenzuela-Fernandez, J.A. Sanchez-Tomero, M. Lopez-Cabrera, R. Selgas (2005) Effects of rapamycin on the epithelial-to-mesenchymal transition of human peritoneal mesothelial cells. Int J Artif Organs *28:* 164–169.

Akhurst, R.J. (2008) TGF-β signaling in epithelial-mesenchymal transition and invasion and metastasis; in Derynck, R., K. Miyazono (eds) The TGF-β Family. New York, Cold Spring Harbor Laboratory Press, pp 939–964.

Alcorn, J.F., A.S. Guala, J. van der Velden, B. McElhinney, C.G. Irvin, R.J. Davis, Y.M. Janssen-Heininger (2008) Jun N-terminal kinase 1 regulates epithelial-to-mesenchymal transition induced by TGF-β_1. J Cell Sci *121:* 1036–1045.

Azhar, M., J. Schultz Jel, I. Grupp, G.W. Dorn, 2nd, P. Meneton, D.G. Molin, A.C. Gittenberger-de Groot, T. Doetschman (2003) Transforming growth factor-β in cardiovascular development and function. Cytokine Growth Factor Rev *14:* 391–407.

Bachelder, R.E., S.O. Yoon, C. Franci, A.G. de Herreros, A.M. Mercurio (2005) Glycogen synthase kinase-3 is an endogenous inhibitor of Snail transcription: implications for the epithelial-mesenchymal transition. J Cell Biol *168:* 29–33.

Bakin, A.V., C. Rinehart, A.K. Tomlinson, C.L. Arteaga (2002) p38 mitogen-activated protein kinase is required for TGF-β-mediated fibroblastic transdifferentiation and cell migration. J Cell Sci *115:* 3193–3206.

Bakin, A.V., A.K. Tomlinson, N.A. Bhowmick, H.L. Moses, C.L. Arteaga (2000) Phosphatidylinositol 3-kinase function is required for transforming growth factor-β-mediated epithelial to mesenchymal transition and cell migration. J Biol Chem *275:* 36803–36810.

Barrallo-Gimeno, A., M.A. Nieto (2005) The Snail genes as inducers of cell movement and survival: implications in development and cancer. Development *132:* 3151–3161.

Batlle, E., E. Sancho, C. Franci, D. Dominguez, M. Monfar, J. Baulida, A. Garcia De Herreros (2000) The transcription factor snail is a repressor of E-cadherin gene expression in epithelial tumour cells. Nat Cell Biol *2:* 84–89.

Bhowmick, N.A., M. Ghiassi, A. Bakin, M. Aakre, C.A. Lundquist, M.E. Engel, C.L. Arteaga, H.L. Moses (2001) Transforming growth factor-β_1 mediates epithelial to mesenchymal transdifferentiation through a RhoA-dependent mechanism. Mol Biol Cell *12:* 27–36.

Bierie, B., H.L. Moses (2006a) TGF-β and cancer. Cytokine Growth Factor Rev *17:* 29–40.

Bierie, B., H.L. Moses (2006b) Tumour microenvironment: TGF-β: the molecular Jekyll and Hyde of cancer. Nat Rev Cancer *6:* 506–520.

Bonafoux, D., W.C. Lee (2009) Strategies for TGF-β modulation: a review of recent patents. Expert Opin Ther Pat *19:* 1759–1769.

Bracken, C.P., P.A. Gregory, N. Kolesnikoff, A.G. Bert, J. Wang, M.F. Shannon, G.J. Goodall (2008) A double-negative feedback loop between ZEB1-SIP1 and the microRNA-200 family regulates epithelial-mesenchymal transition. Cancer Res *68:* 7846–7854.

Burk, U., J. Schubert, U. Wellner, O. Schmalhofer, E. Vincan, S. Spaderna, T. Brabletz (2008) A reciprocal repression between ZEB1 and members of the miR-200 family promotes EMT and invasion in cancer cells. EMBO Rep *9:* 582–589.

Cano, A., M.A. Perez-Moreno, I. Rodrigo, A. Locascio, M.J. Blanco, M.G. del Barrio, F. Portillo, M.A. Nieto (2000). The transcription factor snail controls epithelial-mesenchymal transitions by repressing E-cadherin expression. Nat Cell Biol *2:* 76–83.

Chaudhury, A., G.S. Hussey, P.S. Ray, G. Jin, P.L. Fox, P.H. Howe (2010) TGF-β-mediated phosphorylation of hnRNP E1 induces EMT via transcript-selective translational induction of Dab2 and ILEI. Nat Cell Biol *12:* 286–293.

Cho, H.J., K.E. Baek, S. Saika, M.J. Jeong, J. Yoo (2007) Snail is required for transforming growth factor-β-induced epithelial-mesenchymal transition by activating PI3 kinase/Akt signal pathway. Biochem Biophys Res Commun *353:* 337–343.

Cho, H.J., J. Yoo (2007) Rho activation is required for transforming growth factor-β-induced epithelial-mesenchymal transition in lens epithelial cells. Cell Biol Int *31:* 1225–1230.

Comijn, J., G. Berx, P. Vermassen, K. Verschueren, L. van Grunsven, E. Bruyneel, M. Mareel, D. Huylebroeck, F. van Roy (2001) The two-handed E box binding zinc finger protein SIP1 downregulates E-cadherin and induces invasion. Mol Cell *7:* 1267–1278.

Cui, W., D.J. Fowlis, S. Bryson, E. Duffie, H. Ireland, A. Balmain, R.J. Akhurst (1996) TGF-β_1 inhibits the formation of benign skin tumors, but enhances progression to invasive spindle carcinomas in transgenic mice. Cell *86:* 531–542.

Das, F., N. Ghosh-Choudhury, L. Mahimainathan, B. Venkatesan, D. Feliers, D.J. Riley, B.S. Kasinath, G.G. Choudhury (2008) Raptor-rictor axis in TGF-β-induced protein synthesis. Cell Signal *20:* 409–423.

Deckers, M., M. van Dinther, J. Buijs, I. Que, C. Lowik, G. van der Pluijm, P. ten Dijke (2006) The tumor suppressor Smad4 is required for transforming growth factor-β-induced epithelial to mesenchymal transition and bone metastasis of breast cancer cells. Cancer Res *66:* 2202–2209.

Derynck, R., R.J. Akhurst, A. Balmain (2001) TGF-β signaling in tumor suppression and cancer progression. Nat Genet *29:* 117–129.

Derynck, R., Y.E. Zhang (2003) Smad-dependent and Smad-independent pathways in TGF-β family signaling. Nature *425:* 577–584.

Eger, A., K. Aigner, S. Sonderegger, B. Dampier, S. Oehler, M. Schreiber, G. Berx, A. Cano, H. Beug, R. Foisner (2005) DeltaEF1 is a transcriptional repressor of E-cadherin and regulates epithelial plasticity in breast cancer cells. Oncogene *24:* 2375–2385.

Feng, X.H., R. Derynck (2005) Specificity and versatility in TGF-β signaling through Smads. Annu Rev Cell Dev Biol *21:* 659–693.

Gonzalez, E., T.E. McGraw (2009) The Akt kinases: isoform specificity in metabolism and cancer. Cell Cycle *8:* 2502–2508.

Gordon, K.J., K.C. Kirkbride, T. How, G.C. Blobe (2009) Bone morphogenetic proteins induce pancreatic cancer cell invasiveness through a Smad1-dependent mechanism that involves matrix metalloproteinase-2. Carcinogenesis *30:* 238–248.

Grande, M., A. Franzen, J.O. Karlsson, L.E. Ericson, N.E. Heldin, M. Nilsson (2002) Transforming growth factor-β and epidermal growth factor synergistically stimulate epithelial to mesenchymal transition (EMT) through a MEK-dependent mechanism in primary cultured pig thyrocytes. J Cell Sci *115:* 4227–4236.

Gregory, P.A., A.G. Bert, E.L. Paterson, S.C. Barry, A. Tsykin, G. Farshid, M.A. Vadas, Y. Khew-Goodall, G.J. Goodall (2008) The miR-200 family and miR-205 regulate epithelial to mesenchymal transition by targeting ZEB1 and SIP1. Nat Cell Biol *10:* 593–601.

Gressner, A.M., R. Weiskirchen, K. Breitkopf, S. Dooley (2002) Roles of TGF-β in hepatic fibrosis. Front Biosci *7:* d793–d807.

Guertin, D.A., D.M. Sabatini (2007) Defining the role of mTOR in cancer. Cancer Cell *12:* 9–22.

Guertin, D.A., D.M. Sabatini (2009) The pharmacology of mTOR inhibition. Sci Signal *2:* pe24.

Guertin, D.A., D.M. Stevens, M. Saitoh, S. Kinkel, K. Crosby, J.H. Sheen, D.J. Mullholland, M.A. Magnuson, H. Wu, D.M. Sabatini (2009) mTOR complex 2 is required for the development of prostate cancer induced by Pten loss in mice. Cancer Cell *15:* 148–159.

Gulati, N., M. Karsy, L. Albert, R. Murali, M. Jhanwar-Uniyal (2009) Involvement of mTORC1 and mTORC2 in regulation of glioblastoma multiforme growth and motility. Int J Oncol *35:* 731–740.

Han, G., S.L. Lu, A.G. Li, W. He, C.L. Corless, M. Kulesz-Martin, X.J. Wang (2005) Distinct mechanisms of TGF-β_1-mediated epithelial-to-mesenchymal transition and metastasis during skin carcinogenesis. J Clin Invest *115:* 1714–1723.

Hay, N., N. Sonenberg (2004) Upstream and downstream of mTOR. Genes Dev *18:* 1926–1945.

Holz, M.K., B.A. Ballif, S.P. Gygi, J. Blenis (2005) mTOR and S6K1 mediate assembly of the translation preinitiation complex through dynamic protein interchange and ordered phosphorylation events. Cell *123:* 569–580.

Hoot, K.E., J. Lighthall, G. Han, S.L. Lu, A. Li, W. Ju, M. Kulesz-Martin, E. Böttinger, X.J. Wang (2008) Keratinocyte-specific Smad2 ablation results in increased epithelialmesenchymal transition during skin cancer formation and progression. J Clin Invest *118:* 2722–2732.

Huber, M.A., N. Azoitei, B. Baumann, S. Grunert, A. Sommer, H. Pehamberger, N. Kraut, H. Beug, T. Wirth (2004) NF-kappaB is essential for epithelial-mesenchymal transition and metastasis in a model of breast cancer progression. J Clin Invest *114:* 569–581.

Iliopoulos, D., C. Polytarchou, M. Hatziapostolou, F. Kottakis, I.G. Maroulakou, K. Struhl, P.N. Tsichlis (2009) MicroRNAs differentially regulated by Akt isoforms control EMT and stem cell renewal in cancer cells. Sci Signal *2:* ra62.

Irie, H.Y., R.V. Pearline, D. Grueneberg, M. Hsia, P. Ravichandran, N. Kothari, S. Natesan, J.S. Brugge (2005) Distinct roles of Akt1 and Akt2 in regulating cell migration and epithelial-mesenchymal transition. J Cell Biol *171:* 1023–1034.

Iwano, M., D. Plieth, T.M. Danoff, C. Xue, H. Okada, E.G. Neilson (2002) Evidence that fibroblasts derive from epithelium during tissue fibrosis. J Clin Invest *110:* 341–350.

Jacinto, E., R. Loewith, A. Schmidt, S. Lin, M.A. Ruegg, A. Hall, M.N. Hall (2004) Mammalian TOR complex 2 controls the actin cytoskeleton and is rapamycin insensitive. Nat Cell Biol *6:* 1122–1128.

Julien, S., I. Puig, E. Caretti, J. Bonaventure, L. Nelles, F. van Roy, C. Dargemont, A.G. de Herreros, A. Bellacosa, L. Larue (2007) Activation of NF-kappaB by Akt upregulates Snail expression and induces epithelium mesenchyme transition. Oncogene *26:* 7445–7456.

Kalluri, R., E.G. Neilson (2003) Epithelial-mesenchymal transition and its implications for fibrosis. J Clin Invest *112:* 1776–1784.

Kalluri, R., R.A. Weinberg (2009) The basics of epithelial-mesenchymal transition. J Clin Invest *119:* 1420–1428.

Kang, Y., C.R. Chen, J. Massagué (2003) A self-enabling TGF-β response coupled to stress signaling: Smad engages stress response factor ATF3 for Id1 repression in epithelial cells. Mol Cell *11:* 915–926.

Kishigami, S., Y. Mishina (2005) BMP signaling and early embryonic patterning. Cytokine Growth Factor Rev *16:* 265–278.

Klattig, J., C. Englert (2007) The Mullerian duct: recent insights into its development and regression. Sex Dev *1:* 271–278.

Klymkowsky, M.W., P. Savagner (2009) Epithelial-mesenchymal transition: a cancer researcher's conceptual friend and foe. Am J Pathol *174:* 1588–1593.

Kondo, M., E. Cubillo, K. Tobiume, T. Shirakihara, N. Fukuda, H. Suzuki, K. Shimizu, K. Takehara, A. Cano, M. Saitoh, K. Miyazono (2004) A role for Id in the regulation of TGF-β-induced epithelial-mesenchymal transdifferentiation. Cell Death Differ *11:* 1092–1101.

Kong, W., H. Yang, L. He, J.J. Zhao, D. Coppola, W.S. Dalton, J.Q. Cheng (2008) MicroRNA-155 is regulated by the transforming growth factor-β/Smad pathway and contributes to epithelial cell plasticity by targeting RhoA. Mol Cell Biol *28:* 6773–6784.

Lamouille, S., R. Derynck (2007) Cell size and invasion in TGF-β-induced epithelial to mesenchymal transition is regulated by activation of the mTOR pathway. J Cell Biol *178:* 437–451.

Laplante, M., D.M. Sabatini (2009) mTOR signaling at a glance. J Cell Sci *122:* 3589–3594.

Larue, L., A. Bellacosa (2005) Epithelial-mesenchymal transition in development and cancer: role of phosphatidylinositol 3-kinase/AKT pathways. Oncogene *24:* 7443–7454.

Lee, M.K., C. Pardoux, M.C. Hall, P.S. Lee, D. Warburton, J. Qing, S.M. Smith, R. Derynck (2007) TGF-β activates Erk MAP kinase signaling through direct phosphorylation of ShcA. EMBO J *26:* 3957–3967.

Lee, Y.I., Y.J. Kwon, C.K. Joo (2004) Integrin-linked kinase function is required for transforming growth factor-β-mediated epithelial to mesenchymal transition. Biochem Biophys Res Commun *316:* 997–1001.

Lien, S.C., S. Usami, S. Chien, J.J. Chiu (2006) Phosphatidylinositol 3-kinase/Akt pathway is involved in transforming growth factor-β_1-induced phenotypic modulation of 10T1/2 cells to smooth muscle cells. Cell Signal *18:* 1270–1278.

Lin, C.C., L.L. Chiang, C.H. Lin, C.H. Shih, Y.T. Liao, M.J. Hsu, B.C. Chen (2007) Transforming growth factor-β_1 stimulates heme oxygenase-1 expression via the PI3K/Akt and NF-kappaB pathways in human lung epithelial cells. Eur J Pharmacol *560:* 101–109.

Liu, L., F. Li, J.A. Cardelli, K.A. Martin, J. Blenis, S. Huang (2006) Rapamycin inhibits cell motility by suppression of mTOR-mediated S6K1 and 4E-BP1 pathways. Oncogene *25:* 7029–7040.

Liu, P., H. Cheng, T.M. Roberts, J.J. Zhao (2009) Targeting the phosphoinositide 3-kinase pathway in cancer. Nat Rev Drug Discov *8:* 627–644.

Ma, L., M.F. Lu, R.J. Schwartz, J.F. Martin (2005) Bmp2 is essential for cardiac cushion epithelial-mesenchymal transition and myocardial patterning. Development *132:* 5601–5611.

Masszi, A., A. Kapus (2011) Smaddening complexity: The role of Smad3 in epithelial-myofibroblast transition. Cells Tissues Organs *193:* 41–52.

McDonald, P.C., A.B. Fielding, S. Dedhar (2008) Integrin-linked kinase – essential roles in physiology and cancer biology. J Cell Sci *121:* 3121–3132.

Meindl-Beinker, N.M., S. Dooley (2008) Transforming growth factor-β and hepatocyte transdifferentiation in liver fibrogenesis. J Gastroenterol Hepatol *23 (suppl 1):* S122–S127.

Mercado-Pimentel, M.E., R.B. Runyan (2007) Multiple transforming growth factor-β isoforms and receptors function during epithelial-mesenchymal cell transformation in the embryonic heart. Cells Tissues Organs *185:* 146–156.

Miettinen, P.J., R. Ebner, A.R. Lopez, R. Derynck (1994) TGF-β induced transdifferentiation of mammary epithelial cells to mesenchymal cells: involvement of type I receptors. J Cell Biol *127:* 2021–2036.

Miyazono, K (2009) Transforming growth factor-β signaling in epithelial-mesenchymal transition and progression of cancer. Proc Jpn Acad Ser B Phys Biol Sci *85:* 314–323.

Moreno-Bueno, G., F. Portillo, A. Cano (2008) Transcriptional regulation of cell polarity in EMT and cancer. Oncogene *27:* 6958–6969.

Moustakas, A., C.H. Heldin (2005) Non-Smad TGF-β signals. J Cell Sci *118:* 3573–3584.

Moustakas, A., C.H. Heldin (2007) Signaling networks guiding epithelial-mesenchymal transitions during embryogenesis and cancer progression. Cancer Sci *98:* 1512–1520.

Nakajima, Y., T. Yamagishi, S. Hokari, H. Nakamura (2000) Mechanisms involved in valvuloseptal endocardial cushion formation in early cardiogenesis: roles of transforming growth factor (TGF)-β and bone morphogenetic protein (BMP). Anat Rec *258:* 119–127.

Nawshad, A., D. LaGamba, E.D. Hay (2004) Transforming growth factor-β (TGF-β) signaling in palatal growth, apoptosis and epithelial mesenchymal transformation (EMT). Arch Oral Biol *49:* 675–689.

Nguyen, D.X., J. Massagué (2007) Genetic determinants of cancer metastasis. Nat Rev Genet *8:* 341–352.

Oft, M., K.H. Heider, H. Beug (1998) TGF-β signaling is necessary for carcinoma cell invasiveness and metastasis. Curr Biol *8:* 1243–1252.

Ozdamar, B., R. Bose, M. Barrios-Rodiles, H.R. Wang, Y. Zhang, J.L. Wrana (2005) Regulation of the polarity protein Par6 by TGF-β receptors controls epithelial cell plasticity. Science *307:* 1603–1609.

Padua, D., J. Massagué (2009) Roles of TGF-β in metastasis. Cell Res *19:* 89–102.

Peinado, H., D. Olmeda, A. Cano (2007) Snail, Zeb and bHLH factors in tumour progression: an alliance against the epithelial phenotype? Nat Rev Cancer *7:* 415–428.

Pellegrin, S., H. Mellor (2007) Actin stress fibres. J Cell Sci *120:* 3491–3499.

Pelton, R.W., B.L. Hogan, D.A. Miller, H.L. Moses (1990) Differential expression of genes encoding TGFs β_1, β_2, and β_3 during murine palate formation. Dev Biol *141:* 456–460.

Perez-Moreno, M.A., A. Locascio, I. Rodrigo, G. Dhondt, F. Portillo, M.A. Nieto, A. Cano (2001) A new role for E12/E47 in the repression of E-cadherin expression and epithelial-mesenchymal transitions. J Biol Chem *276:* 27424–27431.

Perk, J., A. Iavarone, R. Benezra (2005) Id family of helix-loop-helix proteins in cancer. Nat Rev Cancer *5:* 603–614.

Piek, E., A. Moustakas, A. Kurisaki, C.H. Heldin, P. ten Dijke (1999) TGF-β type I receptor/ALK-5 and Smad proteins mediate epithelial to mesenchymal transdifferentiation in NMuMG breast epithelial cells. J Cell Sci *112:* 4557–4568.

Pon, Y.L., H.Y. Zhou, A.N. Cheung, H.Y. Ngan, A.S. Wong (2008) p70 S6 kinase promotes epithelial to mesenchymal transition through snail induction in ovarian cancer cells. Cancer Res *68:* 6524–6532.

Portella, G., S.A. Cumming, J. Liddell, W. Cui, H. Ireland, R.J. Akhurst, A. Balmain (1998) Transforming growth factor-β is essential for spindle cell conversion of mouse skin carcinoma in vivo: implications for tumor invasion. Cell Growth Differ *9:* 393–404.

Qiao, M., J.D. Iglehart, A.B. Pardee (2007) Metastatic potential of 21T human breast cancer cells depends on Akt/protein kinase B activation. Cancer Res *67:* 5293–5299.

Robert, F., J. Pelletier (2009) Translation initiation: a critical signaling node in cancer. Expert Opin Ther Targets *13:* 1279–1293.

Rodriguez-Barbero, A., F. Dorado, S. Velasco, A. Pandiella, B. Banas, J.M. Lopez-Novoa (2006) TGF-β_1 induces COX-2 expression and PGE2 synthesis through MAPK and PI3K pathways in human mesangial cells. Kidney Int *70:* 901–909.

Ruzinova, M.B., R. Benezra (2003) Id proteins in development, cell cycle and cancer. Trends Cell Biol *13:* 410–418.

Santibanez, J.F. (2006) JNK mediates TGF-β_1-induced epithelial mesenchymal transdifferentiation of mouse transformed keratinocytes. FEBS Lett *580:* 5385–5391.

Sarbassov, D.D., S.M. Ali, D.H. Kim, D.A. Guertin, R.R. Latek, H. Erdjument-Bromage, P. Tempst, D.M. Sabatini (2004) Rictor, a novel binding partner of mTOR, defines a rapamycin-insensitive and raptor-independent pathway that regulates the cytoskeleton. Curr Biol *14:* 1296–1302.

Sarbassov, D.D., D.A. Guertin, S.M. Ali, D.M. Sabatini (2005) Phosphorylation and regulation of Akt/PKB by the rictor-mTOR complex. Science *307:* 1098–1101.

Schmidt, C.R., Y.J. Gi, T.A. Patel, R.J. Coffey, R.D. Beauchamp, A.S. Pearson (2005) E-cadherin is regulated by the transcriptional repressor SLUG during Ras-mediated transformation of intestinal epithelial cells. Surgery *138:* 306–312.

Schnaper, H.W., T. Hayashida, S.C. Hubchak, A.C. Poncelet (2003) TGF-β signal transduction and mesangial cell fibrogenesis. Am J Physiol Renal Physiol *284:* F243–F252.

Shi, Y., J. Massagué (2003) Mechanisms of TGF-β signaling from cell membrane to the nucleus. Cell *113:* 685–700.

Shirakihara, T., M. Saitoh, K. Miyazono (2007) Differential regulation of epithelial and mesenchymal markers by deltaEF1 proteins in epithelial mesenchymal transition induced by TGF-β. Mol Biol Cell *18:* 3533–3544.

Sorrentino, A., N. Thakur, S. Grimsby, A. Marcusson, V. von Bulow, N. Schuster, S. Zhang, C.H. Heldin, M. Landstrom (2008) The type I TGF-β receptor engages TRAF6 to activate TAK1 in a receptor kinase-independent manner. Nat Cell Biol *10:* 1199–1207.

Tavares, A.L., M.E. Mercado-Pimentel, R.B. Runyan, G.T. Kitten (2006) TGF-β-mediated RhoA expression is necessary for epithelial-mesenchymal transition in the embryonic chick heart. Dev Dyn *235:* 1589–1598.

Theriault, B.L., T.G. Shepherd, M.L. Mujoomdar, M.W. Nachtigal (2007) BMP4 induces EMT and Rho GTPase activation in human ovarian cancer cells. Carcinogenesis *28:* 1153–1162.

Thiery, J.P (2003) Epithelial-mesenchymal transitions in development and pathologies. Curr Opin Cell Biol *15:* 740–746.

Thiery, J.P., H. Acloque, R.Y. Huang, M.A. Nieto (2009) Epithelial-mesenchymal transitions in development and disease. Cell *139:* 871–890.

Thiery, J.P., J.P. Sleeman (2006) Complex networks orchestrate epithelial-mesenchymal transitions. Nat Rev Mol Cell Biol *7:* 131–142.

Thuault, S., U. Valcourt, M. Petersen, G. Manfioletti, C.H. Heldin, A. Moustakas (2006) Transforming growth factor-β employs HMGA2 to elicit epithelial-mesenchymal transition. J Cell Biol *174:* 175–183.

Uttamsingh, S., X. Bao, K.T. Nguyen, M. Bhanot, J. Gong, J.L. Chan, F. Liu, T.T. Chu, L.H. Wang (2008) Synergistic effect between EGF and TGF-β_1 in inducing oncogenic properties of intestinal epithelial cells. Oncogene *27:* 2626–2634.

Valcourt, U., M. Kowanetz, H. Niimi, C.H. Heldin, A. Moustakas (2005) TGF-β and the Smad signaling pathway support transcriptomic reprogramming during epithelial-mesenchymal cell transition. Mol Biol Cell *16:* 1987–2002.

Vardouli, L., A. Moustakas, C. Stournaras (2005) LIM-kinase 2 and cofilin phosphorylation mediate actin cytoskeleton reorganization induced by transforming growth factor-β. J Biol Chem *280:* 11448–11457.
Vincent, T., E.P. Neve, J.R. Johnson, A. Kukalev, F. Rojo, J. Albanell, K. Pietras, I. Virtanen, L. Philipson, P.L. Leopold, R.G. Crystal, A.G. de Herreros, A. Moustakas, R.F. Pettersson, J. Fuxe (2009) A SNAIL1-SMAD3/4 transcriptional repressor complex promotes TGF-β mediated epithelial-mesenchymal transition. Nat Cell Biol *11:* 943–950.
Willis, B.C., Z. Borok (2007) TGF-β-induced EMT: mechanisms and implications for fibrotic lung disease. Am J Physiol Lung Cell Mol Physiol *293:* L525–L534.
Wu, L., R. Derynck (2009) Essential role of TGF-β signaling in glucose-induced cell hypertrophy. Dev Cell *17:* 35–48.
Xie, L., B.K. Law, A.M. Chytil, K.A. Brown, M.E. Aakre, H.L. Moses (2004) Activation of the Erk pathway is required for TGF-β_1-induced EMT in vitro. Neoplasia *6:* 603–610.
Xu, J., S. Lamouille, R. Derynck (2009) TGF-β-induced epithelial to mesenchymal transition. Cell Res *19:* 156–172.
Yamashita, M., K. Fatyol, C. Jin, X. Wang, Z. Liu, Y.E. Zhang (2008) TRAF6 mediates Smad-independent activation of JNK and p38 by TGF-β. Mol Cell *31:* 918–924.
Yang, J., S.A. Mani, J.L. Donaher, S. Ramaswamy, R.A. Itzykson, C. Come, P. Savagner, I. Gitelman, A. Richardson, R.A. Weinberg (2004) Twist, a master regulator of morphogenesis, plays an essential role in tumor metastasis. Cell *117:* 927–939.
Yeh, Y.Y., C.C. Chiao, W.Y. Kuo, Y.C. Hsiao, Y.J. Chen, Y.Y. Wei, T.H. Lai, Y.C. Fong, C.H. Tang (2008) TGF-β_1 increases motility and $\alpha v\beta_3$ integrin up-regulation via PI3K, Akt and NF-kappaB-dependent pathway in human chondrosarcoma cells. Biochem Pharmacol *75:* 1292–1301.
Yi, J.Y., I. Shin, C.L. Arteaga (2005) Type I transforming growth factor-β receptor binds to and activates phosphatidylinositol 3-kinase. J Biol Chem *280:* 10870–10876.
Yilmaz, M., G. Christofori (2009) EMT, the cytoskeleton, and cancer cell invasion. Cancer Metastasis Rev *28:* 15–33.
Yu, L., M.C. Hebert, Y.E. Zhang (2002) TGF-β receptor-activated p38 MAP kinase mediates Smad-independent TGF-β responses. EMBO J *21:* 3749–3759.
Zavadil, J., E.P. Böttinger (2005) TGF-β and epithelial-to-mesenchymal transitions. Oncogene *24:* 5764–5774.
Zeisberg, E.M., O. Tarnavski, M. Zeisberg, A.L. Dorfman, J.R. McMullen, E. Gustafsson, A. Chandraker, X. Yuan, W.T. Pu, A.B. Roberts, E.G. Neilson, M.H. Sayegh, S. Izumo, R. Kalluri (2007) Endothelial-to-mesenchymal transition contributes to cardiac fibrosis. Nat Med *13:* 952–961.
Zeisberg, M., J. Hanai, H. Sugimoto, T. Mammoto, D. Charytan, F. Strutz, R. Kalluri (2003) BMP-7 counteracts TGF-β_1-induced epithelial-to-mesenchymal transition and reverses chronic renal injury. Nat Med *9:* 964–968.
Zeisberg, M., E.G. Neilson (2009) Biomarkers for epithelial-mesenchymal transitions. J Clin Invest *119:* 1429–1437.
Zeisberg, M., A.A. Shah, R. Kalluri (2005) Bone morphogenic protein-7 induces mesenchymal to epithelial transition in adult renal fibroblasts and facilitates regeneration of injured kidney. J Biol Chem *280:* 8094–8100.
Zhou, B.P., J. Deng, W. Xia, J. Xu, Y.M. Li, M. Gunduz, M.C. Hung (2004) Dual regulation of Snail by GSK-3beta-mediated phosphorylation in control of epithelial-mesenchymal transition. Nat Cell Biol *6:* 931–940.

Cells Tissues Organs

Cells Tissues Organs 2011;193:23–40
DOI: 10.1159/000320174

Published online: November 2, 2010

Defining the E-Cadherin Repressor Interactome in Epithelial-Mesenchymal Transition: The PMC42 Model as a Case Study

Honor J. Hugo[a, b] Maria I. Kokkinos[c, d] Tony Blick[a] M. Leigh Ackland[e] Erik W. Thompson[a, f] Donald F. Newgreen[b]

[a]St. Vincent's Institute of Medical Research, [b]Embryology Laboratory, Murdoch Children's Research Institute, Royal Children's Hospital, [c]Pregnancy Research Centre, Department of Perinatal Medicine, and [d]Department of Obstetrics and Gynaecology, University of Melbourne, The Royal Women's Hospital, [e]Centre for Cellular and Molecular Biology, School of Life and Environmental Sciences, Deakin University, and [f]Department of Surgery, University of Melbourne, St Vincent's Hospital, Melbourne, Vic., Australia

Key Words

Breast cancer · Epithelial-mesenchymal transition · E-cadherin transcriptional repression · Inter-regulation

Abstract

Epithelial-mesenchymal transition (EMT) is a feature of migratory cellular processes in all stages of life, including embryonic development and wound healing. Importantly, EMT features cluster with disease states such as chronic fibrosis and cancer. The dissolution of the E-cadherin-mediated adherens junction (AJ) is a key preliminary step in EMT and may occur early or late in the growing epithelial tumour. This is a first step for tumour cells towards stromal invasion, intravasation, extravasation and distant metastasis. The AJ may be inactivated in EMT by directed E-cadherin cleavage; however, it is increasingly evident that the majority of AJ changes are transcriptional and mediated by an expanding group of transcription factors acting directly or indirectly to repress E-cadherin expression. A review of the current literature has revealed that these factors may regulate each other in a hierarchical pattern where Snail1 (formerly Snail) and Snail2 (formerly Slug) are initially induced, leading to the activation of Zeb family members, TCF3, TCF4, Twist, Goosecoid and FOXC2. Within this general pathway, many inter-regulatory relationships have been defined which may be important in maintaining the EMT phenotype. This may be important given the short half-life of Snail1 protein. We have investigated these inter-regulatory relationships in the mesenchymal breast carcinoma cell line PMC42 (also known as PMC42ET) and its epithelial derivative, PMC42LA. This review also discusses several newly described regulators of E-cadherin repressors including oestrogen receptor-α and new discoveries in hypoxia- and growth factor-induced EMT. Finally, we evaluated how these findings may influence approaches to current cancer treatment.

Abbreviations used in this paper

AJ	adherens junction
EGF	epidermal growth factor
EMT	epithelial-mesenchymal transition
ER	oestrogen receptor-α
HDAC	histone deacetylase
HDACi	histone deacetylase inhibitor
KLF8	Kruppel-like factor 8
MDCK	Madin-Darby canine kidney
MET	mesenchymal-epithelial transition
miR	microRNA
MMP	matrix metalloproteinase
NF-κB	nuclear factor-κB
siRNA	small interfering RNA
TGF-β	transforming growth factor-β

KARGER

Fax +41 61 306 12 34
E-Mail karger@karger.ch
www.karger.com

1422–6405/11/1932–0023$38.00/0

Accessible online at:
www.karger.com/cto

Dr. Honor J. Hugo
VBCRC Invasion and Metastasis Unit
St Vincent's Institute, 9 Princes St.
Fitzroy, VIC 3065 (Australia)
Tel. +61 3 9288 2670, Fax +61 3 9416 2676, E-Mail hhugo@svi.edu.au

Introduction

Epithelial-mesenchymal transition (EMT) is a complex set of molecular and cellular changes [for a review, see ref. Hay, 1995; Hugo et al., 2007; Thiery et al., 2009]. The key features of EMT are reduction in cell-cell adhesion, molecular alterations and spatial redistribution of adhesive interactions with extracellular matrix, loss of apico-basal cytoskeletal polarity and gain of front-back polarity. Following EMT, individual cells also show potential for motility and invasion [for a review, see ref. Tsuji et al., 2009]. In normal development, EMT is essential for gastrulation and delamination of neural crest cells from the epiblast and neural epithelia, respectively. Interestingly, the process leading to carcinoma invasion appears descriptively and molecularly similar, and there is increasing attention towards the role of EMT as a critical component of metastasis [Thiery et al., 2006], thought to underlie the spread of malignant cells from a primary carcinoma to distant sites [Geiger and Peeper, 2009].

A major attribute of EMT is the transcriptional or post-transcriptional repression of adherens junction (AJ) cell-cell adhesion molecules, typically E-cadherin, and the subsequent delocalization of AJ-associated molecules like β-catenin. Direct repressors of E-cadherin transcription in EMT are Snail1, Snail2 (formerly Slug), Zeb1 (δEF1), Zeb2 (SIP1) and Kruppel-like factor 8 (KLF8). The indirect E-cadherin repressor group, a rapidly expanding collection of factors whose mechanisms of action in EMT are less defined, includes Twist, Goosecoid, FOXC2, TCF3 (E12/E47), TCF4 (E2.2) and nuclear factor-κB (NF-κB) [for a review, see ref. Thiery et al., 2009]. Along with E-cadherin, the tight junction molecules zona occludens 1 (also called 'TJP1'), occludin and claudin-1 are also delocalized. The expression of epithelial intermediate filament proteins, cytokeratins, is often reduced and the gene encoding the equivalent mesenchymal intermediate filament protein, vimentin, is activated. Matrix metalloproteinases (MMPs) such as MMP-2, MMP-9 and MMP-14 are up-regulated, potentially enabling cells to detach from each other (in part via E-cadherin cleavage) and to exit the tumour mass (via digestion of the basement membrane) [Przybylo and Radisky, 2007; Stallings-Mann and Radisky, 2007].

A notion gathering impetus is that cancer cells which have undergone EMT acquire characteristics of stem cells [for a review, see ref. Hollier et al., 2009; Polyak and Weinberg, 2009]. This has been widely studied in the context of breast cancer. Human mammary cells in which Snail1 or Twist was ectopically expressed, or were treated with transforming growth factor (TGF)-β, underwent an EMT and showed increased stem-like capabilities [Mani et al., 2008]. Additionally, inhibition of pro-EMT Wnt signalling in cells derived from a breast cancer lung metastasis reduced their self-renewal and tumour-seeding capability [DiMeo et al., 2009]. The PMC42 breast carcinoma cell line which undergoes epidermal growth factor (EGF)- or hypoxia-induced EMT (see below) exhibits stem cell characteristics [Whitehead et al., 1983]. Although still a subject of debate [Gupta et al., 2009], alignment of the EMT phenotype with that of stem cells will have considerable implications for our understanding of tumour behaviour, possibly of a similar magnitude to the discovery that the factors and pathways involved in pathological EMT draw from that of normal developmental events.

This review describes the impact of extracellular inducers of EMT, including growth factors, hypoxia and oestrogen, on E-cadherin transcriptional repressor molecules (direct repressor set) in carcinogenesis and summarizes key inter-regulatory/co-operative relationships and hierarchies. We also defined the set of factors which indirectly repress the E-cadherin gene to induce EMT and how these factors inter-relate with the direct repressor set. Finally, we evaluated current chemotherapeutic approaches in light of recent discoveries in the field of EMT.

Growth Factor-Induced EMT

In embryonic EMTs, induction by growth factors is a common theme. For example, neural crest EMT follows exposure of neural epithelia to fibroblast growth factors, Wnts and bone morphogenic protein 4 [for a review, see ref. Sauka-Spengler et al., 2008]. In addition to these, several other growth factors (EGF, hepatocyte growth factor, insulin-like growth factor, fibroblast growth factor and tumor necrosis factor-α) result in elevated Snail1 and/or Snail2 in EMT via signalling through their receptor tyrosine kinases [for a review, see ref. Christiansen and Rajasekaran, 2006]. Subsequently, these activate PI3K and Ras, resulting in activated MAPK and ultimately in Snail1 and Snail2 expression [Peinado et al., 2003]. TGF-β is a consistently described inducer of EMT via its downstream signalling molecule Smad, through which Snail, Zeb1 and Zeb2 are induced [for a review, see ref. Miyazono, 2009]. The protein tyrosine phosphatase, Pez, has also been shown to be a novel inducer of TGF-β signalling in EMT [Wyatt and Khew-Goodall, 2008], and when over-expressed in Madin-Darby canine kidney (MDCK) cells, induced Snail1, Snail2, Zeb1 and Zeb2 [Wyatt et al., 2007]. EGF is a potent stimulator of EMT in several cell types, where its activated receptor has been shown to cause tyrosine phosphorylate β-catenin, leading to its dissociation from the AJ [Nelson and Nusse, 2004; Klymkowsky, 2005]. Endocytosis of E-cadherin also results in the release of β-catenin, which then activates the Wnt pathway resulting in Snail gene transcription, and further, in E-cadherin repression [Lu et al., 2003]. EGF induces EMT-like changes in the PMC42LA breast carcinoma cell line, as shown by gene and protein expression changes and acquisition of motility [Ackland et al., 2003a]. This EGF-induced EMT is enhanced in PMC42LA cells when used in combination with the kinase inhibitor staurosporine, whose initial target is the cytoskeleton [Hugo et al., 2009]. EGF induces EMT in ovarian cancer cells, involving EGF receptor/interleukin-6 receptor co-ordination and activation of the JAK/STAT pathway, resulting in modulation of extracellular matrix interactions through the induction of integrin-$\alpha_6\beta_1$ [Colomiere et al., 2009a, 2009b]. EGF has been shown to induce an EMT in the prostate cancer cell line DU145 [Lu et al., 2003] and in ovarian surface epithelium [Ahmed et al., 2006]. Additionally, hepatocyte growth factor, endothelin-1 and TGF-β have been demonstrated to play a role in the EMT of ovarian cancer [for a review, see ref. Vergara et al., 2009].

Hypoxia

Unrestrained tumour growth with a poorly organized blood supply results in hypoxia [Chaudary and Hill, 2006], and tumours which have hypoxic regions are more likely to metastasize [Boyle and Travers, 2006]. The identification of the gene targets of hypoxia relevant to metastasis, and their connection to genes involved in EMT (such as E-cadherin repressors), has attracted much interest [for reviews, see ref. Chaudary and Hill, 2006; Haase, 2009; Lopez-Novoa and Nieto, 2009]. Twist, for instance, is induced by hypoxia of kidney tubule epithelial cells as a mechanism of renal fibrosis [Sun et al., 2009]. Both the Snail1 and Snail2 genes were shown to be induced by hypoxia in breast carcinoma cells via a Notch-mediated pathway [Chen et al., 2010]. Additionally, Snail1 has been shown to be induced in an EMT of MDA-MB-468 breast cancer cells cultured in hypoxic conditions [Lundgren et al., 2009], and Snail2 contributes to hypoxia-driven metastasis by inducing membrane type 4 MMP [Huang et al., 2009].

Oestrogen Receptor-α Status and Transcriptional Regulation of Snail Family Genes

Primary breast tumours are often oestrogen receptor-α (ER) positive, where oestrogen drives tumour growth through ER-mediated activation of proliferative genes such as c-myb [Drabsch et al., 2007]. A mechanism which essentially segregates EMT from the proliferative region of these ER-positive tumours was discovered by Fujita et al. [2003], who were the first to make the key observation that the absence of MTA3 (oestrogen-dependent component of the Mi-2/NuRd co-repressor) or of ER leads to the up-regulation of Snail1 and the subsequent loss of E-cadherin, and that MTA3 directly repressed Snail1. They then went on to show that MTA3 expression requires ER and oestrogen [Fujita et al., 2004]. Following this finding, the inverse relationship was discovered: Snail1 represses ER [Dhasarathy et al., 2007]. Members of the MTA family have opposing roles in ER regulation with implications for Snail expression: MTA1 represses the ER transactivation function and promotes tumour aggressiveness, whereas MTA3 is induced by oestrogen and represses Snail1 [for a review, see ref. Toh and Nicolson, 2009]. Using publically accessible gene expression data, we have found that highly differentiated, E-cadherin-positive primary breast tumours overlay with ER positivity (data not shown), and Cardamone et al. [2009] showed that E-cadherin expression is sustained by ligand-activated ER in breast cancer cells. ER has a direct role in transcriptionally repressing Snail2 [Ye et al., 2008], and more recently, these authors have demonstrated that oestrogen treatment of breast carcinoma cell lines induced E-cadherin and directly repressed Snail2 expression via the formation of a co-repressor complex of ligand-activated ER, histone deacetylase 1 (HDAC1), and nuclear receptor co-repressor [Ye et al., 2010]. These studies support an inverse relationship between E-cadherin/ER promotion of an epithelial phenotype and Snail1/Snail2 promotion of a mesenchymal phenotype.

Given the oestrogen-MTA3-mediated Snail1 repression axis [Fujita et al., 2004], it seems contradictory that Planas-Silva and Waltz [2007] reported Snail1 and Snail2 up-regulation in an EMT-like change induced by oestrogen in the ER-positive human breast cancer cell line MCF-7. Whether a bona fide EMT-like change was induced as reported in this study is unclear. A fibroblast-like change occurred in <10% oestrogen-treated cultures, and collective rather than single-cell motility was described in which E-cadherin was retained at the membrane. Further, few cells in the MCF-7 colony elongated and detached, and not all colonies acquired motility. Additional controversy on this issue is sparked by Park et al. [2008] who report that Snail1 and Snail2 are up-regulated in an EMT induced by oestrogen in ER-positive epithelial ovarian cancer cells. It is possible that this unexpected finding is specific to the ovary since, of the few reports of oestrogen-driving EMT of ER-positive cells, most are described in the context of ovarian cancer [Ding et al., 2006; Tiezzi et al., 2007; for a review, see ref. Gallo et al., 2009]. Further work is needed to clarify these matters.

It has been reported that oestrogen acts to drive the growth and invasion of ER-negative breast tumors [Gupta and Kuperwasser, 2006]; however, how this occurs is unclear. As for its effect on tumor growth, in a xenograft mouse model of parturition-induced breast carcinoma formation, oestrogen has been shown to promote tumor growth by promoting the recruitment of cells from the bone marrow to form the tumor stroma [Gupta et al., 2007]. Oestrogen has been shown to induce an EMT in ER-negative breast cancer cell lines MCF-10F [Huang et al., 2007]; this model may offer some insight into the ER-independent role of oestrogen in promoting invasion.

Snail Family Genes and EMT

Several transcription factors are seen as upstream coordinators of the complex events that together make up EMT. Often the expression of Snail family genes and other E-cadherin repressors such as Zeb1 and Twist can be immunohistochemically detected at sites of EMT at the leading edge of an invading tumour [Come et al., 2004; Yang et al., 2004; Franci et al., 2006; Spaderna et al., 2006]. The Snail family of genes encode zinc finger-containing transcription factors Snail1 and Snail2 [for a review, see ref. Nieto, 2002]. These genes are frequently and causally associated with EMT in embryonic development [Nieto, 2002] and carcinogenesis [Batlle et al., 2000; Cano and Nieto, 2000; Yokoyama et al., 2001] where they down-regulate the expression of cadherins, typically E-cadherin. Snail family proteins repress E-cadherin transcription by binding the E-box E-pal element in the E-cadherin promoter. The same mechanism is found in other E-cadherin repressors involved in carcinogenesis such as Zeb1 and Zeb2 [Comijn et al., 2001; Guaita et al., 2002; Yang et al., 2004]. Snail1 can recruit HDACs to the E-cadherin promoter to aid in transcriptional repression [Hemavathy and Ashraf, 2000]. Snail1 transfected into E-cadherin-positive epithelial cells leads to repression of E-cadherin, occludin and claudin expression, the latter two also containing conserved E-box elements in their promoters [Batlle et al., 2000; Cano and Nieto, 2000]. The mesenchymal genes vimentin and fibronectin are up-regulated in response to Snail1, as is Zeb1 [Guaita et al., 2002]. Snail1 has been reported to repress genes for mucin-1 [Guaita et al., 2002], vitamin D_3 receptor [Palmer et al., 2004], p53 [Kajita et al., 2004] and cyclin D2 [Vega et al., 2004], the latter enabling apoptosis resistance and decreased proliferation. Snail1 transfected into squamous cell lines induces MMP-2 via a non-transcriptional mechanism [Yokoyama et al., 2003], by stimulating the growth factor Wnt5a [Yokoyama et al., 2003], Zeb1 and LEF1 [Guaita et al., 2002; Yokoyama et al., 2003]. Snail1 protein immunolocalization correlated with integrin-linked kinase, suggesting that integrin-linked kinase induces Snail1 in ductal pancreatic adenocarcinoma [Schaeffer et al., 2010]. This pathway has been demonstrated in prostate adenocarcinoma cells [McPhee et al., 2008]. Snail2 up-regulation correlated with E-cadherin down-regulation in oesophageal squamous cell carcinoma and correlated with a poor clinical outcome [Uchikado et al., 2005]. Snail3 is expressed in skin melanotic melanoma, lung epidermoid carcinoma and germ cell tumours, and given its high homology with Snail1 and Snail2 in its N-terminal SNAG domain [Katoh, 2003], it is likely that Snail3 expression plays a role in carcinogenesis and embryogenesis.

The PMC42 Cell Line and Its Derivative PMC42LA Are a Unique System to Study EMT

The human breast cancer cell line PMC42 [Whitehead et al., 1983, 1984], here termed 'PMC42ET', expresses many characteristics of mesenchymal cells such as low junctional E-cadherin but high vimentin expression. From this cell line, a sub-line termed 'PMC42LA' with epithelial properties in 2D and 3D culture was derived [Ackland et al., 2001, 2003a, 2003b]. These cells have highly related karyotypes [L. Campbell, Victorian Cancer Cytogenetics Service, St. Vincent's Hospital, pers. commun.] despite their major differences in epithelial/mesenchymal properties. Both the parental PMC42ET and the PMC42LA sub-line show stem cell properties [Whitehead et al., 1983, 1984; Lebret et al., 2006]. As mentioned above, the PMC42LA cells can be induced to undergo an EMT by exposure to EGF [Ackland et al., 2003a], after which the cells closely resemble PMC42ET cells. EMT-like changes can also be induced by exposure to medium conditioned by breast cancer

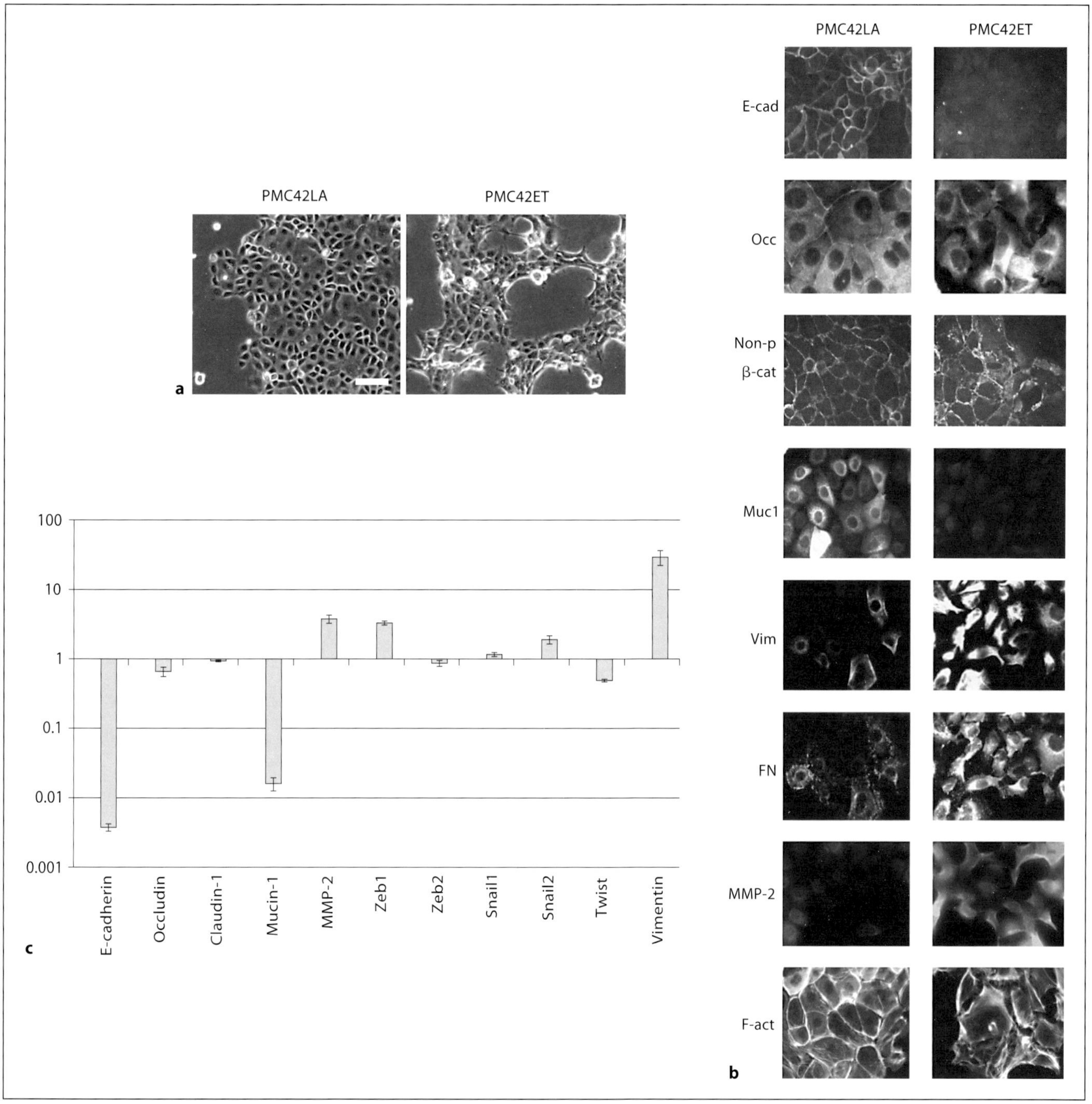

Fig. 1. PMC42LA and PMC42ET breast carcinoma cells display typical epithelial and mesenchymal morphological and gene expression patterns, respectively. **a** Cell morphologies (phase). Scale bar = 150 μm. **b** Immunohistochemistry. E-cad = E-cadherin; Occ = occludin; Non-p β-cat: non-phosphorylated β-catenin; Muc1 = mucin-1; Vim = vimentin; FN = fibronectin; F-act = F-actin. **c** PMC42ET real-time PCR expression data normalized to PMC42LA (corrected for L32). E-cadherin, occludin, mucin-1, vimentin, Zeb1, MMP-2, Snail1 and Snail2 immunohistochemical profiles are supported by real-time data. The E-cadherin repressor gene Twist shows a paradoxical variation relative to E-cadherin. Details of antibodies used are found in table 1, and all quantitative RT-PCR primer sequences of genes examined in this and subsequent figures are found in table 2.

Table 1. Antibodies and probes used for fluorescent labelling

Antibody/probe	Species	Source	Dilution
Primary antibodies/probes			
E-cadherin (HECD1)	mouse, hybridoma supernatant	Dr. Alpha Yap (Inst. Mol. Biosci., University of Queensland)	1:2
Occludin	rabbit	Zymed	1:100
Non-phosphorylated β-catenin	mouse	Upstate (Millipore)	1:100
Vimentin (V9)	mouse	Sigma-Aldrich	1:400
Fibronectin	rabbit	Biogenix	1:150
MMP-2	sheep	Dr. Gillian Murphy (Strangeways laboratory, Cambridge)	1:200
Mucin-1	mouse	[Xing et al., 1998]	1:250
Phalloidin (F-actin)	fungus	Molecular Probes (Invitrogen)	1:400
Secondary antibodies/probes			
Anti-mouse: Alexa 488	goat	Molecular Probes (Invitrogen)	1:2,000
Anti-rabbit: Alexa 594	donkey	Molecular Probes (Invitrogen)	1:2,000
Anti-rat biotin	donkey	Jackson Laboratory	1:100

Table 2. Quantitative RT-PCR primer sequences

Gene	Forward primer sequence	Reverse primer sequence
E-cadherin	GGCACAGATGGTGTGATTACAGTCAAAA	GTCCCAGGCGTAGACCAAGAAA
Occludin	AAGGTCAAAGAGAACAGAGCAAGA	TATTCCCTGATCCAGTCCTCCTC
Claudin-1	GATGAGGTGCAGAAGATGAGG	AGAAGGCAGAGAGAAGCAGC
Mucin-1	ACCATCCTATGAGCGAGTACC	GCCACCATTACCTGCAGAAAC
Vimentin	GCTTCAGAGAGAGGAAGCCGAAAA	TTTCCAAGCCTGACCTCACGG
MMP-2	CGGCCGCAGTGACGGAAA	CATCCTGGGACAGACGGAAG
N-cadherin	GACGGTTCGCCATCCAGAC	TCGATTGGTTTGACCACGG
Zeb1	GCCAATAAGCAAACGATTCTG	TTTGGCTGGATCACTTTCAAG
Zeb2	GGTCCAGATCGAAGCAGCTCAAT	GTGACTTCTATGTTTGTTCACATT
Snail1	CTGCGGGAAGGCCTTCTCT	CGCCTGGCACTGGTACTTCTT
Snail2	CGGACCCACACATTACCTTGTGTTT	CACAGCAGCCAGATTCCTCATGTTT
Twist	GGACAAGCTGAGCAAGATTCAGA	TCTGGAGGACCTGGTAGAGGAA
Snail1 for siRNA knockdown	CCAGACCCACTCAGATGTCAA	GGCAGAGGACACAGAACCAGAAAA
Snail2 for siRNA knockdown	CGGACCCACACATTACCTTGTTTT	CACAGCAGCCAGATTCCTCATGTTT
Zeb1 for siRNA knockdown	CAAAATGGGGTTTTCACTGG	CCACCTTGTTGTATGGGTGA
Zeb2 for siRNA knockdown	TTTACTTGGGTTTCCCACCA	CTTCAGCCTTGCAGTCCATT
RPL32 (housekeeping gene)	CAGGGTTCGTAGAAGATTCAAGGG	GATCGCTCACAATGTTTCCTCCAAG

Snail1, Snail2, Zeb1 or Zeb2 for siRNA knockdown denotes primers used to check the efficacy of respective gene knockdowns.

fibroblasts [Lebret et al., 2006]. These characteristics provide a useful resource for studying EMT in the context of human breast cancer.

We have compared the expression of E-cadherin repressor genes and epithelial and mesenchymal-associated gene products between these 2 lines (fig. 1; tables 1, 2). Given the results of this comparative study, we were then confident that PMC42LA is a suitable model in which to drive the over-expression of Snail1, Snail2 or Zeb1 to examine the consequences on EMT (fig. 2a, 3a; table 3) and that PMC42ET was suitable to examine the effects of knockdown of these genes in promoting a reversal of EMT – a mesenchymal-epithelial transition (MET) (fig. 2b, c, 3b). These studies allowed for the examination of inter-regulatory relationships between the E-cadherin repressors manipulated in each cell line. The relationships are indicated in the schematic representation shown in figure 4. Green lines are relationships derived from

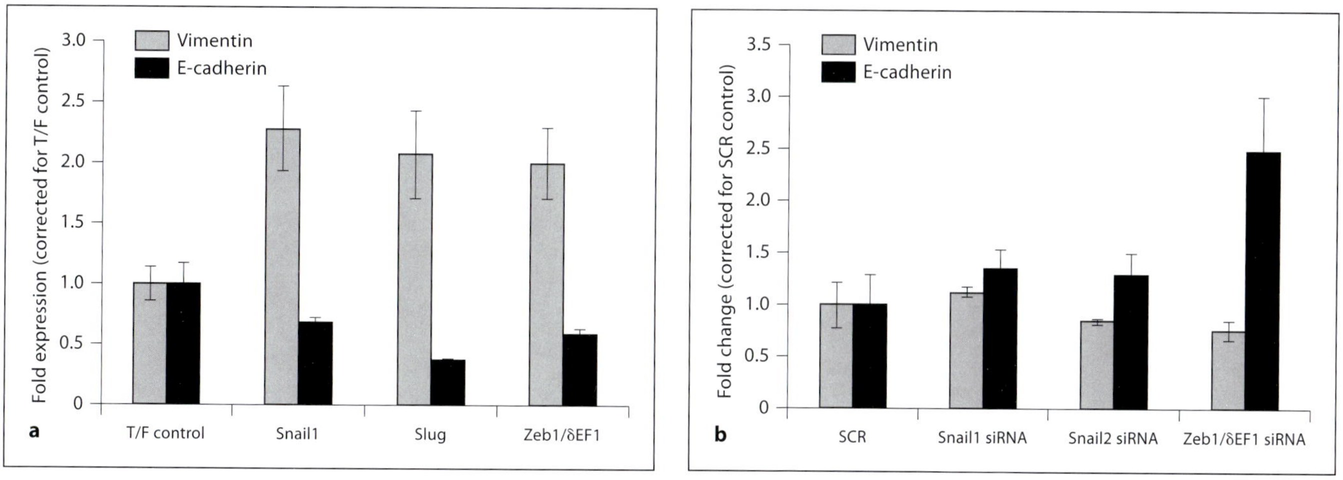

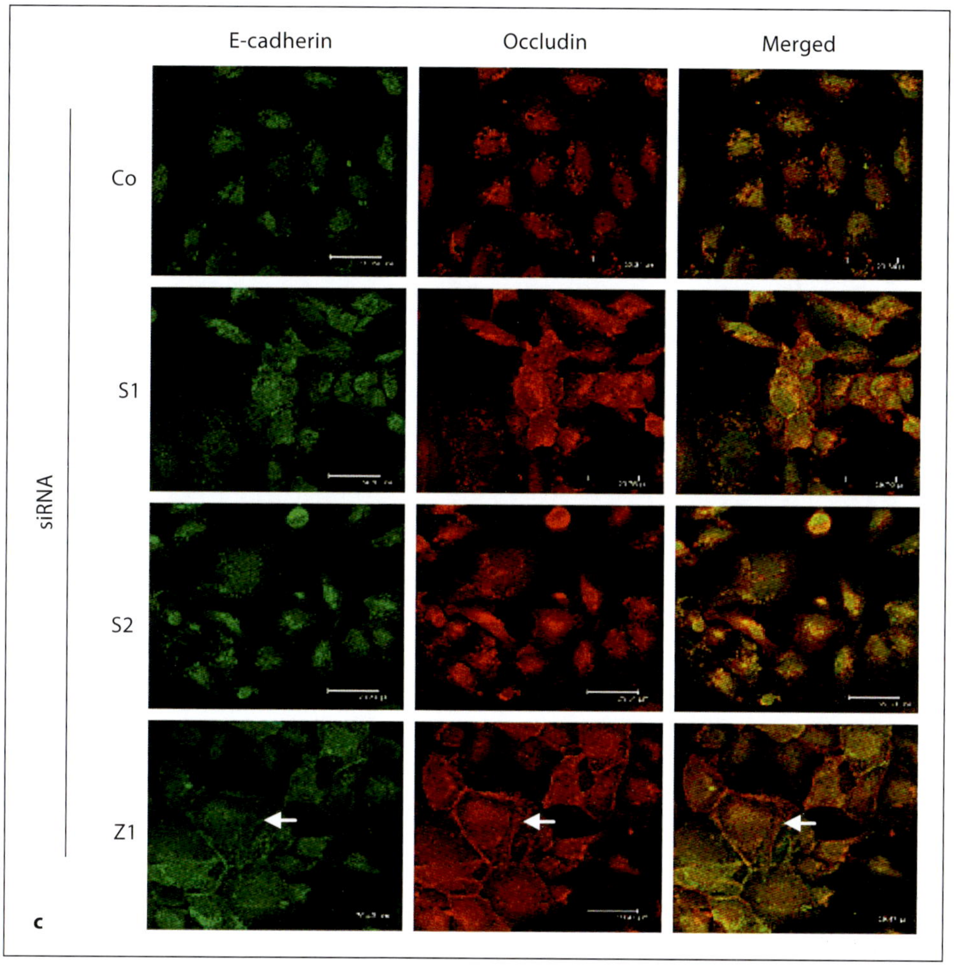

Fig. 2. Expression changes of the E-cadherin repressor gene set when Snail1, Snail2 or Zeb1 was transiently over-expressed (in PMC42LA, **a**) or reduced (in PMC42ET, **b**). All results shown are quantitative PCR fold change – i.e. corrected for transfection (T/F) control or scrambled siRNA (SCR) control, respectively. Results are represented as the mean ± SEM. **c** siRNA knockdown of Zeb1/δEF1 led to the greatest E-cadherin and occludin membrane expression. Arrows indicate E-cadherin at the cell membrane co-localizing with occludin, as seen in the merged images. Co = Control; S1 = Snail1; S2 = Snail2; Z1 = Zeb1. Scale bars = 29 μm.

over-expression studies, whereas red lines are derived from the small interfering RNA (siRNA) work. These relationships are overlaid on the known relationships demonstrated in the literature (black lines), and the connections will be discussed throughout this article.

The re-expression of E-cadherin by Snail1, Snail2 or Zeb1 knockdown in PMC42ET cells (fig. 2b) indicates that the E-cadherin promoter is not irreversibly silenced, as occurs in promoter mutations [Vos et al., 1997]. As a negative control, knockdown of Zeb2 did not change vi-

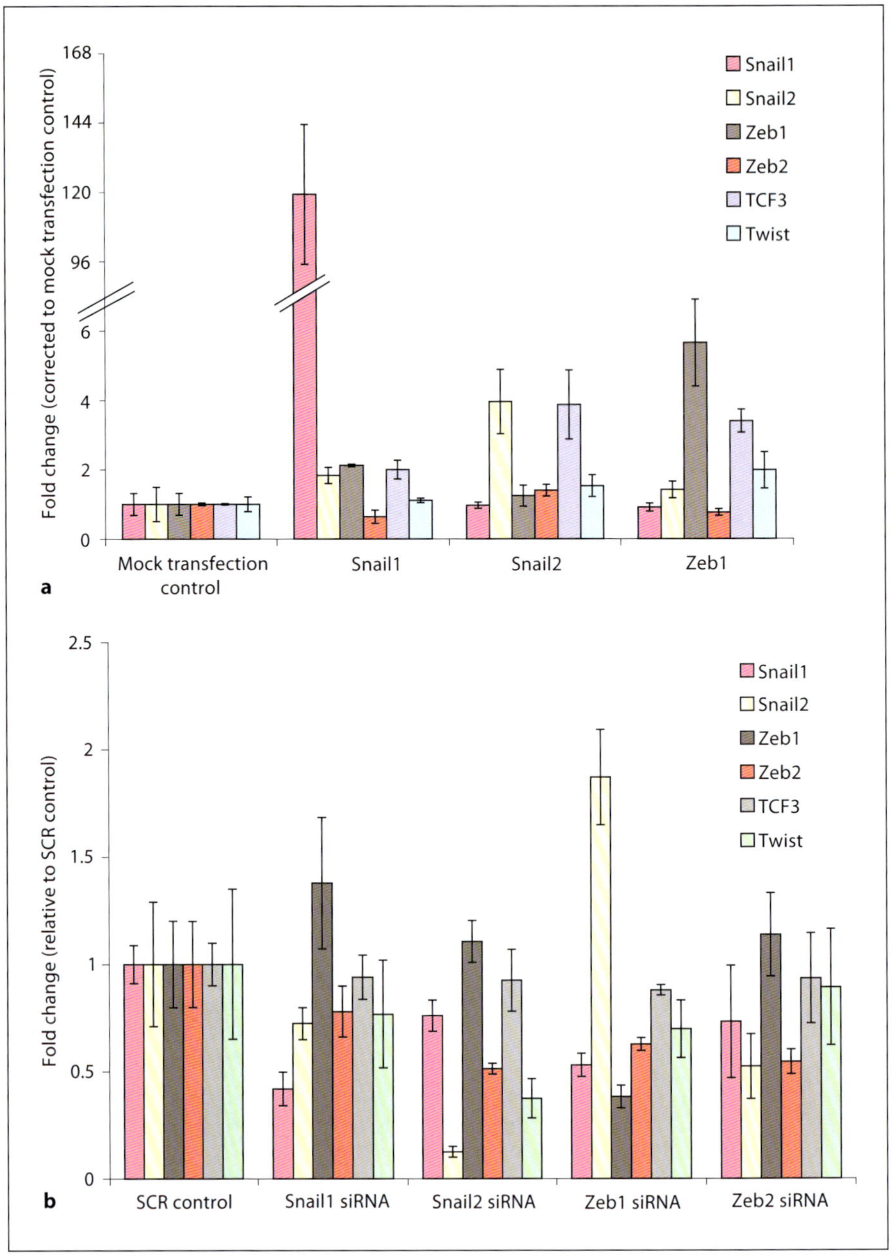

Fig. 3. EMT/MET changes (with respect to E-cadherin and vimentin expression) when Snail1, Snail2 or Zeb1 was transiently over-expressed (PMC42LA) or reduced (PMC42ET). All results shown are quantitative PCR fold change – i.e. corrected for transfection control or scrambled siRNA (SCR) control, respectively. Results represent the mean ± SEM. Sequences of siRNAs used are found in table 3.

Table 3. siRNAs transfected into PMC42ET cells

siRNA	Sequence
Scrambled siRNA control	AAGAGCAACUCGAAGCAGUCC
Snail1	CCGAAUGUCCCUGCUCCACAA
Snail2	AAGGACACAUUAGAACUCACA
Zeb1	GATGGTAATGTAATAAGGCAAG
Zeb2	AAGTGAGGTACAAAAGGTTCTACAGATTGTGGACAATACTGTTTCCAGGCAAAA

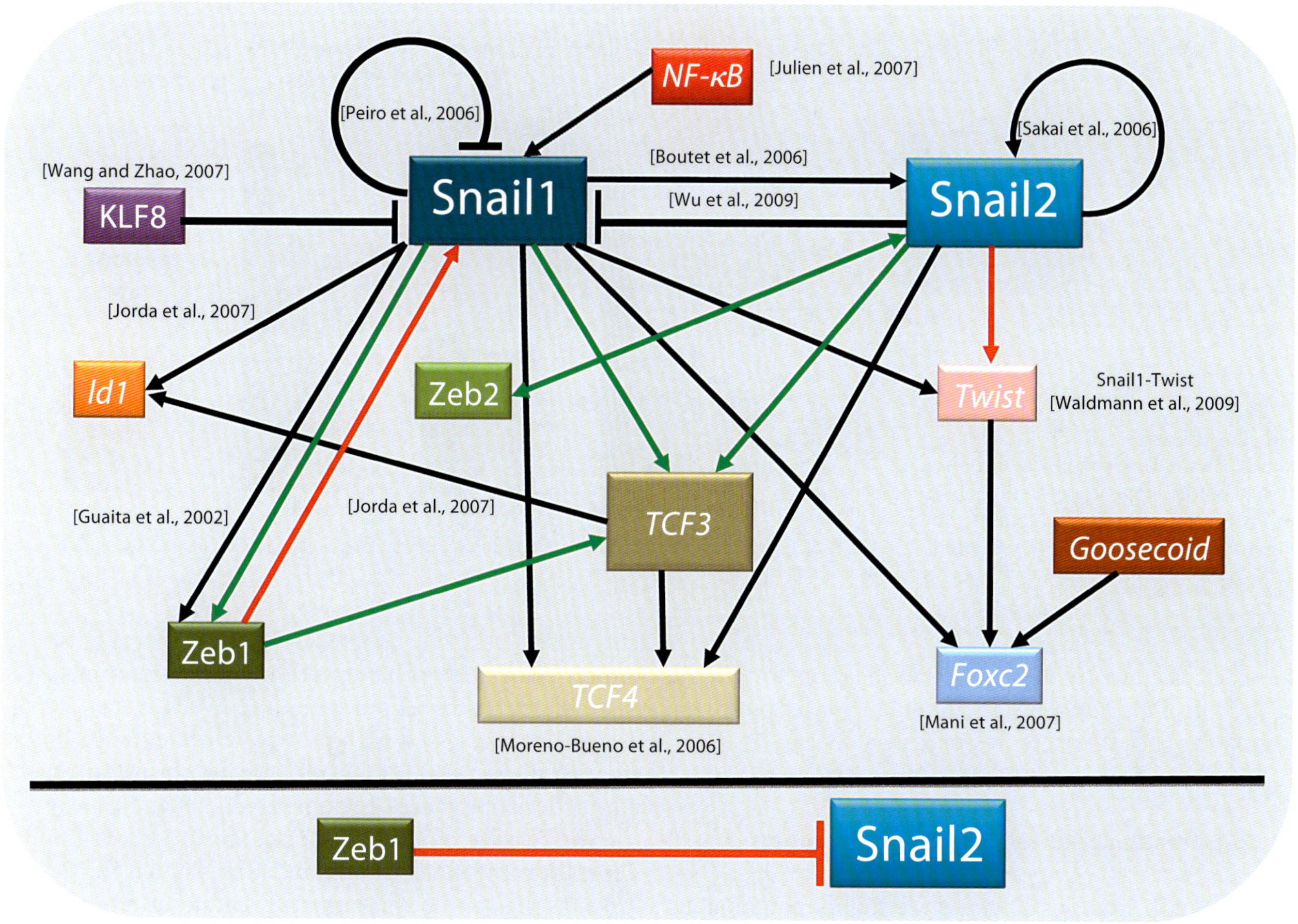

Fig. 4. Summary of E-cadherin repressor gene interactions (interactome) derived from over-expression and siRNA studies performed in PMC42LA and PMC42ET, respectively. Arrows suggest gene induction. Zeb2 over-expression studies in PMC42LA were not performed. Published interactions are shown as black arrows (references in brackets). These interactions are not necessarily restricted to cancer. Factors in italics are indirect E-cadherin repressors (Twist as an indirect or direct repressor has not been established). Red arrows indicate regulatory relationships derived from siRNA studies, whereas green arrows indicate regulation derived from over-expression studies. Id1 = Inhibitor of differentiation 1.

mentin or E-cadherin expression (data not shown). The ability to re-express E-cadherin in late-stage tumour cell metastasis may permit MET and re-differentiation of relatively well-organized breast carcinoma at secondary sites, as seen so spectacularly in colon cancer secondary sites [Brabletz et al., 2005], as well as in the Dunning rat carcinoma model [Oltean et al., 2006].

EGF treatment causes EMT in PMC42LA cells, resulting in induction of vimentin [Ackland et al., 2003a], and PMC42ET cells, although already more mesenchymal than PMC42LA, also show intensified expression of EMT responses with EGF treatment (data not shown). We investigated this in the context of E-cadherin repressor knockdown (fig. 5). It is interesting to note that although a transient knockdown of Snail1, Snail2 or Zeb1 raised epithelial gene expression despite EGF treatment (which is otherwise mesenchymalizing), knockdown of these genes was not sufficient to block the induction of the mesenchymal marker vimentin (fig. 5). It may be that in PMC42ET, sustained vimentin transcription is enabled by a separate set of factors to those that induce it in EMT. These include a combination of the known vimentin promoter-activating proteins poly(ADP-ribose) polymerase 1, AP-1, PAE3, Sp1, Stat3 or ZBP-89 [Rittling et al., 1989; Chen et al., 1996; Wu et al., 2004; Chu et al., 2007]. Hence, in post-EMT mesenchymal cells, mesenchymal charac-

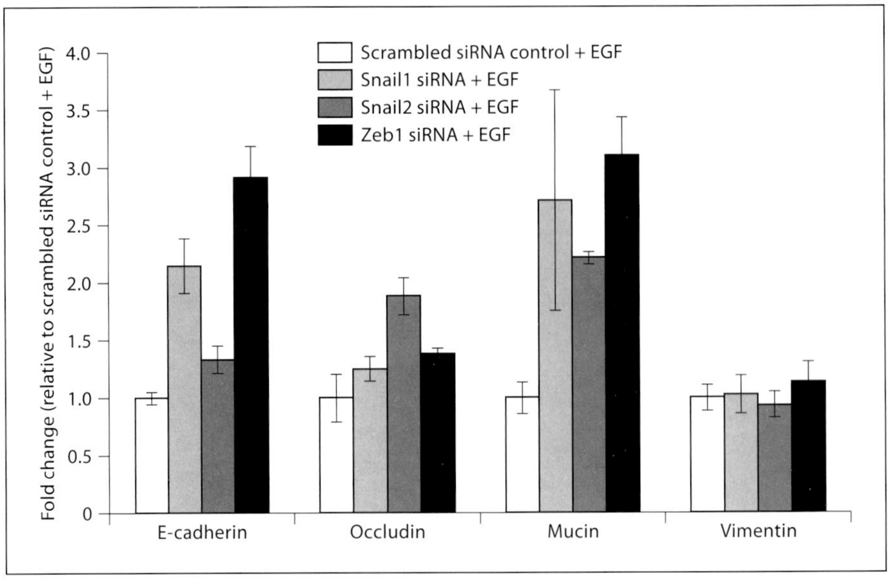

Fig. 5. Although siRNA knockdown of Snail1, Snail2 or Zeb1 blocked the reduction of epithelial gene expression observed in PMC42ET with EGF (data not shown), vimentin induction was not impaired.

ters such as vimentin expression may be refractory to the reduction of the initial EMT stimulus (achieved by down-regulating E-cadherin repressor gene activity).

Co-Operation between Snail Family Members

The Snail1 and Snail2 genes are highly homologous and, in certain circumstances, can replace each other functionally: for example, the consequences of reduced Snail2 expression in avian embryonic neural crest can be avoided by transfection of Snail1 [Nieto, 2002]. However, these genes appear to possess somewhat distinct roles. For instance, the knockout of the Snail1 gene is lethal during gastrulation in the mouse embryo [Ip and Gridley, 2002], whereas Snail2 knockout mice are viable and fertile [Jiang et al., 1998]. In human breast cancer biopsies, a correlation was found between Snail1 expression, reduced E-cadherin expression and invasive grade of tumours [Blanco et al., 2002; Come et al., 2004; Elloul et al., 2005]. Snail1 expression has been found in infiltrating ductal carcinomas associated with lymph node metastases [Cheng et al., 2001; Blanco et al., 2002] and distant metastases. These include effusions [Elloul et al., 2005; Come et al., 2006] as well as the recurrence of breast carcinomas [Moody et al., 2005]. It may be of clinical significance to examine Snail1 expression in the stroma of these tumours, as stromal Snail1 positivity was suggested to be an informative indicator of poor prognosis of low-stage colon tumours [Franci et al., 2009]. Snail2 expression is associated with breast tumour effusions, metastasis and recurrence [Elloul et al., 2005; Martin et al., 2005], but is also associated with partially differentiated breast cancers [Come et al., 2006], reflective of the role of Snail2 in the developing breast [Come et al., 2004].

The relative efficiency of E-cadherin transcriptional repression by Snail1 and Snail2 was studied in MDCK cells, as the canine and human E-cadherin promoter E-pal elements are relatively well conserved [Bolos et al., 2003]. In this study, Snail1 was found to bind with higher affinity than Snail2 to the E-cadherin repressor domain. Both Snail1 and Snail2 co-operate to repress the vitamin D receptor in colon cancer progression [Larriba et al., 2009, 2010]. Vitamin D receptor repression was shown to be specific to Snail family genes and not to other EMT inducers. Indeed, Snail1 has been reported to induce Snail2 expression [Boutet et al., 2006] whereas Snail2 forms a ternary complex with wild-type p53 and Mdm2 to degrade Snail1 [Wu et al., 2009]. Further differences between these factors have been reported: Snail1 represses its own transcription [Peiro et al., 2006] whereas Snail2 has been shown to activate its own promoter in avian neural crest cells [Sakai et al., 2006].

A possible further role for Snail2 may be in the induction of the gene Twist, as siRNA directed against Snail2 in PMC42 cells reduced Twist expression (fig. 3b). Indeed, Twist and Snail2 appear to be able to replace each other functionally: Twist and Snail2 have recently been shown to share the same transcriptional target, Cerberus, in early *Drosophila* development [Zhang and Klymkowsky, 2009], and a similar Twist-Snail2 shared role has been shown in the restoration of the normal phenotype disrupted by Xc-myc knockdown in the developing *Xenopus* embryo [Rodrigues et al., 2008].

We also observed that ectopic expression of Snail2 in PMC42LA cells caused TCF3 (E12/E47) expression to increase (fig. 3a). A putative reciprocal regulatory relationship derived from over-expression studies was also observed for Snail2 and Zeb2. Up-regulation of Snail2 significantly correlated with Zeb2 expression in intestinal carcinomas [Castro Alves et al., 2007] suggesting that Snail2 and Zeb2 may act synergistically to down-regulate E-cadherin in these tumours. It may be possible that a similar inductive relationship is observed with Snail1 and Zeb1 [Guaita et al., 2002]; EGF and staurosporine treatment of PMC42LA [Hugo et al., 2009] occurs with Snail2 and Zeb2. Further studies similar to those performed by Guaita et al. [2002] are required to determine whether this is a direct transcriptional relationship.

Twist in EMT

Twist has been defined as a target gene of Snail1 in malignant pheochromocytomas [Waldmann et al., 2009]. Indeed, Twist is up-regulated along with Snail1 in EMT of pancreatic and breast tumour cells induced by vascular endothelial growth factor [Yang et al., 2006; Wanami et al., 2008]. In addition to these cancers, Twist is over-expressed in uterine, gastric and squamous cell cancers, hepatocarcinoma and melanoma, where in many cases, it is a predictor of metastasis [for a review, see ref. Peinado et al., 2007]. Twist is over-expressed in metastatic breast cancer cells [Yang et al., 2004] where it mediates the induction of Akt2 to facilitate cell survival, migration and invasion [Cheng et al., 2008]. As mentioned earlier, cells which have undergone an EMT acquire characteristics of breast cancer stem cells defined by a $CD24^{low}/CD44^{high}$ status. Transfection of Twist into breast cancer cells has also been demonstrated to achieve this status ($CD24^{low}/CD44^{high}$ and stem cell characteristics), mediated by the down-regulation of CD24 expression [Vesuna et al., 2009].

There is controversy as to whether Twist represses E-cadherin directly by binding to its promoter. It was thought for some time that Twist repressed E-cadherin indirectly [Peinado et al., 2007], until studies by Vesuna et al. [2008] demonstrated direct binding via chromatin immunoprecipitation assays. Some reviews [Gavert and Ben-Ze'ev, 2008; Feng et al., 2009; Kasper et al., 2009] and papers [Li and Mattingly, 2008] acknowledge this finding; however, others do not [Yang and Weinberg, 2008; Baranwal and Alahari, 2009; Thiery and Sleeman, 2009]. These 3 negative reports are supported by unpublished data cited in the study by Yang and Weinberg [2008]. Twist is an inducer of FOXC2 [Mani et al., 2007], a non-transcriptional repressor of E-cadherin important in EMT (described below).

ZEB Family Members in EMT

Zeb1 is emerging as an important EMT regulator [Peinado et al., 2007]. The over-expression of Zeb1 predicts a poor prognosis in uterine cancer [Spoelstra et al., 2006] and is associated with E-cadherin down-regulation in Snail1-negative tumours of the colon [Pena et al., 2006]. Its expression in the prostate cancer cell line PC-3 enables crossing of the endothelial barrier, rather than invasion [Drake et al., 2009]. Zeb1 down-regulates the transcription of epithelial-related genes: E-cadherin [Eger et al., 2005], mucin-1 [Guaita et al., 2002], the desmosomal protein plakophilin 3 [Aigner et al., 2007b], the cell polarity genes Crumbs3 and HUGL2, and the tight junction protein Pals1 [Aigner et al., 2007a; Spaderna et al., 2008].

Our observations after transiently knocking down Zeb1 in PMC42ET cells suggest another target for down-regulation: Snail2 (fig. 3b, 4), which was also borne out by stable Zeb1 knockdown in the same cell line (data not shown). This pathway suggests a mechanism through which Snail1, in inducing Zeb1 [Guaita et al., 2002], may repress Snail2 in order to mediate Snail1-specific patterning in embryological development [Murray and Gridley, 2006a, 2006b].

The inhibition of Zeb1 along with Rho is important in a full MET in mouse mammary gland cells [Das et al., 2009]. We observed that PMC42ET breast carcinoma cells stably expressing short hairpin RNA against Zeb1 exhibit gene expression changes consistent with a MET and grow as tight clusters in 2D culture [Hugo et al., manuscript in preparation]. Zeb1 knockout mice show severe thymocyte deficiency [Takagi et al., 1998] consistent with interleukin-2 being a target of Zeb1 [Williams et al., 1991]. Given that interleukin-2 deficiency is a risk factor for breast cancer relapse [Arduino et al., 1996], and Zeb1 represses homologues of p53 important in differentiation [Fontemaggi et al., 2005], Zeb1 over-expression in cancer EMT is likely to have a greater role than just E-cadherin down-regulation. Zeb2 is also an important regulator of tumour invasion, often acting in co-operation with Zeb1.

An example is NF-κB activation leading to Zeb1 and Zeb2 up-regulation in mammary epithelial cells [Chua et al., 2007]. Snail2 and Zeb2 up-regulation closely correlate with E-cadherin down-regulation in intestinal cancer [Castro Alves et al., 2007] and are coupled with MMP-2 up-regulation in ovarian cancer [Elloul et al., 2005]. Zeb2 expression is suggested to be increased by Snail1 via a natural antisense transcript which overlaps a 5′ splice site in an intron, thus preventing splicing of this part of the gene. This is important because an internal ribosomal entry site within this intron is necessary for Zeb2 expression, hence the preservation of this intron promotes Zeb2 expression [Beltran et al., 2008].

Temporal Differences in the Snail1-Zeb1 Regulatory Pathway

Snail1 is sensitive to GSK-3β phosphorylation, a target for proteasomal degradation. Thus, it is rendered highly unstable with a half-life of approximately 25 min in MCF-7 and HEK 293 cells engineered to express Snail1 [Zhou et al., 2004]. However, Snail1 induces Zeb1 in various epithelial cell lines, and only in the cell lines where Snail1 and Zeb1 were co-expressed was E-cadherin severely down-regulated [Guaita et al., 2002]. These authors found that Zeb1 was induced by Snail1 after a lag period. Indeed, we have shown that Zeb1 is induced as a late event in an EMT driven by Snail1 in PMC42LA breast carcinoma cells treated with EGF and staurosporine [Hugo et al., 2009]. Snail1 over-expression by transfection in PMC42LA caused the same effect after 72 h (fig. 3a, 4, green arrow). In the study by Guaita et al. [2002], Zeb1 activation was maintained even after Snail1 expression declined. Similarly, in our study, Snail1 siRNA knockdown in PMC42ET cells did not affect Zeb1 expression (fig. 3b).

Post-Transcriptional Regulation of the ZEB Family

It is rapidly emerging that non-coding messenger RNAs of the microRNA (miR)-200 family and miR-205 promote the epithelial phenotype by negatively regulating Zeb1 and Zeb2 [Cano and Nieto, 2008; Gregory et al., 2008]. The expression of the miR-200 family in regulating Zeb transcription factors in the progression of ovarian cancer distinctly contrasts to its expression in the progression of other cancers, switching from a miR-200 family^{low} and Zeb1/2^{high} state to a miR-200 family^{high} and Zeb1/2^{low} phenotype in the process of malignant transformation [Bendoraite et al., 2010]. This may relate to previous work indicating the need for ovarian surface epithelial cells, which are mesothelially derived, to acquire E-cadherin expression for malignancy [Auersperg et al., 1999]. This in turn may have bearing on the need for a MET in order for metastases to grow [for a review, see ref. Hugo et al., 2007]. The anomalous position of ovarian cancers with respect to the influence of oestrogen on EMT has already been mentioned. On the other hand, Zeb1 acts as a direct transcriptional repressor of miRs miR-141 and miR-200c [Burk et al., 2008]. The ability of Zeb1 to repress these miRs was proposed by Burk et al. [2008] to be important for Zeb1 to maintain the mesenchymal phenotype. Some miRs oppose metastasis (miR-31) [Valastyan et al., 2009] and some promote it, such as miR-10b-promoted migration and invasion directed by Twist [Ma et al., 2007]. Additionally, miR-9-directed E-cadherin down-regulation to induce EMT is under the positive control of MYC and MYCN [Ma et al., 2010]. miR regulation of EMT is a field which is likely to rapidly expand over the next few years.

Hierarchy of Direct E-Cadherin Repressor Genes

It is evident that a large number of intracellular signalling pathways converge in Snail1 and Snail2 induction [for a review, see ref. Thiery and Sleeman, 2009]. Indeed, Peinado et al. [2007] made the key observation that EMT in development and carcinoma progression initially features Snail1 induction resulting in Snail2, Zeb, TCF3 and Twist induction, which serve to enforce the mesenchymal phenotype and promote migration. Given the induction pathways outlined in figure 4, these Snail1-induced feed-forward pathways could be extended to include the less well-characterized indirect E-cadherin repressor molecules such as TCF4. We have observed indications of E-cadherin repressor gene hierarchy in the induction of EMT by staurosporine combined with EGF, where early induction of Snail1 (3 h) leads to Zeb1 induction after 3 days [Hugo et al., 2009]. Indeed, of all the E-cadherin repressors examined in PMC42LA (epithelial) and PMC42ET (mesenchymal) cell lines (fig. 1), Zeb1 showed the highest expression differential, suggesting that Zeb1 maintains the mesenchymal phenotype. Consistently, we have found that the mesenchymal PMC42ET cells lack expression of the miR-200 family members relative to the epithelial PMC42LA subline [Fabra-Fres, Thompson and Goodall, unpubl. observation]. We also have data to suggest that Zeb1 stable knockdown in PMC42ET restores many aspects of the epithelial phenotype including E-cadherin and zona occludens 1 expression and the polarity factor HUGL2 (Lgl2) in 3D culture (data not shown).

KLF8 is a downstream effector of focal adhesion kinase [Zhao et al., 2003] and is up-regulated in several types of invasive human cancers including breast carcinoma [Wang and Zhao, 2007a]. KLF8 transcriptionally down-regulates the key E-cadherin repressor gene Snail1, along with E-cadherin, and has been shown to promote EMT in an immortalized normal human breast epithelial cell line (MCF-10A) [Wang et al., 2007b]. Finally, we have suggested through over-expression studies (fig. 3a) that TCF3, an important direct E-cadherin repressor gene [Perez-Moreno et al., 2001], fits into the Snail family hierarchical model. Specifically, we show that this gene is induced by the elevated expression of Snail1, Snail2 and Zeb1 in the EMT-inducible epithelial breast cancer line, PMC42LA. Indeed, TCF3 and Snail1 co-operate to induce inhibitor of differentiation 1 gene [Jorda et al., 2007] and also co-operate to promote invasion and angiogenesis [Peinado et al., 2004] (fig. 4). Further work is necessary to determine whether Snail2 and Zeb1 induction of TCF3 is physiologically relevant.

Indirect E-Cadherin Repressors

The set of indirect repressors of E-cadherin in the induction of EMT summarized include factors defined by their inductive effects on the direct E-cadherin repressor set in addition to their non-transcriptional effects on E-cadherin. For example, Snail1 protein stabilization is promoted by NF-κB [Wu et al., 2009], as is Snail1 expression [Julien et al., 2007]. Ladybird homeobox 1, a gene regulated in development, has been shown to induce the expression of Zeb1, Zeb2 and Snail1 in MCF-10A cells during the induction of EMT [Yu et al., 2009]. FOXC2 plays a role in the EMT of renal epithelial cells in response to injury [Hader et al., 2009] and is triggered by a number of signals, including TGF-β_1 and several EMT-inducing transcription factors, such as Snail, Twist and Goosecoid in mammary cells [for a review, see ref. Mani et al., 2007]. FOXC2 does not act to repress E-cadherin expression but rather to promote its cytoplasmic re-localization [Yang and Weinberg, 2008]. Through insight gained from its role in early development, Goosecoid has been discovered as a down-stream effector gene in the TGF-β signalling pathway of EMT induction in breast cancer cells [Hartwell et al., 2006]. Inhibitor of differentiation 1 is induced rapidly in human proximal tubular epithelial cells after TGF-β_1 treatment [Li et al., 2007] and in MDCK cells in response to expression of Snail1 and TCF3 [Jorda et al., 2007]. TCF4 is another indirect repressor of E-cadherin which has been demonstrated to be up-regulated by TCF3, Snail1 and Snail2 in MDCK cells [Moreno-Bueno et al., 2006; Sobrado et al., 2009], and we have shown increased TCF4 in a subset of breast cancer cells lines with mesenchymal traits [Blick et al., 2008].

Clinical Perspectives

Traditional cancer chemotherapies aim to eradicate tumour cells by shutting down the cell cycle, based on basic early studies linking cancer with continuous cellular division [Calkins, 1908]. These therapies may be effective for the short-term treatment of cancer in patients who have later-stage cancer, but present severe side effects. Although momentous advances have been made in how cancer is treated with surgical, radiological and adjuvant therapy approaches since the early observations of Calkins [1908], recurrence remains a serious problem [Gluck, 2007; Jones, 2008]. The 5-year relative survival rate for breast cancer is 86%, dropping to 52% 20 years after diagnosis [Brenner, 2002]. One potential roadblock to the anti-proliferative approach is the observation that proliferation is down-regulated in EMT. Several direct E-cadherin repressors act to attenuate the cell cycle: Snail1 regulates components of the early to late G1 transition and the G1/S checkpoint, including the repression of cyclin D2 transcription and the increase in p21/Cip1 [Vega et al., 2004], Zeb2 represses cyclin D1 [Mejlvang et al., 2007], and activation of Snail2 significantly reduces proliferation of epidermal keratinocytes [Turner et al., 2006]. The reduction or inhibition of cell proliferation is thought to favour invasion versus tumour growth [Thiery et al., 2009] enabling invading cancer cells to survive and propagate at distant secondary or tertiary sites. Thus, these escaped cells remain as 'silent assassins', dormant but with lethal potential and refractory to anti-proliferative therapies. However, the inverse relationship between EMT and proliferation should not be extended too far, since in an embryonic post-EMT model, invasion of tissue by mesenchymal neural crest cells requires proliferation to be effective [Simpson et al., 2007]. It may be necessary to differentiate between cells in the process of EMT and those after the event, only the former being subject to proliferative blockade.

In addition to down-regulating proliferation, it is known that both Snail1 and Snail2 confer resistance to paclitaxel, adriamycin and radiation by antagonizing apoptosis mediated by p53 [Kurrey et al., 2009]. Approaches are being taken to specifically capture tumour cells [Myung et al., 2010] in the circulation which could be used to investigate whether they exhibit characteristics of an EMT [Paterlini-Brechot and Benali, 2007]. This may have important clinical implications for cancer [Andreopoulou and Christofanilli, 2010; Nelson, 2010].

Promotion of the EMT phenotype may also accelerate cancer metastasis via a contribution to immunotherapeutic resistance, as Snail1 has been shown to activate immunosuppressive cytokines and impair the normal development of dendritic cells [Kudo-Saito et al., 2009].

Some current chemotherapeutics may actually promote an EMT, which raises the question of how effective these may be in inhibiting tumour development and spread. The use of HDAC inhibitors (HDACi) in the treatment of cancers is rapidly expanding [Frew et al., 2009; Marks and Yu, 2009], with potential for breast cancer treatment [Thomas et al., 2009]. In the study by Thomas et al. [2009], it is reported that HDACi treatment of ER-positive tumours reduced the expression of ER and its downstream targets and, paradoxically, that HDACi treatment restored the efficacy of anti-oestrogen therapy in a preclinical model, as measured by a reduction in tumour growth. However, work by Ye et al. [2008, 2010] has shown that ER represses Snail2 expression in ER-positive breast carcinoma cells in a complex involving HDAC1 and nuclear receptor co-repressor and that treatment with an HDACi led to the release of this repression. Thus, although HDACi treatment may be effective in reducing breast tumour growth, it may promote EMT via the release of Snail2 transcriptional repression. For chemotherapies to be fully effective in eradicating cancers they will need to target the immediate problem of unrestrained cell growth and the clandestine problem of EMT. Salinomycin has been discovered to selectively target the mesenchymal cell [Gupta and Kuperwasser, 2009], although it is toxic to humans [Story and Doube, 2004]. The development of a non-toxic analogue of this compound could prove to be an important step forward in the treatment of cancer.

References

Ackland, M.L., A. Michalczyk, R.H. Whitehead (2001) PMC42, a novel model for the differentiated human breast. Exp Cell Res *263:* 14–22.

Ackland, M.L., D.F. Newgreen, M. Fridman, M.C. Waltham, A. Arvanitis, J. Minichiello, J.T. Price, E.W. Thompson (2003a) Epidermal growth factor-induced epithelio-mesenchymal transition in human breast carcinoma cells. Lab Invest *83:* 435–448.

Ackland, M.L., J. Ward, C.M. Ackland, M. Greaves, M. Walker (2003b) Extracellular matrix induces formation of organoids and changes in cell surface morphology in cultured human breast carcinoma cells PMC42-LA. In Vitro Cell Dev Biol Anim *39:* 428–433.

Ahmed, N., S. Maines-Bandiera, M.A. Quinn, W.G. Unger, S. Dedhar, N. Auersperg (2006) Molecular pathways regulating EGF-induced epithelio-mesenchymal transition in human ovarian surface epithelium. Am J Physiol Cell Physiol *290:* C1532–C1542.

Aigner, K., B. Dampier, L. Descovich, M. Mikula, A. Sultan, M. Schreiber, W. Mikulits, T. Brabletz, D. Strand, P. Obrist, W. Sommergruber, N. Schweifer, A. Wernitznig, H. Beug, R. Foisner, A. Eger (2007a) The transcription factor ZEB1 (deltaEF1) promotes tumour cell dedifferentiation by repressing master regulators of epithelial polarity. Oncogene *26:* 6979–6988.

Aigner, K., L. Descovich, M. Mikula, A. Sultan, B. Dampier, S. Bonne, F. van Roy, W. Mikulits, M. Schreiber, T. Brabletz, W. Sommergruber, N. Schweifer, A. Wernitznig, H. Beug, R. Foisner, A. Eger (2007b) The transcription factor ZEB1 (deltaEF1) represses Plakophilin 3 during human cancer progression. FEBS Lett *581:* 1617–1624.

Andreopoulou, E., M. Cristofanilli (2010) Circulating tumor cells as prognostic marker in metastatic breast cancer. Expert Rev Anticancer Ther *10:* 171–177.

Arduino, S., M. Tessarolo, R. Bellino, S. Colombatto, L. Leo, T. Wierdis, A. Lanza (1996) Reduced IL-2 level concentration in patients with breast cancer as a possible risk factor for relapse. Eur J Gynaecol Oncol *17:* 535–537.

Auersperg, N., J. Pan, B.D. Grove, T. Peterson, J. Fisher, S. Maines-Bandiera, A. Somasiri, C.D. Roskelley (1999) E-cadherin induces mesenchymal-to-epithelial transition in human ovarian surface epithelium. Proc Natl Acad Sci USA *96:* 6249–6254.

Baranwal, S., S.K. Alahari (2009) Molecular mechanisms controlling E-cadherin expression in breast cancer. Biochem Biophys Res Commun *384:* 6–11.

Batlle, E., E. Sancho, C. Franci, D. Dominguez, M. Monfar, J. Baulida, A. Garcia De Herreros (2000) The transcription factor snail is a repressor of E-cadherin gene expression in epithelial tumour cells. Nat Cell Biol *2:* 84–89.

Beltran, M., I. Puig, C. Pena, J.M. Garcia, A.B. Alvarez, R. Pena, F. Bonilla, A.G. de Herreros (2008) A natural antisense transcript regulates Zeb2/Sip1 gene expression during Snail1-induced epithelial-mesenchymal transition. Genes Dev *22:* 756–769.

Bendoraite, A., E.C. Knouf, K.S. Garg, R.K. Parkin, E.M. Kroh, K.C. O'Briant, A.P. Ventura, A.K. Godwin, B.Y. Karlan, C.W. Drescher, N. Urban, B.S. Knudsen, M. Tewari (2010) Regulation of miR-200 family microRNAs and ZEB transcription factors in ovarian cancer: evidence supporting a mesothelial-to-epithelial transition. Gynecol Oncol *116:* 117–125.

Blanco, M.J., G. Moreno-Bueno, D. Sarrio, A. Locascio, A. Cano, J. Palacios, M.A. Nieto (2002) Correlation of Snail expression with histological grade and lymph node status in breast carcinomas. Oncogene *21:* 3241–3246.

Blick, T., E. Widodo, H. Hugo, M. Waltham, M.E. Lenburg, R.M. Neve, E.W. Thompson (2008) Epithelial mesenchymal transition traits in human breast cancer cell lines. Clin Exp Metastasis *25:* 629–642.

Bolos, V., H. Peinado, M.A. Perez-Moreno, M.F. Fraga, M. Esteller, A. Cano (2003) The transcription factor Slug represses E-cadherin expression and induces epithelial to mesenchymal transitions: a comparison with Snail and E47 repressors. J Cell Sci *116:* 499–511.

Boutet, A., C.A. De Frutos, P.H. Maxwell, M.J. Mayol, J. Romero, M.A. Nieto (2006) Snail activation disrupts tissue homeostasis and induces fibrosis in the adult kidney. EMBO J *25:* 5603–5613.

Boyle, R.G., S. Travers (2006) Hypoxia: targeting the tumour. Anticancer Agents Med Chem *6:* 281–286.

Brabletz, T., F. Hlubek, S. Spaderna, O. Schmalhofer, E. Hiendlmeyer, A. Jung, T. Kirchner (2005) Invasion and metastasis in colorectal cancer: epithelial-mesenchymal transition, mesenchymal-epithelial transition, stem cells and beta-catenin. Cells Tissues Organs *179:* 56–65.

Brenner, H. (2002) Long-term survival rates of cancer patients achieved by the end of the 20th century: a period analysis. Lancet *360:* 1131–1135.

Burk, U., J. Schubert, U. Wellner, O. Schmalhofer, E. Vincan, S. Spaderna, T. Brabletz (2008) A reciprocal repression between ZEB1 and members of the miR-200 family promotes EMT and invasion in cancer cells. EMBO Rep *9:* 582–589.

Calkins, G.N. (1908) The so-called rhythms of growth-energy in mouse cancer. J Exp Med *10:* 283–307.

Cano, A., M.A. Nieto (2008) Non-coding RNAs take centre stage in epithelial-to-mesenchymal transition. Trends Cell Biol *18:* 357–359.

Cano, A., M.A. Perez-Moreno, I. Rodrigo, A. Locascio, M.J. Blanco, M.G. del Barrio, F. Portillo, M.A. Nieto (2000) The transcription factor snail controls epithelial-mesenchymal transitions by repressing E-cadherin expression. Nat Cell Biol *2:* 76–83.

Cardamone, M.D., C. Bardella, A. Gutierrez, L. Di Croce, M.G. Rosenfeld, M.F. Di Renzo, M. De Bortoli (2009) ERalpha as ligand-independent activator of CDH-1 regulates determination and maintenance of epithelial morphology in breast cancer cells. Proc Natl Acad Sci USA *106:* 7420–7425.

Castro Alves, C., E. Rosivatz, C. Schott, R. Hollweck, I. Becker, M. Sarbia, F. Carneiro, K.F. Becker (2007) Slug is overexpressed in gastric carcinomas and may act synergistically with SIP1 and Snail in the down-regulation of E-cadherin. J Pathol *211:* 507–515.

Chaudary, N., R.P. Hill (2006) Hypoxia and metastasis in breast cancer. Breast Dis *26:* 55–64.

Chen, J., N. Imanaka, J.D. Griffin (2010) Hypoxia potentiates Notch signaling in breast cancer leading to decreased E-cadherin expression and increased cell migration and invasion. Br J Cancer *102:* 351–360.

Chen, J.H., C. Vercamer, Z. Li, D. Paulin, B. Vandenbunder, D. Stehelin (1996) PEA3 transactivates vimentin promoter in mammary epithelial and tumor cells. Oncogene *13:* 1667–1675.

Cheng, C.W., P.E. Wu, J.C. Yu, C.S. Huang, C.T. Yue, C.W. Wu, C.Y. Shen (2001) Mechanisms of inactivation of E-cadherin in breast carcinoma: modification of the two-hit hypothesis of tumor suppressor gene. Oncogene *20:* 3814–3823.

Cheng, G.Z., W. Zhang, L.H. Wang (2008) Regulation of cancer cell survival, migration, and invasion by Twist: AKT2 comes to interplay. Cancer Res *68:* 957–960.

Christiansen, J.J., A.K. Rajasekaran (2006) Reassessing epithelial to mesenchymal transition as a prerequisite for carcinoma invasion and metastasis. Cancer Res *66:* 8319–8326.

Chu, S., H. Xu, T.J. Ferro, P.X. Rivera (2007) Poly(ADP-ribose) polymerase-1 regulates vimentin expression in lung cancer cells. Am J Physiol Lung Cell Mol Physiol *293:* L1127–L1134.

Chua, H.L., P. Bhat-Nakshatri, S.E. Clare, A. Morimiya, S. Badve, H. Nakshatri (2007) NF-kappaB represses E-cadherin expression and enhances epithelial to mesenchymal transition of mammary epithelial cells: potential involvement of ZEB-1 and ZEB-2. Oncogene *26:* 711–724.

Colomiere, M., J. Findlay, L. Ackland, N. Ahmed (2009a) Epidermal growth factor-induced ovarian carcinoma cell migration is associated with JAK2/STAT3 signals and changes in the abundance and localization of alpha6beta1 integrin. Int J Biochem Cell Biol *41:* 1034–1045.

Colomiere, M., A.C. Ward, C. Riley, M.K. Trenerry, D. Cameron-Smith, J. Findlay, L. Ackland, N. Ahmed (2009b) Cross talk of signals between EGFR and IL-6R through JAK2/STAT3 mediate epithelial-mesenchymal transition in ovarian carcinomas. Br J Cancer *100:* 134–144.

Come, C., V. Arnoux, F. Bibeau, P. Savagner (2004) Roles of the transcription factors snail and slug during mammary morphogenesis and breast carcinoma progression. J Mammary Gland Biol Neoplasia *9:* 183–193.

Come, C., F. Magnino, F. Bibeau, P. De Santa Barbara, K.F. Becker, C. Theillet, P. Savagner (2006) Snail and slug play distinct roles during breast carcinoma progression. Clin Cancer Res *12:* 5395–5402.

Comijn, J., G. Berx, P. Vermassen, K. Verschueren, L. van Grunsven, E. Bruyneel, M. Mareel, D. Huylebroeck, F. van Roy (2001) The two-handed E box binding zinc finger protein SIP1 downregulates E-cadherin and induces invasion. Mol Cell *7:* 1267–1278.

Das, S., B.N. Becker, F.M. Hoffmann, J.E. Mertz (2009) Complete reversal of epithelial to mesenchymal transition requires inhibition of both ZEB expression and the Rho pathway. BMC Cell Biol *10:* 94.

Dhasarathy, A., M. Kajita, P.A. Wade (2007) The transcription factor snail mediates epithelial to mesenchymal transitions by repression of estrogen receptor-alpha. Mol Endocrinol *21:* 2907–2918.

DiMeo, T.A., K. Anderson, P. Phadke, C. Fan, C.M. Perou, S. Naber, C. Kuperwasser (2009) A novel lung metastasis signature links Wnt signaling with cancer cell self-renewal and epithelial-mesenchymal transition in basal-like breast cancer. Cancer Res *69:* 5364–5373.

Ding, J.X., Y.J. Feng, L.Q. Yao, M. Yu, H.Y. Jin, L.H. Yin (2006) The reinforcement of invasion in epithelial ovarian cancer cells by 17 beta-estradiol is associated with up-regulation of Snail. Gynecol Oncol *103:* 623–630.

Drabsch, Y., H. Hugo, R. Zhang, D.H. Dowhan, Y.R. Miao, A.M. Gewirtz, S.C. Barry, R.G. Ramsay, T.J. Gonda (2007) Mechanism of and requirement for estrogen-regulated MYB expression in estrogen-receptor-positive breast cancer cells. Proc Natl Acad Sci USA *104:* 13762–13767.

Drake, J.M., G. Strohbehn, T.B. Bair, J.G. Moreland, M.D. Henry (2009) ZEB1 enhances transendothelial migration and represses the epithelial phenotype of prostate cancer cells. Mol Biol Cell *20:* 2207–2217.

Eger, A., K. Aigner, S. Sonderegger, B. Dampier, S. Oehler, M. Schreiber, G. Berx, A. Cano, H. Beug, R. Foisner (2005) DeltaEF1 is a transcriptional repressor of E-cadherin and regulates epithelial plasticity in breast cancer cells. Oncogene *24:* 2375–2385.

Elloul, S., M.B. Elstrand, J.M. Nesland, C.G. Trope, G. Kvalheim, I. Goldberg, R. Reich, B. Davidson (2005) Snail, Slug, and Smad-interacting protein 1 as novel parameters of disease aggressiveness in metastatic ovarian and breast carcinoma. Cancer *103:* 1631–1643.

Feng, M.Y., K. Wang, Q.T. Shi, X.W. Yu, J.S. Geng (2009) Gene expression profiling in TWIST-depleted gastric cancer cells. Anat Rec (Hoboken) *292:* 262–270.

Fontemaggi, G., A. Gurtner, A. Damalas, A. Costanzo, Y. Higashi, A. Sacchi, S. Strano, G. Piaggio, G. Blandino (2005) DeltaEF1 repressor controls selectively p53 family members during differentiation. Oncogene *24:* 7273–7280.

Franci, C., M. Gallen, F. Alameda, T. Baro, M. Iglesias, I. Virtanen, A. Garcia de Herreros (2009) Snail1 protein in the stroma as a new putative prognosis marker for colon tumours. PLoS One *4:* e5595.

Franci, C., M. Takkunen, N. Dave, F. Alameda, S. Gomez, R. Rodriguez, M. Escriva, B. Montserrat-Sentis, T. Baro, M. Garrido, F. Bonilla, I. Virtanen, A. Garcia de Herreros (2006) Expression of Snail protein in tumor-stroma interface. Oncogene *25:* 5134–5144.

Frew, A.J., R.W. Johnstone, J.E. Bolden (2009) Enhancing the apoptotic and therapeutic effects of HDAC inhibitors. Cancer Lett *280:* 125–133.

Fujita, N., D.L. Jaye, M. Kajita, C. Geigerman, C.S. Moreno, P.A. Wade (2003) MTA3, a Mi-2/NuRD complex subunit, regulates an invasive growth pathway in breast cancer. Cell *113:* 207–219.

Fujita, N., M. Kajita, P. Taysavang, P.A. Wade (2004) Hormonal regulation of metastasis-associated protein 3 transcription in breast cancer cells. Mol Endocrinol *18:* 2937–2949.
Gallo, D., C. Ferlini, G. Scambia (2010) The epithelial-mesenchymal transition and the estrogen-signaling in ovarian cancer. Curr Drug Targets *11:* 474–481.
Gavert, N., A. Ben-Ze'ev (2008) Epithelial-mesenchymal transition and the invasive potential of tumors. Trends Mol Med *14:* 199–209.
Geiger, T.R., D.S. Peeper (2009) Metastasis mechanisms. Biochim Biophys Acta *1796:* 293–308.
Gluck, S. (2007) The prevention and management of distant metastases in women with breast cancer. Cancer Invest *25:* 6–13.
Gregory, P.A., C.P. Bracken, A.G. Bert, G.J. Goodall (2008) MicroRNAs as regulators of epithelial-mesenchymal transition. Cell Cycle *7:* 3112–3118.
Guaita, S., I. Puig, C. Franci, M. Garrido, D. Dominguez, E. Batlle, E. Sancho, S. Dedhar, A.G. De Herreros, J. Baulida (2002) Snail induction of epithelial to mesenchymal transition in tumor cells is accompanied by MUC1 repression and ZEB1 expression. J Biol Chem *277:* 39209–39216.
Gupta, P.B., C. Kuperwasser (2006) Contributions of estrogen to ER-negative breast tumor growth. J Steroid Biochem Mol Biol *102:* 71–78.
Gupta, P.B., T.T. Onder, G. Jiang, K. Tao, C. Kuperwasser, R.A. Weinberg, E.S. Lander (2009) Identification of selective inhibitors of cancer stem cells by high-throughput screening. Cell *138:* 645–659.
Gupta, P.B., D. Proia, O. Cingoz, J. Weremowicz, S.P. Naber, R.A. Weinberg, C. Kuperwasser (2007) Systemic stromal effects of estrogen promote the growth of estrogen receptor-negative cancers. Cancer Res *67:* 2062–2071.
Haase, V.H. (2009) Oxygen regulates epithelial-to-mesenchymal transition: insights into molecular mechanisms and relevance to disease. Kidney Int *76:* 492–499.
Hader, C., A. Marlier, L. Cantley (2009) Mesenchymal-epithelial transition in epithelial response to injury: the role of Foxc2. Oncogene *29:* 1031–1040.
Hartwell, K.A., B. Muir, F. Reinhardt, A.E. Carpenter, D.C. Sgroi, R.A. Weinberg (2006) The Spemann organizer gene, Goosecoid, promotes tumor metastasis. Proc Natl Acad Sci USA *103:* 18969–18974.
Hay, E.D. (1995) An overview of epithelio-mesenchymal transformation. Acta Anat (Basel) *154:* 8–20.
Hemavathy, K., S.I. Ashraf, Y.T. Ip (2000) Snail/slug family of repressors: slowly going into the fast lane of development and cancer. Gene *257:* 1–12.
Hollier, B.G., K. Evans, S.A. Mani (2009) The epithelial-to-mesenchymal transition and cancer stem cells: a coalition against cancer therapies. J Mammary Gland Biol Neoplasia *14:* 29–43.
Huang, C.H., W.H. Yang, S.Y. Chang, S.K. Tai, C.H. Tzeng, J.Y. Kao, K.J. Wu, M.H. Yang (2009) Regulation of membrane-type 4 matrix metalloproteinase by SLUG contributes to hypoxia-mediated metastasis. Neoplasia *11:* 1371–1382.
Huang, Y., S.V. Fernandez, S. Goodwin, P.A. Russo, I.H. Russo, T.R. Sutter, J. Russo (2007) Epithelial to mesenchymal transition in human breast epithelial cells transformed by 17beta-estradiol. Cancer Res *67:* 11147–11157.
Hugo, H., M.L. Ackland, T. Blick, M.G. Lawrence, J.A. Clements, E.D. Williams, E.W. Thompson (2007) Epithelial-mesenchymal and mesenchymal-epithelial transitions in carcinoma progression. J Cell Physiol *213:* 374–383.
Hugo, H.J., R. Wafai, T. Blick, E.W. Thompson, D.F. Newgreen (2009) Staurosporine augments EGF-mediated EMT in PMC42-LA cells through actin depolymerisation, focal contact size reduction and Snail1 induction – a model for cross-modulation. BMC Cancer *9:* 235.
Ip, Y.T., T. Gridley (2002) Cell movements during gastrulation: snail dependent and independent pathways. Curr Opin Genet Dev *12:* 423–429.
Jiang, R., Y. Lan, C.R. Norton, J.P. Sundberg, T. Gridley (1998) The Slug gene is not essential for mesoderm or neural crest development in mice. Dev Biol *198:* 277–285.
Jones, S.E. (2008) Metastatic breast cancer: the treatment challenge. Clin Breast Cancer *8:* 224–233.
Jorda, M., A. Vinyals, A. Marazuela, E. Cubillo, D. Olmeda, E. Valero, A. Cano, A. Fabra (2007) Id-1 is induced in MDCK epithelial cells by activated Erk/MAPK pathway in response to expression of the Snail and E47 transcription factors. Exp Cell Res *313:* 2389–2403.
Julien, S., I. Puig, E. Caretti, J. Bonaventure, L. Nelles, F. van Roy, C. Dargemont, A.G. de Herreros, A. Bellacosa, L. Larue (2007) Activation of NF-kappaB by Akt upregulates Snail expression and induces epithelium mesenchyme transition. Oncogene *26:* 7445–7456.
Kajita, M., K.N. McClinic, P.A. Wade (2004) Aberrant expression of the transcription factors snail and slug alters the response to genotoxic stress. Mol Cell Biol *24:* 7559–7566.
Kasper, M., V. Jaks, M. Fiaschi, R. Toftgard (2009) Hedgehog signalling in breast cancer. Carcinogenesis *30:* 903–911.
Katoh, M. (2003) Identification and characterization of human SNAIL3 (SNAI3) gene in silico. Int J Mol Med *11:* 383–388.
Klymkowsky, M.W. (2005) Beta-catenin and its regulatory network. Hum Pathol *36:* 225–227.
Kudo-Saito, C., H. Shirako, T. Takeuchi, Y. Kawakami (2009) Cancer metastasis is accelerated through immunosuppression during Snail-induced EMT of cancer cells. Cancer Cell *15:* 195–206.
Kurrey, N.K., S.P. Jalgaonkar, A.V. Joglekar, A.D. Ghanate, P.D. Chaskar, R.Y. Doiphode, S.A. Bapat (2009) Snail and slug mediate radioresistance and chemoresistance by antagonizing p53-mediated apoptosis and acquiring a stem-like phenotype in ovarian cancer cells. Stem Cells *27:* 2059–2068.
Larriba, M.J., F. Bonilla, A. Munoz (2010) The transcription factors Snail1 and Snail2 repress vitamin D receptor during colon cancer progression. J Steroid Biochem Mol Biol.
Larriba, M.J., E. Martin-Villar, J.M. Garcia, F. Pereira, C. Pena, A.G. de Herreros, F. Bonilla, A. Munoz (2009) Snail2 cooperates with Snail1 in the repression of vitamin D receptor in colon cancer. Carcinogenesis *30:* 1459–1468.
Lebret, S.C., D.F. Newgreen, M.C. Waltham, J.T. Price, E.W. Thompson, M.L. Ackland (2006) Myoepithelial molecular markers in human breast carcinoma PMC42-LA cells are induced by extracellular matrix and stromal cells. In Vitro Cell Dev Biol Anim *42:* 298–307.
Li, Q., R.R. Mattingly (2008) Restoration of E-cadherin cell-cell junctions requires both expression of E-cadherin and suppression of ERK MAP kinase activation in Ras-transformed breast epithelial cells. Neoplasia *10:* 1444–1458.
Li, Y., J. Yang, J.H. Luo, S. Dedhar, Y. Liu (2007) Tubular epithelial cell dedifferentiation is driven by the helix-loop-helix transcriptional inhibitor Id1. J Am Soc Nephrol *18:* 449–460.
Lopez-Novoa, J.M., M.A. Nieto (2009) Inflammation and EMT: an alliance towards organ fibrosis and cancer progression. EMBO Mol Med *1:* 303–314.
Lu, Z., S. Ghosh, Z. Wang, T. Hunter (2003) Downregulation of caveolin-1 function by EGF leads to the loss of E-cadherin, increased transcriptional activity of beta-catenin, and enhanced tumor cell invasion. Cancer Cell *4:* 499–515.
Lundgren, K., B. Nordenskjold, G. Landberg (2009) Hypoxia, Snail and incomplete epithelial-mesenchymal transition in breast cancer. Br J Cancer *101:* 1769–1781.
Ma, L., J. Teruya-Feldstein, R.A. Weinberg (2007) Tumour invasion and metastasis initiated by microRNA-10b in breast cancer. Nature *449:* 682–688.
Ma, L., J. Young, H. Prabhala, E. Pan, P. Mestdagh, D. Muth, J. Teruya-Feldstein, F. Reinhardt, T.T. Onder, S. Valastyan, F. Westermann, F. Speleman, J. Vandesompele, R.A. Weinberg (2010) miR-9, a MYC/MYCN-activated microRNA, regulates E-cadherin and cancer metastasis. Nat Cell Biol *12:* 247–256.
Mani, S.A., W. Guo, M.J. Liao, E.N. Eaton, A. Ayyanan, A.Y. Zhou, M. Brooks, F. Reinhard, C.C. Zhang, M. Shipitsin, L.L. Campbell, K. Polyak, C. Brisken, J. Yang, R.A. Weinberg (2008) The epithelial-mesenchymal transition generates cells with properties of stem cells. Cell *133:* 704–715.

Mani, S.A., J. Yang, M. Brooks, G. Schwaninger, A. Zhou, N. Miura, J.L. Kutok, K. Hartwell, A.L. Richardson, R.A. Weinberg (2007) Mesenchyme Forkhead 1 (FOXC2) plays a key role in metastasis and is associated with aggressive basal-like breast cancers. Proc Natl Acad Sci USA *104:* 10069–10074.

Marks, P.A., W.S. Xu (2009) Histone deacetylase inhibitors: potential in cancer therapy. J Cell Biochem *107:* 600–608.

Martin, T.A., A. Goyal, G. Watkins, W.G. Jiang (2005) Expression of the transcription factors snail, slug, and twist and their clinical significance in human breast cancer. Ann Surg Oncol *12:* 488–496.

McPhee, T.R., P.C. McDonald, A. Oloumi, S. Dedhar (2008) Integrin-linked kinase regulates E-cadherin expression through PARP-1. Dev Dyn *237:* 2737–2747.

Mejlvang, J., M. Kriajevska, C. Vandewalle, T. Chernova, A.E. Sayan, G. Berx, J.K. Mellon, E. Tulchinsky (2007) Direct repression of cyclin D1 by SIP1 attenuates cell cycle progression in cells undergoing an epithelial mesenchymal transition. Mol Biol Cell *18:* 4615–4624.

Miyazono, K. (2009) Transforming growth factor-beta signaling in epithelial-mesenchymal transition and progression of cancer. Proc Jpn Acad Ser B Phys Biol Sci *85:* 314–323.

Moody, S.E., D. Perez, T.C. Pan, C.J. Sarkisian, C.P. Portocarrero, C.J. Sterner, K.L. Notorfrancesco, R.D. Cardiff, L.A. Chodosh (2005) The transcriptional repressor Snail promotes mammary tumor recurrence. Cancer Cell *8:* 197–209.

Moreno-Bueno, G., E. Cubillo, D. Sarrio, H. Peinado, S.M. Rodriguez-Pinilla, S. Villa, V. Bolos, M. Jorda, A. Fabra, F. Portillo, J. Palacios, A. Cano (2006) Genetic profiling of epithelial cells expressing E-cadherin repressors reveals a distinct role for Snail, Slug, and E47 factors in epithelial-mesenchymal transition. Cancer Res *66:* 9543–9556.

Murray, S.A., T. Gridley (2006a) Snail1 gene function during early embryo patterning in mice. Cell Cycle *5:* 2566–2570.

Murray, S.A., T. Gridley (2006b) Snail family genes are required for left-right asymmetry determination, but not neural crest formation, in mice. Proc Natl Acad Sci USA *103:* 10300–10304.

Myung, J.H., C.A. Launiere, D.T. Eddington, S. Hong (2010) Enhanced tumor cell isolation by a biomimetic combination of E-selectin and anti-EpCAM: implications for the effective separation of circulating tumor cells (CTCs). Langmuir *26:* 8589–8596.

Nelson, N.J. (2010) Circulating tumor cells: will they be clinically useful? J Natl Cancer Inst *102:* 146–148.

Nelson, W.J., R. Nusse (2004) Convergence of Wnt, beta-catenin, and cadherin pathways. Science *303:* 1483–1487.

Nieto, M.A. (2002) The snail superfamily of zinc-finger transcription factors. Nat Rev Mol Cell Biol *3:* 155–166.

Oltean, S., B.S. Sorg, T. Albrecht, V.I. Bonano, R.M. Brazas, M.W. Dewhirst, M.A. Garcia-Blanco (2006) Alternative inclusion of fibroblast growth factor receptor 2 exon IIIc in Dunning prostate tumors reveals unexpected epithelial mesenchymal plasticity. Proc Natl Acad Sci USA *103:* 14116–14121.

Palmer, H.G., M.J. Larriba, J.M. Garcia, P. Ordonez-Moran, C. Pena, S. Peiro, I. Puig, R. Rodriguez, R. de la Fuente, A. Bernad, M. Pollan, F. Bonilla, C. Gamallo, A.G. de Herreros, A. Munoz (2004) The transcription factor SNAIL represses vitamin D receptor expression and responsiveness in human colon cancer. Nat Med *10:* 917–919.

Park, S.H., L.W. Cheung, A.S. Wong, P.C. Leung (2008) Estrogen regulates Snail and Slug in the down-regulation of E-cadherin and induces metastatic potential of ovarian cancer cells through estrogen receptor alpha. Mol Endocrinol *22:* 2085–2098.

Paterlini-Brechot, P., N.L. Benali (2007) Circulating tumor cells (CTC) detection: clinical impact and future directions. Cancer Lett *253:* 180–204.

Peinado, H., F. Marin, E. Cubillo, H.J. Stark, N. Fusenig, M.A. Nieto, A. Cano (2004) Snail and E47 repressors of E-cadherin induce distinct invasive and angiogenic properties in vivo. J Cell Sci *117:* 2827–2839.

Peinado, H., D. Olmeda, A. Cano (2007) Snail, Zeb and bHLH factors in tumour progression: an alliance against the epithelial phenotype? Nat Rev Cancer *7:* 415–428.

Peinado, H., M. Quintanilla, A. Cano (2003) Transforming growth factor beta-1 induces snail transcription factor in epithelial cell lines: mechanisms for epithelial mesenchymal transitions. J Biol Chem *278:* 21113–21123.

Peiro, S., M. Escriva, I. Puig, M.J. Barbera, N. Dave, N. Herranz, M.J. Larriba, M. Takkunen, C. Franci, A. Munoz, I. Virtanen, J. Baulida, A. Garcia de Herreros (2006) Snail1 transcriptional repressor binds to its own promoter and controls its expression. Nucleic Acids Res *34:* 2077–2084.

Pena, C., J.M. Garcia, V. Garcia, J. Silva, G. Dominguez, R. Rodriguez, C. Maximiano, A. Garcia de Herreros, A. Munoz, F. Bonilla (2006) The expression levels of the transcriptional regulators p300 and CtBP modulate the correlations between SNAIL, ZEB1, E-cadherin and vitamin D receptor in human colon carcinomas. Int J Cancer *119:* 2098–2104.

Perez-Moreno, M.A., A. Locascio, I. Rodrigo, G. Dhondt, F. Portillo, M.A. Nieto, A. Cano (2001) A new role for E12/E47 in the repression of E-cadherin expression and epithelial-mesenchymal transitions. J Biol Chem *276:* 27424–27431.

Planas-Silva, M.D., P.K. Waltz (2007) Estrogen promotes reversible epithelial-to-mesenchymal-like transition and collective motility in MCF-7 breast cancer cells. J Steroid Biochem Mol Biol *104:* 11–21.

Polyak, K., R.A. Weinberg (2009) Transitions between epithelial and mesenchymal states: acquisition of malignant and stem cell traits. Nat Rev Cancer *9:* 265–273.

Przybylo, J.A., D.C. Radisky (2007) Matrix metalloproteinase-induced epithelial-mesenchymal transition: tumor progression at Snail's pace. Int J Biochem Cell Biol *39:* 1082–1088.

Rittling, S.R., L. Coutinho, T. Amram, M. Kolbe (1989) AP-1/jun binding sites mediate serum inducibility of the human vimentin promoter. Nucleic Acids Res *17:* 1619–1633.

Rodrigues, C.O., S.T. Nerlick, E.L. White, J.L. Cleveland, M.L. King (2008) A Myc-Slug (Snail2)/Twist regulatory circuit directs vascular development. Development *135:* 1903–1911.

Sakai, D., T. Suzuki, N. Osumi, Y. Wakamatsu (2006) Cooperative action of Sox9, Snail2 and PKA signaling in early neural crest development. Development *133:* 1323–1333.

Sauka-Spengler, T., M. Bronner-Fraser (2008) A gene regulatory network orchestrates neural crest formation. Nat Rev Mol Cell Biol *9:* 557–568.

Schaeffer, D.F., K. Assi, K. Chan, A.K. Buczkowski, S.W. Chung, C.H. Scudamore, A. Weiss, B. Salh, D.A. Owen (2010) Tumor expression of integrin-linked kinase (ILK) correlates with the expression of the E-cadherin repressor Snail: an immunohistochemical study in ductal pancreatic adenocarcinoma. Virchows Arch *456:* 261–268.

Simpson, M.J., D.C. Zhang, M. Mariani, K.A. Landman, D.F. Newgreen (2007) Cell proliferation drives neural crest cell invasion of the intestine. Dev Biol *302:* 553–568.

Sobrado, V.R., G. Moreno-Bueno, E. Cubillo, L.J. Holt, M.A. Nieto, F. Portillo, A. Cano (2009) The class I bHLH factors E2-2A and E2-2B regulate EMT. J Cell Sci *122:* 1014–1024.

Spaderna, S., O. Schmalhofer, F. Hlubek, G. Berx, A. Eger, S. Merkel, A. Jung, T. Kirchner, T. Brabletz (2006) A transient, EMT-linked loss of basement membranes indicates metastasis and poor survival in colorectal cancer. Gastroenterology *131:* 830–840.

Spaderna, S., O. Schmalhofer, M. Wahlbuhl, A. Dimmler, K. Bauer, A. Sultan, F. Hlubek, A. Jung, D. Strand, A. Eger, T. Kirchner, J. Behrens, T. Brabletz (2008) The transcriptional repressor ZEB1 promotes metastasis and loss of cell polarity in cancer. Cancer Res *68:* 537–544.

Spoelstra, N.S., N.G. Manning, Y. Higashi, D. Darling, M. Singh, K.R. Shroyer, R.R. Broaddus, K.B. Horwitz, J.K. Richer (2006) The transcription factor ZEB1 is aberrantly expressed in aggressive uterine cancers. Cancer Res *66:* 3893–3902.

Stallings-Mann, M., D. Radisky (2007) Matrix metalloproteinase-induced malignancy in mammary epithelial cells. Cells Tissues Organs *185:* 104–110.

Story, P., A. Doube (2004) A case of human poisoning by salinomycin, an agricultural antibiotic. NZ Med J *117:* U799.

Sun, S., X. Ning, Y. Zhang, Y. Lu, Y. Nie, S. Han, L. Liu, R. Du, L. Xia, L. He, D. Fan (2009) Hypoxia-inducible factor-1alpha induces Twist expression in tubular epithelial cells subjected to hypoxia, leading to epithelial-to-mesenchymal transition. Kidney Int *75:* 1278–1287.

Takagi, T., H. Moribe, H. Kondoh, Y. Higashi (1998) DeltaEF1, a zinc finger and homeodomain transcription factor, is required for skeleton patterning in multiple lineages. Development *125:* 21–31.

Thiery, J.P., H. Acloque, R.Y. Huang, M.A. Nieto (2009) Epithelial-mesenchymal transitions in development and disease. Cell *139:* 871–890.

Thiery, J.P., J.P. Sleeman (2006) Complex networks orchestrate epithelial-mesenchymal transitions. Nat Rev Mol Cell Biol *7:* 131–142.

Thomas, S., P.N. Munster (2009) Histone deacetylase inhibitor induced modulation of anti-estrogen therapy. Cancer Lett *280:* 184–191.

Tiezzi, D.G., S.V. Fernandez, J. Russo (2007) Epithelial mesenchymal transition during the neoplastic transformation of human breast epithelial cells by estrogen. Int J Oncol *31:* 823–827.

Toh, Y., G.L. Nicolson (2009) The role of the MTA family and their encoded proteins in human cancers: molecular functions and clinical implications. Clin Exp Metastasis *26:* 215–227.

Tsuji, T., S. Ibaragi, G.F. Hu (2009) Epithelial-mesenchymal transition and cell cooperativity in metastasis. Cancer Res *69:* 7135–7139.

Turner, F.E., S. Broad, F.L. Khanim, A. Jeanes, S. Talma, S. Hughes, C. Tselepis, N.A. Hotchin (2006) Slug regulates integrin expression and cell proliferation in human epidermal keratinocytes. J Biol Chem *281:* 21321–21331.

Uchikado, Y., S. Natsugoe, H. Okumura, T. Setoyama, M. Matsumoto, S. Ishigami, T. Aikou (2005) Slug expression in the E-cadherin preserved tumors is related to prognosis in patients with esophageal squamous cell carcinoma. Clin Cancer Res *11:* 1174–1180.

Valastyan, S., F. Reinhardt, N. Benaich, D. Calogrias, A.M. Szasz, Z.C. Wang, J.E. Brock, A.L. Richardson, R.A. Weinberg (2009) A pleiotropically acting microRNA, miR-31, inhibits breast cancer metastasis. Cell *137:* 1032–1046.

Vega, S., A.V. Morales, O.H. Ocana, F. Valdes, I. Fabregat, M.A. Nieto (2004) Snail blocks the cell cycle and confers resistance to cell death. Genes Dev *18:* 1131–1143.

Vergara, D., B. Merlot, J.P. Lucot, P. Collinet, D. Vinatier, I. Fournier, M. Salzet (2010) Epithelial-mesenchymal transition in ovarian cancer. Cancer Lett *291:* 59–66.

Vesuna, F., A. Lisok, B. Kimble, V. Raman (2009) Twist modulates breast cancer stem cells by transcriptional regulation of CD24 expression. Neoplasia *11:* 1318–1328.

Vesuna, F., P. van Diest, J.H. Chen, V. Raman (2008) Twist is a transcriptional repressor of E-cadherin gene expression in breast cancer. Biochem Biophys Res Commun *367:* 235–241.

Vos, C.B., A.M. Cleton-Jansen, G. Berx, W.J. de Leeuw, N.T. ter Haar, F. van Roy, C.J. Cornelisse, J.L. Peterse, M.J. van de Vijver (1997) E-cadherin inactivation in lobular carcinoma in situ of the breast: an early event in tumorigenesis. Br J Cancer *76:* 1131–1133.

Waldmann, J., E.P. Slater, P. Langer, M. Buchholz, A. Ramaswamy, M.K. Walz, K.W. Schmid, G. Feldmann, D.K. Bartsch, V. Fendrich (2009) Expression of the transcription factor snail and its target gene twist are associated with malignancy in pheochromocytomas. Ann Surg Oncol *16:* 1997–2005.

Wanami, L.S., H.Y. Chen, S. Peiro, A. Garcia de Herreros, R.E. Bachelder (2008) Vascular endothelial growth factor-A stimulates Snail expression in breast tumor cells: implications for tumor progression. Exp Cell Res *314:* 2448–2453.

Wang, X., J. Zhao (2007a) KLF8 transcription factor participates in oncogenic transformation. Oncogene *26:* 456–461.

Wang, X., M. Zheng, G. Liu, W. Xia, P.J. McKeown-Longo, M.C. Hung, J. Zhao (2007b) Kruppel-like factor 8 induces epithelial to mesenchymal transition and epithelial cell invasion. Cancer Res *67:* 7184–7193.

Whitehead, R.H., I. Bertoncello, L.M. Webber, J.S. Pedersen (1983) A new human breast carcinoma cell line (PMC42) with stem cell characteristics. 1. Morphologic characterization. J Natl Cancer Inst *70:* 649–661.

Whitehead, R.H., S.J. Quirk, A.A. Vitali, J.W. Funder, R.L. Sutherland, L.C. Murphy (1984) A new human breast carcinoma cell line (PMC42) with stem cell characteristics. 3. Hormone receptor status and responsiveness. J Natl Cancer Inst *73:* 643–648.

Williams, T.M., D. Moolten, J. Burlein, J. Romano, R. Bhaerman, A. Godillot, M. Mellon, F.J. Rauscher 3rd, J.A. Kant (1991) Identification of a zinc finger protein that inhibits IL-2 gene expression. Science *254:* 1791–1794.

Wu, Y., J. Deng, P.G. Rychahou, S. Qiu, B.M. Evers, B.P. Zhou (2009) Stabilization of snail by NF-kappaB is required for inflammation-induced cell migration and invasion. Cancer Cell *15:* 416–428.

Wu, Y., I. Diab, X. Zhang, E.S. Izmailova, Z.E. Zehner (2004) Stat3 enhances vimentin gene expression by binding to the antisilencer element and interacting with the repressor protein, ZBP-89. Oncogene *23:* 168–178.

Wyatt, L., Y. Khew-Goodall (2008) PTP-Pez: a novel regulator of TGFbeta signaling. Cell Cycle *7:* 2290–2295.

Wyatt, L., C. Wadham, L.A. Crocker, M. Lardelli, Y. Khew-Goodall (2007) The protein tyrosine phosphatase Pez regulates TGFbeta, epithelial-mesenchymal transition, and organ development. J Cell Biol *178:* 1223–1235.

Yang, A.D., E.R. Camp, F. Fan, L. Shen, M.J. Gray, W. Liu, R. Somcio, T.W. Bauer, Y. Wu, D.J. Hicklin, L.M. Ellis (2006) Vascular endothelial growth factor receptor-1 activation mediates epithelial to mesenchymal transition in human pancreatic carcinoma cells. Cancer Res *66:* 46–51.

Yang, J., S.A. Mani, J.L. Donaher, S. Ramaswamy, R.A. Itzykson, C. Come, P. Savagner, I. Gitelman, A. Richardson, R.A. Weinberg (2004) Twist, a master regulator of morphogenesis, plays an essential role in tumor metastasis. Cell *117:* 927–939.

Yang, J., R.A. Weinberg (2008) Epithelial-mesenchymal transition: at the crossroads of development and tumor metastasis. Dev Cell *14:* 818–829.

Ye, Y., Y. Xiao, W. Wang, K. Yearsley, J.X. Gao, S.H. Barsky (2008) ERalpha suppresses slug expression directly by transcriptional repression. Biochem J *416:* 179–187.

Ye, Y., Y. Xiao, W. Wang, K. Yearsley, J.X. Gao, B. Shetuni, S.H. Barsky (2010) ERalpha signaling through slug regulates E-cadherin and EMT. Oncogene *29:* 1451–1462.

Yokoyama, K., N. Kamata, R. Fujimoto, S. Tsutsumi, M. Tomonari, M. Taki, H. Hosokawa, M. Nagayama (2003) Increased invasion and matrix metalloproteinase-2 expression by Snail-induced mesenchymal transition in squamous cell carcinomas. Int J Oncol *22:* 891–898.

Yokoyama, K., N. Kamata, E. Hayashi, T. Hoteiya, N. Ueda, R. Fujimoto, M. Nagayama (2001) Reverse correlation of E-cadherin and snail expression in oral squamous cell carcinoma cells in vitro. Oral Oncol *37:* 65–71.

Yu, M., G.A. Smolen, J. Zhang, B. Wittner, B.J. Schott, E. Brachtel, S. Ramaswamy, S. Maheswaran, D.A. Haber (2009) A developmentally regulated inducer of EMT, LBX1, contributes to breast cancer progression. Genes Dev *23:* 1737–1742.

Zhang, C., M.W. Klymkowsky (2009) Unexpected functional redundancy between Twist and Slug (Snail2) and their feedback regulation of NF-kappaB via Nodal and Cerberus. Dev Biol *331:* 340–349.

Zhao, J., Z.C. Bian, K. Yee, B.P. Chen, S. Chien, J.L. Guan (2003) Identification of transcription factor KLF8 as a downstream target of focal adhesion kinase in its regulation of cyclin D1 and cell cycle progression. Mol Cell *11:* 1503–1515.

Zhou, B.P., J. Deng, W. Xia, J. Xu, Y.M. Li, M. Gunduz, M.C. Hung (2004) Dual regulation of Snail by GSK-3beta-mediated phosphorylation in control of epithelial-mesenchymal transition. Nat Cell Biol *6:* 931–940.

Cells
Tissues
Organs

Cells Tissues Organs 2011;193:41–52
DOI: 10.1159/000320180

Published online: November 3, 2010

Smaddening Complexity: The Role of Smad3 in Epithelial-Myofibroblast Transition

András Masszi András Kapus

Keenan Research Centre, Li Ka Shing Knowledge Institute, St. Michael's Hospital, and Department of Surgery, University of Toronto, Toronto, Ont., Canada

Key Words

Transforming growth factor-β · Receptor Smads · α-Smooth muscle actin · Myogenic program · Epithelial-mesenchymal transition · Myocardin-related transcription factor · Intercellular contacts

Abstract

Epithelial-mesenchymal transition (EMT) has emerged as a major mechanism in the pathogenesis of organ fibrosis. The epithelium has been proposed to be a significant source of matrix-producing fibroblasts and of myofibroblasts (MFs), a motile and contractile cell type hallmarked by the expression of α-smooth muscle actin (SMA). Importantly, tissue accumulation of MFs shows strong correlation with the severity and progression of fibrotic diseases. The pleiotropic cytokine transforming growth factor-β_1 has been long known as the chief inducer of fibrosis, EMT and MF generation. Accordingly, receptor Smads (Smad2 and particularly Smad3), the direct targets of the activated transforming growth factor-β receptor have been implicated as critical mediators in fibrogenesis and EMT. However, evidence is accumulating that the role of Smad3 is complex and apparently controversial; in fact, Smad3 may differentially affect the various components of EMT, including the loss of epithelial markers (de-epithelialization), the production of extracellular matrix (fibrogenesis) and the expression of SMA (myogenic program). In this review, we revisit the role of Smad3 in epithelial-myofibroblast transition (EMyT). We first summarize the evidence supporting the thesis that Smad3 is a key mediator of EMT and MF generation; next, we present evidence supporting the antithesis that Smad3 is in fact a negative regulator of SMA expression and the activation of the myogenic program in the epithelium; finally, we propose a synthesis, which depicts Smad3 as a timekeeper and context-dependent modulator of EMyT. We suggest that EMyT is composed of an early, mesenchymal, Smad3-promoted phase and a late, myogenic, Smad3-inhibitable phase.

Abbreviations used in this paper

CArG	CC(A/T)rich GG box
ECM	extracellular matrix
EMT	epithelial-mesenchymal transition
EMyT	epithelial-myofibroblast transition
KO	knockout
MF	myofibroblast
MRTF	myocardin-related transcription factor
MyoD	myogenic differentiation factor
R-Smad	receptor Smad
SBE	Smad-binding element
SMA	α-smooth muscle actin
SRF	serum response factor
TGF-β	transforming growth factor-β

KARGER

Fax +41 61 306 12 34
E-Mail karger@karger.ch
www.karger.com

1422–6405/11/1932–0041$38.00/0

Accessible online at:
www.karger.com/cto

Dr. András Kapus
Saint Michael's Hospital Research Institute, Queen Wing 7-009
30 Bond Street
Toronto, ON M5B 1W8 (Canada)
Tel. +1 416 864 6060, ext. 2839, Fax +1 416 864 5167, E-Mail kapusa@smh.toronto.on.ca

Prelude: Organ Fibrosis and Epithelial-Myofibroblast Transition

In his landmark review, Thomas Wynn [2007] called attention to the striking fact that nearly 45% of all deaths in the developed world are attributable to some form of tissue or organ fibrosis. The prime examples for these currently incurable fibroproliferative diseases and pathologies include idiopathic pulmonary fibrosis and other forms of interstitial lung disease, liver cirrhosis, tubulointerstitial fibrosis, glomerulosclerosis, scleroderma and a variety of cardiovascular disorders [Iredale, 2007; Varga and Abraham, 2007; Gharaee-Kermani et al., 2009; Liu, 2010]. Despite the obvious diversity of the above conditions, the basic mechanisms underlying these fibrotic diseases are essentially common. Organ fibrosis can be viewed as a process of chronic and destructive tissue remodeling due to repeated or continuous cycles of injury and failed repair. Various triggering factors, such as pathogen-induced or autoimmune inflammation, ischemia, chemical or mechanical trauma and other noxae precipitate tissue injury, which in turn initiates the accumulation and activation of fibroblasts and their contractile counterparts, the myofibroblasts (MFs), hallmarked by the expression of α-smooth muscle actin (SMA) [Hinz et al., 2007]. These mesenchymal cells are then responsible for excessive production of extracellular matrix (ECM) components and the ensuing tissue contraction, the distinguishing features of progressive organ scarring [Wynn, 2008].

As the accumulation of MFs (and thus SMA) shows strong correlation with the severity and progression of fibrosis, the source of MFs has become the focus of intensive research. MFs can originate from resident fibroblasts, pericytes, bone marrow-derived circulating fibrocytes and monocytes/macrophages [Hinz, 2007; Wynn, 2008]. Moreover, fibroblasts and MFs can derive from differentiated cells with apico-basal polarity such as the endothelium or the epithelium, through the process of endothelial-mesenchymal [Zeisberg et al., 2007a] and epithelial-mesenchymal transition (EMT) [Kalluri and Weinberg, 2009]. Indeed, the epithelium, once seen as a passive victim of fibrogenesis, has emerged as an active participant, through a mechanism that directly couples the loss of epithelial properties with the gain of mesenchymal features. While the capacity of epithelial cells to transform into fibroblasts and MFs have undoubtedly been demonstrated in vitro [for a review, see ref. Xu et al., 2009; Zeisberg and Neilson, 2009], the participation of EMT in fibrogenesis in vivo is more controversial. Studies employing genetic tagging and tracking of epithelial cells have provided differing results depending on the particular model, the mode of lineage tracing and – most importantly – on the marker that is used as the indicator of EMT. Thus, the presence of EMT (or rather SMA expression in the epithelium) has been questioned in obstruction-induced kidney fibrosis [Humphreys et al., 2010] and chemically induced liver fibrosis [Taura et al., 2010]. On the other hand, a substantial set of studies have indicated that a sizable portion of mesenchymal cells (including MFs) originates from the epithelium in pulmonary [Kim et al., 2006, 2009b; Tanjore et al., 2009], renal [Iwano et al., 2002], liver [Zeisberg et al., 2007b] and intestinal [Flier et al., 2010] fibrosis. Moreover, the observed co-expression of epithelial and fibroblast markers (e.g., FSP1) in epithelial cells during fibrogenesis provides strong support for the presence and significance of EMT [Strutz et al., 1995].

Fibrogenic EMT, is a profound phenotypic change characterized by (1) the loss of intercellular contacts, i.e. the dissolution of tight and adherent junctions and the down-regulation of their components (such as claudin and E-cadherin); (2) excessive ECM production (e.g., collagen, fibronectin), and (3) dramatic remodeling of the cytoskeleton, which manifests in shape change, increased cell contractility and motility [Kalluri and Weinberg, 2009]. Moreover, the process may progress further, culminating in the expression of SMA, an event that reflects the activation of a myogenic program in the transformed epithelium. To distinguish this full-blown, MF-generating form of EMT, we will use the term 'epithelial-myofibroblast transition' or 'EMyT' [Masszi et al., 2010]. Overall, the process of EMyT follows a defined chronology, from the loss of contacts, through ECM production to SMA expression.

The pleiotropic cytokine, transforming growth factor-β (TGF-β), produced by inflammatory cells, fibroblasts and the epithelium itself, has long been recognized as the single most important inducer of EMT and EMyT [Xu et al., 2009; see also Lamouille and Derynck, 2011, and Allington and Schiemann, 2011, in the current issue]. However, recent studies have called attention to the fact that an intact epithelium can be rather resistant to the EMyT-provoking (SMA-inducing) effect of TGF-β, suggesting that TGF-β, albeit necessary, may not be sufficient for this process [Masszi et al., 2004, 2010]. Instead, TGF-β acts together with other inputs, such as an initial loss or injury of the intercellular contacts [Masszi et al., 2004; Fan et al., 2007; Tamiya et al., 2009; Zheng et al., 2009], enhanced cell contractility or tension [Wipff et al., 2007;

Gomez et al., 2010], increased matrix stiffness [Hinz, 2009] or the activation of integrins [Kim et al., 2009a, 2009b]. In the presence of at least 1 of these additional stimuli (i.e. in a '2-hit' scenario) massive EMyT can ensue. Such regulation may explain the self-augmenting/propagating and spatially restricted nature of EMyT, because (1) TGF-β will preferentially transform injured areas in the tissue; (2) once local susceptibility is established, TGF-β will exert a positive feedback by promoting the development of these costimulatory factors (e.g., it facilitates contact downregulation, contraction, ECM stiffness), and (3) enhanced mechanical tension (e.g., due to matrix stiffness + SMA expression) can activate latent TGF-β [Wipff et al., 2007].

Cognizant of this complex scenario, the main aim of this review is to highlight how critical regulatory/signaling events converge to mobilize the myogenic program in the epithelium during EMyT. We will focus primarily on the complex and apparently controversial role(s) of Smad3, one of the main signal transducers of TGF-β.

Thesis: Smad3 Is a Key Mediator of EMT and MF Generation

TGF-β regulates a plethora of cellular responses through a wide range of signaling pathways [Taylor and Wrana, 2008]. Upon TGF-β binding, the type II TGF-β receptor recruits the type I receptor, a transmembrane Ser/Thr kinase. The most important TGF-β-specific effectors are the Smad proteins. The activated receptor complex phosphorylates receptor (R)-Smad proteins (Smad2 and Smad3) on a serine residue in their C-terminal SSXS motif. R-Smads then bind to Smad4, and the complex translocates to the nucleus, where it acts on Smad-binding elements (SBE), and activates an array of genes suppressing epithelial and inducing mesenchymal characteristics. In addition to the Smad pathway, TGF-β can also activate the extracellular signal-regulated kinase, c-Jun N-terminal kinase and p38 mitogen-activated protein kinase, the phosphatidyl-inositol 3-kinase/Akt kinase and Rho/Rho kinase pathways, which were all implicated in the regulation of EMT [Derynck and Zhang, 2003; Moustakas and Heldin, 2005; see also Lamouille and Derynck, 2011, in the current issue].

Substantial literature suggests that R-Smads are key mediators in TGF-β-induced fibrosis and EMT [Roberts et al., 2006]. Strong support for this view originates from studies using Smad3 knockout (KO) mice [Yang et al., 1999], which exhibit reduced susceptibility to matrix deposition and EMT in various models of skin [Flanders et al., 2003; Lakos et al., 2004], lens [Saika et al., 2004], lung [Bonniaud et al., 2004] and kidney fibrosis [Sato et al., 2003]. Nonetheless, experiments using pharmacological inhibitors and mutant type I TGF-β receptors with selectively altered downstream signaling potential revealed that Smad signaling is necessary but not sufficient to induce EMT [Yu et al., 2002].

The Smad pathway targets each functional section of EMT/EMyT. Thus, TGF-β downregulates intercellular junctions in a Smad-dependent manner by inducing the expression of the members of the Slug/Snail family [Thuault et al., 2006]. These proteins are strong suppressors of E-cadherin [Come et al., 2004], occludin [Wang et al., 2007] and claudin-1 [Martinez-Estrada et al., 2006]. One of the mechanisms underlying Slug induction is the association of Smad3 with myocardin-related transcription factor (MRTF), a key myogenic transcriptional coactivator (see below); this complex was reported to bind to and drive the Slug promoter through non-classical SBEs [Morita et al., 2007]. In addition, Smads directly interact with the zinc finger factors ZEB1 and ZEB2 [Postigo, 2003], which are strong suppressors of the E-cadherin gene. This interaction has been shown to modulate Smad-dependent transcription and may also impact on ZEB-dependent repression.

During fibrogenesis, ECM accumulation is achieved both by increased synthesis of matrix components and by alterations in the expression or activity of their metabolizing enzymes. The Smad pathway targets both sides of this intricate balance. Namely, Smad3 induces the expression of several collagen isoforms and regulates the expression of various matrix metalloproteinases and tissue type inhibitor of metalloproteases [Verrecchia et al., 2001]. Smad-dependent upregulation of matrix metalloproteinases can also contribute to the degradation of cell contacts [Zheng et al., 2009]. In addition, the altered ECM can induce intracellular signaling through integrins and the integrin-linked kinase, which has been implicated as a major mediator of EMT [Li et al., 2009]. Furthermore, Smad3 is a direct inducer of plasminogen activator inhibitor-1, the expression of which is both a contributor and a widely used, sensitive indicator of the process of mesenchymalization and fibrosis [Eddy and Fogo, 2006].

The Smad pathway can also contribute to the regulation of the myogenic program in several ways. In fact, the SMA promoter is a hub of various cis-elements, which integrates the combined action of many transcription factors (fig. 1). Some of these will be considered here. Of

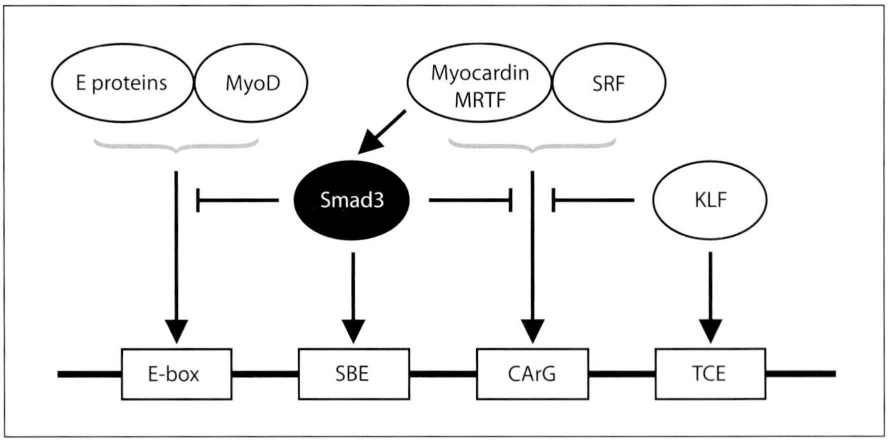

Fig. 1. Regulatory elements of the SMA promoter. The SMA promoter, a typical myogenic promoter, integrates multiple regulatory signals through a variety of different DNA cis-elements, including 1 or more copies of the E-box, SBE, CArG-box and TGF-β control element (TCE). (For the sake of clarity, only a single element of each type is shown.) The scheme also indicates the corresponding transcription factors. The complexity of the regulation is further increased by the fact that the various transcription factors, in addition to acting on their own cognate DNA boxes, interact with each other, thereby enhancing or mitigating the transcriptional activity of their partners (see text for further explanation). While not mentioned in the text, it is worth noting here that KLFs were reported to inhibit myocardin [Liu et al., 2005] and Smad3 [Hu et al., 2007] as well. KLF = Kruppel-like factor(s).

particular relevance, Smad3-specific SBEs have been described in the promoter of SMA, as well as in that of SM22α, a related smooth muscle marker. Indeed, in TGF-β-stimulated fibroblasts, Smad3 was shown to bind to these sites, and overexpression of Smad3 activated the corresponding promoter constructs, at least through one of the SBEs [Hu et al., 2003; Qiu et al., 2003]. Moreover, the SM22α promoter was synergistically activated through SBE by Smad3 in a complex with myocardin [Qiu et al., 2005]. This finding is intriguing, since members of the myocardin family (myocardin, MRTF-A and MRTF-B) are master regulators of muscle-related genes in their 'own right' as well [Parmacek, 2007]. These recently discovered proteins are Rho-GTPase-regulated transcriptional coactivators, which not only stimulate but also confer muscle specificity to serum response factor (SRF) [Wang et al., 2001; Miralles et al., 2003]. The SRF/MRTF complex targets the CC(A/T)richTT (CArG) cis-elements or CArG boxes, present in the SMA promoter and in many other cytoskeletal or muscle genes, which together constitute the 'CArGome' [Sun et al., 2006]. Interestingly, SRF can directly interact with Smad3 as well [Qiu et al., 2003; Lee et al., 2007]. This complex was proposed to exert enhanced transcriptional activity on CArGs (an effect that may be promyogenic) [Qiu et al., 2003] but reduced the activity on SBE (a mechanism whereby SRF can inhibit the apoptotic effect of Smad3) [Lee et al., 2007]. Another layer of complexity, namely the intrinsic role of the MRTF in EMyT and its interplay with Smad3, will be discussed in the Antithesis section. Finally, it is worth noting that in addition to impacting the Smad and MRTF/SRF pathways and their interactions [Elberg et al., 2008; Masszi et al., 2010], TGF-β was reported to drive the SMA promoter via the TGF-β control element as well [Tomasek et al., 2005], which is a target of Kruppel-like factors.

Taken together, both observational evidence and mechanistic insight support the concept that Smad3 is an important mediator of the TGF-β-induced EMT and EMyT.

Antithesis: Smad3 Is a Negative Regulator of the Myogenic Program

While R-Smads have repeatedly been shown to play an important role in fibrogenesis, 2 sets of stubbornly accumulating facts suggest that their overall role may be more complex, and the view that they unambiguously promote MF generation should be revisited. First, the progression of fibrosis, and especially the concomitant accumulation of MFs is often accompanied by a reduction in Smad3 (or Smad2) expression or the overexpression of enzymes involved in R-Smad degradation. Second, experimental elimination of Smad3 (or Smad2) can actually facilitate rather than inhibit SMA expression under various conditions. Experimental evidence substantiating these statements is summarized below.

Dramatic decrease in Smad3 levels was reported in ureteral obstruction-induced kidney fibrosis [Poncelet et al., 2007] and bleomycin-triggered lung fibrosis [Zhao and Geverd, 2002]. Under these conditions, the loss of Smad3 was concomitant with increased SMA expression and tissue accumulation of MFs. Reduced glomerular Smad2 expression and increased levels of Smad ubiquitination regulatory factor-2 have been detected in experimental serum nephritis [Togawa et al., 2003]. Similar observations were made in patients with chronic nephropathies characterized by progressive fibrosis [Tan et al., 2008].

In addition to these in vivo and clinical studies, cell biological approaches have provided strong backing to the idea that certain aspects of EMT or EMyT, and particularly the ensuing SMA expression, are coincident with (and presumably causally linked to) the reduction in R-Smad levels or functions. EMT, induced by the synergistic effect of TGF-β and the expression of an oncogenic Ras, was accompanied by the gradual downregulation of Smad3 in distal tubular (Madin-Darby canine kidney) cells [Nicolas et al., 2003]. Forced re-expression of Smad3 did not re-establish the epithelial morphology, but restored the TGF-β-induced cell cycle arrest. In human mesangial and tubular cells, TGF-β caused robust downregulation of Smad3 (but not Smad2) protein, enhanced Smad3 ubiquitination and suppressed Smad3 mRNA transcription [Poncelet et al., 2007]. Again, these events ran in parallel with EMT and SMA expression. Our studies have shown that tubular EMyT provoked by a two-hit scheme (TGF-β + cell contact injury, see further details below) caused a near-complete loss of Smad3, without affecting Smad2. Moreover, during the course of EMyT, the activity of the SMA promoter exhibited an inverse correlation with the actual cellular level of Smad3 [Masszi et al., 2010]. It is worth noting that the Smad3-eliminating effect of TGF-β is not restricted to epithelia since TGF-β dramatically reduced Smad3 mRNA in lung fibroblasts [Yanagisawa et al., 1998] and strongly suppressed Smad3 protein expression in dermal fibroblasts as well [Bhattacharyya et al., 2008]. In other cellular systems, SMA expression appeared to correlate with Smad2 downregulation. In human proximal tubular epithelial cells, TGF-β triggered the loss of Smad anchor for receptor activation, which in turn led to ubiquitination and degradation of Smad2, an event coincident with SMA expression [Runyan et al., 2009]. Finally, pioneering studies, performed nearly a decade ago, already called attention to the apparent 'Smad paradox' showing that the development of MFs from hepatic stellate cells [Bauer and Schuppan, 2001; Dooley et al., 2001] or from skin fibroblasts [Reisdorf et al., 2001] is associated with impaired (as opposed to enhanced) Smad3 (and/or Smad2) signaling. Although no reduction in the total Smad3 expression was detected, the transdifferentiated MFs contained much less nuclear and phosphorylated Smad3 than their progenitors.

While these observations are suggestive of an inhibitory role of R-Smads in EMyT, they are purely correlative or coincidental. However, recent studies applying targeted silencing of R-Smads have begun to establish a definitive cause-effect relationship between Smad downregulation and the development of EMT/EMyT. Intriguingly, keratinocyte-specific ablation of Smad2 promoted EMT during skin carcinogenesis [Hoot et al., 2008]. siRNA-mediated knockdown of Smad anchor for receptor activation (and thus Smad2) was sufficient to induce SMA expression in the epithelium [Runyan et al., 2009]. Downregulation of Smad2 in transformed kidney tubular cells significantly augmented basal SMA expression [Phanish et al., 2006]. Despite this positive effect of Smad2 knockdown on SMA levels in unstimulated cells, these authors interpreted their result to mean that both Smad2 and Smad3 contribute to SMA expression, because the elimination of these proteins diminished the TGF-β-induced rise in SMA. In contrast, our results revealed that while Smad3 silencing does not induce SMA expression itself, it hugely potentiates SMA mRNA and protein expression provoked by other stimuli [Masszi et al., 2010]. Importantly, as detailed below, our studies not only demonstrated that downregulation of Smad3 facilitates SMA expression but also provided insight into the mechanism underlying this counterintuitive effect.

Our aim was to explore the mechanism whereby a myogenic program is mobilized in the epithelium. Ironically, our intention was to verify the classic view, namely that Smad3 is a contributor to SMA expression. Our previous studies have shown that TGF-β is not sufficient to induce SMA expression in intact monolayers of LLC-PK1 tubular cells [Masszi et al., 2004; Fan et al., 2007]. The other prerequisite is the absence or disruption of E-cadherin-dependent cell contacts, e.g., by wounding or low calcium medium. This 2-hit model proved to be a highly efficient approach to dissect the underlying signaling. We have shown that TGF-β or low calcium medium can drive the SMA promoter, but the individual application of these stimuli causes only modest promoter activation, which does not manifest in SMA protein expression. In contrast, their combination has a synergistic effect on the promoter and induces SMA protein expression. How do these inputs act and synergize? We and others have shown that contact injury activates Rho GTPases, which in turn induce nuclear translocation of MRTF [Fan et al., 2007; Busche et al., 2008]. Nuclear MRTF interacts with SRF and the complex acts on CArG boxes present in the SMA promoter. How can we integrate the TGF-β/Smad3 signaling into this picture? The answer seemed straightforward enough, since in addition to CArG boxes, the SMA promoter contains SBEs as well. It was thus conceivable that CArGs and SBEs are responsible for the contact-dependent and TGF-β/Smad3-dependent activation of the SMA promoter, respectively. We surmised that these factors might synergize through their concomitant action on their own cis-elements. Alternatively, since Smad3 can bind to MRTF [Morita et al., 2007], the complex might exert enhanced effects through SBEs and/or CArGs. As discussed, previous observations gave credence to both of these possibilities: Smad3 has been reported to activate SMA [Hu et al., 2003] and SM22α [Qiu et al., 2003] through SBE, the Smad3/myocardin complex can synergistically drive SM22α [Qiu et al., 2005], while the Smad3/MRTF complex has been shown to induce expression of Slug, a repressor of the E-cadherin gene [Morita et al., 2007]. However, to our surprise, the picture emerging from our studies delineates a mechanism that is quite different from these predictions [Masszi et al., 2010]. We first performed a detailed promoter analysis, mutating each CArG and SBE (individually and combined) in the SMA promoter. This showed that CArGs are necessary and sufficient for the effect of the individual stimuli (TGF-β or contact injury) and their synergy, while SBEs are dispensable with regard to either stimulus. Further, overexpression of Smad3 not only failed to stimulate the SMA promoter, but strongly inhibited its MRTF-induced activation. Smad3 silencing enhanced the binding of MRTF to CArG, vastly potentiated the contact injury (low calcium)-induced expression of SMA mRNA, and rendered contact injury (without TGF-β) sufficient to induce SMA protein expression. These findings, together with the observation that the 2-hit stimulation induced the loss of Smad3 (which was coincident with SMA promoter activation and SMA expression) implied that Smad3 is a potent inhibitor of SMA expression. The most plausible mechanism of this action is that Smad3 binds to MRTFs and prevents the effect of the latter on the SRF/CArG complex. Consistent with this interpretation, our promoter studies have shown that a deletion mutant of MRTF, which has diminished capacity to bind Smad3, is much less sensitive to the MRTF-inhibiting action of Smad3. Further, since Smad3 can directly bind to SRF as well [Lee et al., 2007], it is conceivable that an SRF/Smad3 interaction might also contribute to the inhibition of SMA expression. In any case, these results depict Smad3 as an efficient break on the myogenic program.

While this conclusion may be surprising in the context of SMA expression during EMT, the concept that Smad3 is a strong antimyogenic factor has been well established in the field of skeletal muscle research. Smad3 physically interacts with and thereby inhibits 2 critically important myogenic transcription factors, MyoD [Liu et al., 2001] and myocyte enhancer factor 2 [Liu et al., 2004]. Binding of Smad3 to these factors prevents their association with their transcriptional coactivators (e.g., E47 for MyoD), and thus, the interaction of the complex with the corresponding cis-element (e.g., the E-box in case of MyoD). Remarkably, this mechanism of action is fully analogous to the above-described interference of Smad3 with the MRTF/SRF/CArG complex. Interestingly, the SMA promoter also harbors E-boxes [Kumar et al., 2003], and it remains to be tested whether Smad3 could alter SMA expression in the epithelium via these loci as well. Another Smad-dependent antimyogenic mechanism involves MRTF itself. In proliferating myoblasts, Smad1/4 binds to MRTF, and the complex drives the transcription of the inhibitor of DNA binding 3 gene. The inhibitor of DNA binding 3 protein then interacts with and blocks the action of myogenic regulatory factors such as MyoD [Iwasaki et al., 2008]. Finally, TGF-β, through a partially Smad-dependent mechanism, downregulates Notch3, which results in enhanced SMA expression [Kennard et al., 2008]. Again, it awaits elucidation whether any of these pathways is operative during EMyT.

Taken together, there is ample evidence showing that R-Smads are downregulated under various fibrotic conditions, that the loss of R-Smads is often coincident with and causally linked to enhanced SMA expression and that Smad3 can act as a strong negative regulator of the MRTF/SRF complex, the chief driver of the SMA promoter.

Synthesis: Smad3 Is a Timekeeper and Context-Dependent Modulator of EMyT

How can we reconcile or rather integrate these apparently disparate facts and views into a coherent picture? We will attempt to do this in a 2-step process. First, we will scrutinize the validity and limitations of the directly contradictory findings or inferences. Next, we will envisage EMyT as a dynamic process with various phases and explore the role of Smad3 in each of these.

First, we consider the 2 strongest arguments supporting the notion that Smad3 is a key input for SMA expression during EMyT.

Argument 1: Smad3 KO Animals Seem to Be Protected against EMT and Show Less SMA Expression in Fibrotic Disease Models

To address this point, the first key question is: are Smad3 KO animals truly devoid of Smad3 protein? The Smad3 KO animals used in most studies harbor an exon 8 deletion, leading to the loss of the last 89 amino acids of Smad3. As this truncation cancels the critical SSXS motif, it leads to a functional null mutant. However, the mRNA encoding the truncated protein is present, and thus, the truncated protein per se (albeit less stable) might still be expressed at some level in different tissues [Yang et al., 1999]. Importantly, this C-terminally truncated Smad3 can still interact with various partners, as indicated by the fact that it exerts dominant negative effects [Yang et al., 1999]. Is it therefore possible that a truncated Smad3 protein, which remains expressed at low levels, has lost its pro-fibrotic effect but kept its anti-myogenic (MRTF-interfering) capacity? This question warrants future studies. The other type of Smad3 KO mice, which contains an exon 2 deletion [Zhu et al., 1998], has not been used in fibrotic disease models. However, the phenotype of the two 'Smad3$^{-/-}$' mice is different: exon 2 animals succumb to intestinal tumors while the exon 8 mice succumb to autoimmunity. This difference might be (at least in part) due to the distinct functional repertoire of the truncated proteins. But irrespective of the question whether Smad3 is fully eliminated or not, do Smad3 KO animals consistently exhibit impaired SMA expression and MF generation? Here the literature is widely divided, with various groups reporting markedly suppressed, unchanged or even elevated SMA expression depending on the fibrogenic model used and the particular time point and the tissues examined [see e.g. ref. Flanders et al., 2003; Lakos et al., 2004; Saika et al., 2004; Arany et al., 2006; Banh et al., 2006; Bujak et al., 2007]. However, it is clear that EMT and MF generation can occur in Smad3 KO animals [Banh et al., 2006; Ramirez et al., 2006; Patel et al., 2010]. Nonetheless, the presence of WT Smad3 is obviously important for fibrogenesis, and this process itself promotes the accumulation of MFs. In fact, Smad3 acts at multiple levels, and its direct and indirect effects may have a very different impact. For example, Smad3 KO animals exhibit impaired recruitment of and TGF-β production by macrophages at the site of injury, and many (albeit not all) of the fibrotic effects were restored by local TGF-β addition [Ashcroft et al., 1999]. Thus, impaired MF accumulation might be partly due to reduced TGF-β levels, rather than to an absolute need for Smad3 in SMA expression per se. Nonetheless, in 1 study that tested this aspect, TGF-β failed to induce SMA expression in tubular cells from Smad3 KO animals [Sato et al., 2003]. However, it awaits elucidation whether this particular finding represents a true Smad3 requirement, is due to the presence of a truncated Smad3 protein or simply reflects the fact that the response was tested at a single, very early time point. In summary, clarification of the exact nature of Smad3 'deletion' and the ensuing compensatory reactions in Smad3 KO animals will undoubtedly facilitate the correct interpretation of the experimental results.

Arguments 2: The SMA Promoter Does Contain SBEs and Overexpression of Smad3 Has Been Reported to Drive the Promoter or Enhance SMA Expression in Certain Systems

Indeed, these findings imply that the activity of the SMA promoter can be enhanced by Smad3; or rather that one of the impacts of Smad3 on the promoter is stimulatory. Importantly, the overall effect will be determined by the integration of the positive and negative inputs, such as the direct stimulatory action through SBEs and the indirect inhibitory action, e.g., through Smad3-mediated interference with MRTF. Two aspects are noteworthy in this regard. First, that the sporadically reported positive action of Smad3 overexpression (when at all present) is rather weak [Hu et al., 2003; Uemura et al., 2005]. In contrast, the positive effect of Smad3 silencing on SMA expression is robust [Masszi et al., 2010]. Second, the effect of Smad3 overexpression on the SMA promoter is fully context dependent: e.g. the stimulatory effect was found in lung fibroblasts [Hu et al., 2003], while Smad3 failed to drive the SMA promoter in the multipotential 10T1/2 cell line [Qiu et al., 2005] and in kidney tubular cells [Masszi et al., 2010]. This raises a key issue: the overall outcome will depend upon the interplay between Smad3 and its partners, as dictated by the level of Smad3 expression together with the presence and activation state of Smad3-interacting proteins, as determined by the cell type, stimulus and developmental stage. Indeed, Smad3 is a highly promiscuous molecule, which is known to interact with many proteins involved in EMT/EMyT, including Sp1 [Subramanian et al., 2004], β-catenin [Tian and Phillips, 2002], Kruppel-like factors [Hu et al., 2007], MRTF [Morita et al., 2007],

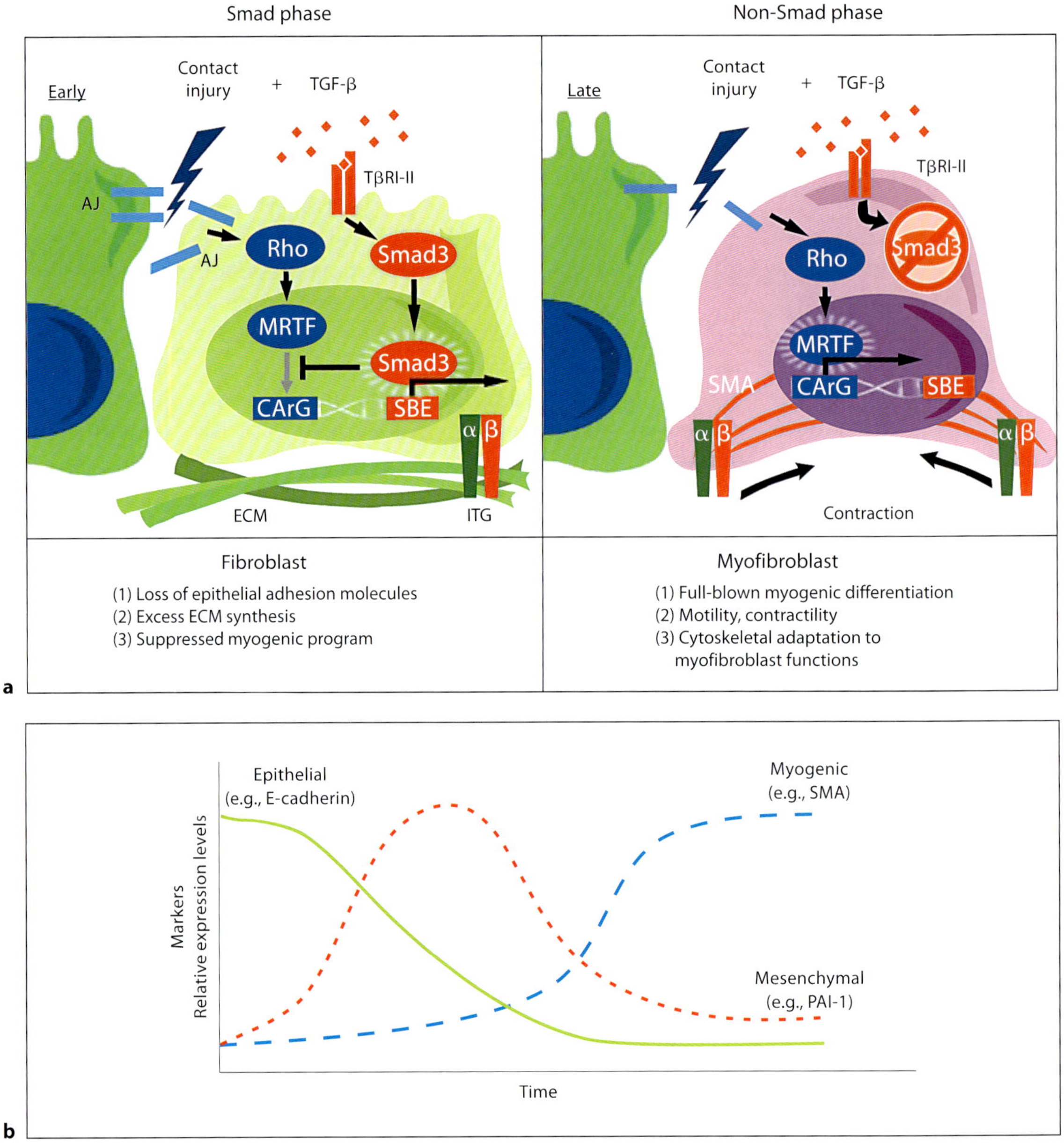

Fig. 2. Integrated model of EMyT. **a** Based on our 2-hit model (see details in text), we propose that EMyT consists of 2, biochemically and transcriptionally distinguishable phases. The phases correspond to the presence or absence (decrease) of Smad3, which acts as a switch between them. The early Smad-dependent phase includes the loss of epithelial adherent junctions (AJ) and the expression of mesenchymal markers, resulting in ECM accumulation. These steps are induced by TGF-β via its receptor complex (TβRI-II) and are augmented by cell contact injury. Many events of the ensuing mesenchymal reprogramming are mediated via SBEs in the DNA. On the other hand, Smad3 puts the myogenic program on hold by inhibiting MRTF. The late phase is initiated by the loss of Smad3, which liberates MRTF and leads to the expression of CArGome genes. The chronological order of these steps is strictly regulated by the presence and interactions of Smad3. **b** Time-dependent changes in critical marker genes during EMyT as deduced from the biphasic model. PAI-1 = Plasminogen activator inhibitor-1.

SRF [Lee et al., 2007] and others [Brown et al., 2008]. Since the SRF/MRTF pathway is a key input in SMA regulation, the impact of Smad3 on this mechanism may be predominant. Overall, this scenario poses an intriguing general possibility. Could the myogenic versus antimyogenic impact of Smad3 primarily depend on tissue type and developmental stage? Specifically, the antimyogenic effect may dominate in the epithelium (and in skeletal muscle) whereas the promyogenic impact may carry more weight in tissue fibroblasts. Is it possible that Smad3 plays a differential role in epithelial-MF vs. fibroblast-MF transition? Do MFs carry their past, i.e. is their origin critical for their later fate and function? Moreover, even 'tissue fibroblasts' represent a heterogeneous group in this regard since fibroblasts isolated from various tissues exert a markedly different capacity to produce SMA [Hinz, 2007]. Could this be (partly) related to differences in their Smad3 levels and turnover? Furthermore, it remains to be elucidated whether a change in the Smad3/Smad2 ratio could account for some of the observed changes during EMyT. Since these Smads act through both common and distinct effectors [Brown et al., 2007], a change in either of them might influence the efficiency of signaling through the other. While such a shift in their balance cannot be the sole mechanism in the control of the myogenic program (e.g., the MRTF-inhibiting effect is fully Smad3 specific), it may significantly contribute to the overall outcome. These exciting questions mark the direction for future research.

The Phases of EMyT – An Integrated View

EMyT is a well-orchestrated process with a defined chronology, which starts with the loss of epithelial characteristics, continues with the acquisition of mesenchymal features and culminates in the activation of the myogenic program. We propose that EMyT can be dissected into 2 major phases, distinguished by the presence and role of Smad3 (fig. 2). Thus, EMyT is composed of a Smad3-promoted, early, mesenchymal 'Smad phase' and a Smad3-inhibitable, late, myogenic, 'non-Smad phase'. Early on, active Smad3 contributes to the downregulation of epithelial markers, e.g., E-cadherin, and plays a major role in the induction of several mesenchymal genes. The latter can be exemplified by plasminogen activator inhibitor-1. This mesenchymal phase is likely an important preparatory period for MF development. On the other hand, Smad3 puts the myogenic program on hold in the injured epithelium, thereby postponing the commitment toward the MF phenotype. However, upon continued stimulation, Smad3 is degraded, which unleashes the myogenic program. This view depicts Smad3 as an important switch or timekeeper that contributes to major fate-determining decisions during EMyT [Masszi et al., 2010]. This basic theme can then be modified by various cell type- and stimulus-specific inputs.

Clearly, this paradigm raises a plethora of questions and calls attention to major unresolved issues. While recent research has identified various factors and signaling pathways that impact Smad3 ubiquitination and degradation [Lo and Massague, 1999; Fukuchi et al., 2001; Izzi and Attisano, 2004; Guo et al., 2008a, 2008b; Gao et al., 2009], our understanding of these processes is quite rudimentary. Moreover, the mechanisms whereby critical EMT-promoting inputs – such as disruption of cell contacts, increased tissue tension, or integrin activation – regulate the transcription and/or metabolism of Smad3 (or Smad2) remain to be established. If Smad3 is a general inhibitor of CArG-dependent transcription, its degradation may also influence the expression of other CArG-dependent proteins (e.g., myosins and integrins), many of which are involved in the maintenance of the MF phenotype. Furthermore, it is not clear if (or to what extent) epithelium-derived MFs contribute to the progressive aspects of fibrosis, or if alternatively they represent a perhaps failed, but much less harmful repair attempt. Namely, the loss of Smad3 is expected to result in decreased expression of several mesenchymal (fibrogenic) genes, while the ensuing higher contractility is a physiological factor during wound closure. On the other hand, the antiproliferative effect of TGF-β is probably lost in the absence of Smad3. Do epithelium-derived MFs represent a less fibrogenic but more rapidly dividing subset of MFs? This possibility would be consistent with the finding that Smad3 KO animals show accelerated wound epithelialization and closure [Ashcroft et al., 1999; Flanders et al., 2003].

Unraveling the complex modus operandi of R-Smads, these multi-faceted regulators of tissue plasticity, will undoubtedly lead to important insight into the pathogenesis of organ fibrosis. Given these complexities, it seems unlikely that general inhibition of R-Smads will represent an ideal therapy. However, better understanding of their roles, interactions, synthesis, traffic and degradation holds promise for developing improved treatments to halt or reverse this devastating disease entity.

Acknowledgements

The authors are indebted to Ms. Pam Speight for her comments and suggestions. The authors' own experimental work was supported by research grants to A.K. from the Canadian Institutes of Health Research and from the Kidney Foundation of Canada.

References

Allington, T.M., W.P. Schiemann (2011) The cain and Abl of epithelial-mesenchymal transition and transforming growth factor-β in mammary epithelial cells. Cells Tissues Organs *193:* 98–113.

Arany, P.R., K.C. Flanders, T. Kobayashi, C.K. Kuo, C. Stuelten, K.V. Desai, R. Tuan, S.I. Rennard, A.B. Roberts (2006) Smad3 deficiency alters key structural elements of the extracellular matrix and mechanotransduction of wound closure. Proc Natl Acad Sci USA *103:* 9250–9255.

Ashcroft, G.S., X. Yang, A.B. Glick, M. Weinstein, J.L. Letterio, D.E. Mizel, M. Anzano, T. Greenwell-Wild, S.M. Wahl, C. Deng, A.B. Roberts (1999) Mice lacking Smad3 show accelerated wound healing and an impaired local inflammatory response. Nat Cell Biol *1:* 260–266.

Banh, A., P.A. Deschamps, J. Gauldie, P.A. Overbeek, J.G. Sivak, J.A. West-Mays (2006) Lens-specific expression of TGF-beta induces anterior subcapsular cataract formation in the absence of Smad3. Invest Ophthalmol Vis Sci *47:* 3450–3460.

Bauer, M., D. Schuppan (2001) TGFbeta1 in liver fibrosis: time to change paradigms? FEBS Lett *502:* 1–3.

Bhattacharyya, S., S.J. Chen, M. Wu, M. Warner-Blankenship, H. Ning, G. Lakos, Y. Mori, E. Chang, C. Nihijima, K. Takehara, C. Feghali-Bostwick, J. Varga (2008) Smad-independent transforming growth factor-beta regulation of early growth response-1 and sustained expression in fibrosis: implications for scleroderma. Am J Pathol *173:* 1085–1099.

Bonniaud, P., M. Kolb, T. Galt, J. Robertson, C. Robbins, M. Stampfli, C. Lavery, P.J. Margetts, A.B. Roberts, J. Gauldie (2004) Smad3 null mice develop airspace enlargement and are resistant to TGF-beta-mediated pulmonary fibrosis. J Immunol *173:* 2099–2108.

Brown, K.A., A.J. Ham, C.N. Clark, N. Meller, B.K. Law, A. Chytil, N. Cheng, J.A. Pietenpol, H.L. Moses (2008) Identification of novel Smad2 and Smad3 associated proteins in response to TGF-beta1. J Cell Biochem *105:* 596–611.

Brown, K.A., J.A. Pietenpol, H.L. Moses (2007) A tale of two proteins: differential roles and regulation of Smad2 and Smad3 in TGF-beta signaling. J Cell Biochem *101:* 9–33.

Bujak, M., G. Ren, H.J. Kweon, M. Dobaczewski, A. Reddy, G. Taffet, X.F. Wang, N.G. Frangogiannis (2007) Essential role of Smad3 in infarct healing and in the pathogenesis of cardiac remodeling. Circulation *116:* 2127–2138.

Busche, S., A. Descot, S. Julien, H. Genth, G. Posern (2008) Epithelial cell-cell contacts regulate SRF-mediated transcription via Rac-actin-MAL signalling. J Cell Sci *121:* 1025–1035.

Come, C., V. Arnoux, F. Bibeau, P. Savagner (2004) Roles of the transcription factors snail and slug during mammary morphogenesis and breast carcinoma progression. J Mammary Gland Biol Neoplasia *9:* 183–193.

Derynck, R., Y.E. Zhang (2003) Smad-dependent and Smad-independent pathways in TGF-beta family signalling. Nature *425:* 577–584.

Dooley, S., B. Delvoux, M. Streckert, L. Bonzel, M. Stopa, P. ten Dijke, A.M. Gressner (2001) Transforming growth factor beta signal transduction in hepatic stellate cells via Smad2/3 phosphorylation, a pathway that is abrogated during in vitro progression to myofibroblasts. TGFbeta signal transduction during transdifferentiation of hepatic stellate cells. FEBS Lett *502:* 4–10.

Eddy, A.A., A.B. Fogo (2006) Plasminogen activator inhibitor-1 in chronic kidney disease: evidence and mechanisms of action. J Am Soc Nephrol *17:* 2999–3012.

Elberg, G., L. Chen, D. Elberg, M.D. Chan, C.J. Logan, M.A. Turman (2008) MKL1 mediates TGF-beta1-induced alpha-smooth muscle actin expression in human renal epithelial cells. Am J Physiol Renal Physiol *294:* F1116–F1128.

Fan, L., A. Sebe, Z. Peterfi, A. Masszi, A.C. Thirone, O.D. Rotstein, H. Nakano, C.A. McCulloch, K. Szaszi, I. Mucsi, A. Kapus (2007) Cell contact-dependent regulation of epithelial-myofibroblast transition via the rho-rho kinase-phospho-myosin pathway. Mol Biol Cell *18:* 1083–1097.

Flanders, K.C., C.D. Major, A. Arabshahi, E.E. Aburime, M.H. Okada, M. Fujii, T.D. Blalock, G.S. Schultz, A. Sowers, M.A. Anzano, J.B. Mitchell, A. Russo, A.B. Roberts (2003) Interference with transforming growth factor-beta/ Smad3 signaling results in accelerated healing of wounds in previously irradiated skin. Am J Pathol *163:* 2247–2257.

Flier, S.N., H. Tanjore, E.G. Kokkotou, H. Sugimoto, M. Zeisberg, R. Kalluri (2010) Identification of epithelial to mesenchymal transition as a novel source of fibroblasts in intestinal fibrosis. J Biol Chem DOI: 10.1074/jbc.M110.102012.

Fukuchi, M., T. Imamura, T. Chiba, T. Ebisawa, M. Kawabata, K. Tanaka, K. Miyazono (2001) Ligand-dependent degradation of Smad3 by a ubiquitin ligase complex of ROC1 and associated proteins. Mol Biol Cell *12:* 1431–1443.

Gao, S., C. Alarcon, G. Sapkota, S. Rahman, P.Y. Chen, N. Goerner, M.J. Macias, H. Erdjument-Bromage, P. Tempst, J. Massague (2009) Ubiquitin ligase Nedd4L targets activated Smad2/3 to limit TGF-beta signaling. Mol Cell *36:* 457–468.

Gharaee-Kermani, M., B. Hu, S.H. Phan, M.R. Gyetko (2009) Recent advances in molecular targets and treatment of idiopathic pulmonary fibrosis: focus on TGFbeta signaling and the myofibroblast. Curr Med Chem *16:* 1400–1417.

Gomez, E.W., Q.K. Chen, N. Gjorevski, C.M. Nelson (2010) Tissue geometry patterns epithelial-mesenchymal transition via intercellular mechanotransduction. J Cell Biochem DOI: 10.1002/jcb.22545.

Guo, X., A. Ramirez, D.S. Waddell, Z. Li, X. Liu, X.F. Wang (2008a) Axin and GSK3- control Smad3 protein stability and modulate TGF-β signaling. Genes Dev *22:* 106–120.

Guo, X., D.S. Waddell, W. Wang, Z. Wang, N.T. Liberati, S. Yong, X. Liu, X.F. Wang (2008b) Ligand-dependent ubiquitination of Smad3 is regulated by casein kinase 1 gamma 2, an inhibitor of TGF-beta signaling. Oncogene *27:* 7235–7247.

Hinz, B. (2007) Formation and function of the myofibroblast during tissue repair. J Invest Dermatol *127:* 526–537.

Hinz, B. (2009) Tissue stiffness, latent TGF-beta1 activation, and mechanical signal transduction: implications for the pathogenesis and treatment of fibrosis. Curr Rheumatol Rep *11:* 120–126.

Hinz, B., S.H. Phan, V.J. Thannickal, A. Galli, M.L. Bochaton-Piallat, G. Gabbiani (2007) The myofibroblast: one function, multiple origins. Am J Pathol *170:* 1807–1816.

Hoot, K.E., J. Lighthall, G. Han, S.L. Lu, A. Li, W. Ju, M. Kulesz-Martin, E. Bottinger, X.J. Wang (2008) Keratinocyte-specific Smad2 ablation results in increased epithelial-mesenchymal transition during skin cancer formation and progression. J Clin Invest *118:* 2722–2732.

Hu, B., Z. Wu, T. Liu, M.R. Ullenbruch, H. Jin, S.H. Phan (2007) Gut-enriched Kruppel-like factor interaction with Smad3 inhibits myofibroblast differentiation. Am J Respir Cell Mol Biol *36:* 78–84.

Hu, B., Z. Wu, S.H. Phan (2003) Smad3 mediates transforming growth factor-beta-induced alpha-smooth muscle actin expression. Am J Respir Cell Mol Biol *29:* 397–404.

Humphreys, B.D., S.L. Lin, A. Kobayashi, T.E. Hudson, B.T. Nowlin, J.V. Bonventre, M.T. Valerius, A.P. McMahon, J.S. Duffield (2010) Fate tracing reveals the pericyte and not epithelial origin of myofibroblasts in kidney fibrosis. Am J Pathol *176:* 85–97.

Iredale, J.P. (2007) Models of liver fibrosis: exploring the dynamic nature of inflammation and repair in a solid organ. J Clin Invest *117:* 539–548.

Iwano, M., D. Plieth, T.M. Danoff, C. Xue, H. Okada, E.G. Neilson (2002) Evidence that fibroblasts derive from epithelium during tissue fibrosis. J Clin Invest *110:* 341–350.

Iwasaki, K., K. Hayashi, T. Fujioka, K. Sobue (2008) Rho/Rho-associated kinase signal regulates myogenic differentiation via myocardin-related transcription factor-A/Smad-dependent transcription of the Id3 gene. J Biol Chem *283:* 21230–21241.

Izzi, L., L. Attisano (2004) Regulation of the TGFbeta signalling pathway by ubiquitin-mediated degradation. Oncogene *23:* 2071–2078.

Kalluri, R., R.A. Weinberg (2009) The basics of epithelial-mesenchymal transition. J Clin Invest *119:* 1420–1428.

Kennard, S., H. Liu, B. Lilly (2008) Transforming growth factor-beta (TGF-β_1) down-regulates Notch3 in fibroblasts to promote smooth muscle gene expression. J Biol Chem *283:* 1324–1333.

Kim, K.K., M.C. Kugler, P.J. Wolters, L. Robillard, M.G. Galvez, A.N. Brumwell, D. Sheppard, H.A. Chapman (2006) Alveolar epithelial cell mesenchymal transition develops in vivo during pulmonary fibrosis and is regulated by the extracellular matrix. Proc Natl Acad Sci USA *103:* 13180–13185.

Kim, K.K., Y. Wei, C. Szekeres, M.C. Kugler, P.J. Wolters, M.L. Hill, J.A. Frank, A.N. Brumwell, S.E. Wheeler, J.A. Kreidberg, H.A. Chapman (2009b) Epithelial cell alpha3beta1 integrin links beta-catenin and Smad signaling to promote myofibroblast formation and pulmonary fibrosis. J Clin Invest *119:* 213–224.

Kim, Y., M.C. Kugler, Y. Wei, K.K. Kim, X. Li, A.N. Brumwell, H.A. Chapman (2009a) Integrin alpha3beta1-dependent beta-catenin phosphorylation links epithelial Smad signaling to cell contacts. J Cell Biol *184:* 309–322.

Kumar, M.S., J.A. Hendrix, A.D. Johnson, G.K. Owens (2003) Smooth muscle alpha-actin gene requires two E-boxes for proper expression in vivo and is a target of class I basic helix-loop-helix proteins. Circ Res *92:* 840–847.

Lakos, G., S. Takagawa, S.J. Chen, A.M. Ferreira, G. Han, K. Masuda, X.J. Wang, L.A. DiPietro, J. Varga (2004) Targeted disruption of TGF-beta/Smad3 signaling modulates skin fibrosis in a mouse model of scleroderma. Am J Pathol *165:* 203–217.

Lamouille, S., R. Derynck (2011) Emergence of the phosphoinositide 3-kinase-akt-mammalian target of rapamycin axis in transforming growth factor-β-induced epithelial-mesenchymal transition. Cells Tissues Organs *193:* 8–22.

Lee, H.J., C.H. Yun, S.H. Lim, B.C. Kim, K.G. Baik, J.M. Kim, W.H. Kim, S.J. Kim (2007) SRF is a nuclear repressor of Smad3-mediated TGF-beta signaling. Oncogene *26:* 173–185.

Li, Y., X. Tan, C. Dai, D.B. Stolz, D. Wang, Y. Liu (2009) Inhibition of integrin-linked kinase attenuates renal interstitial fibrosis. J Am Soc Nephrol *20:* 1907–1918.

Liu, D., B.L. Black, R. Derynck (2001) TGF-beta inhibits muscle differentiation through functional repression of myogenic transcription factors by Smad3. Genes Dev *15:* 2950–2966.

Liu, D., J.S. Kang, R. Derynck (2004) TGF-beta-activated Smad3 represses MEF2-dependent transcription in myogenic differentiation. EMBO J *23:* 1557–1566.

Liu, Y., S. Sinha, O.G. McDonald, Y. Shang, M.H. Hoofnagle, G.K. Owens (2005) Kruppel-like factor 4 abrogates myocardin-induced activation of smooth muscle gene expression. J Biol Chem *280:* 9719–9727.

Liu, Y. (2010) New insights into epithelial-mesenchymal transition in kidney fibrosis. J Am Soc Nephrol *21:* 212–222.

Lo, R.S., J. Massague (1999) Ubiquitin-dependent degradation of TGF-beta-activated smad2. Nat Cell Biol *1:* 472–478.

Martinez-Estrada, O.M., A. Culleres, F.X. Soriano, H. Peinado, V. Bolos, F.O. Martinez, M. Reina, A. Cano, M. Fabre, S. Vilaro (2006) The transcription factors Slug and Snail act as repressors of Claudin-1 expression in epithelial cells. Biochem J *394:* 449–457.

Masszi, A., L. Fan, L. Rosivall, C.A. McCulloch, O.D. Rotstein, I. Mucsi, A. Kapus (2004) Integrity of cell-cell contacts is a critical regulator of TGF-beta1-induced epithelial-to-myofibroblast transition: role for beta-catenin. Am J Pathol *165:* 1955–1967.

Masszi, A., P. Speight, E. Charbonney, M. Lodyga, H. Nakano, K. Szaszi, A. Kapus (2010) Fate-determining mechanisms in epithelial-myofibroblast transition: major inhibitory role for Smad3. J Cell Biol *188:* 383–399.

Miralles, F., G. Posern, A.I. Zaromytidou, R. Treisman (2003) Actin dynamics control SRF activity by regulation of its coactivator MAL. Cell *113:* 329–342.

Morita, T., T. Mayanagi, K. Sobue (2007) Dual roles of myocardin-related transcription factors in epithelial mesenchymal transition via slug induction and actin remodeling. J Cell Biol *179:* 1027–1042.

Moustakas, A., C.H. Heldin (2005) Non-Smad TGF-beta signals. J Cell Sci *118:* 3573–3584.

Nicolas, F.J., K. Lehmann, P.H. Warne, C.S. Hill, J. Downward (2003) Epithelial to mesenchymal transition in Madin-Darby canine kidney cells is accompanied by down-regulation of Smad3 expression, leading to resistance to transforming growth factor-beta-induced growth arrest. J Biol Chem *278:* 3251–3256.

Parmacek, M.S. (2007) Myocardin-related transcription factors: critical coactivators regulating cardiovascular development and adaptation. Circ Res *100:* 633–644.

Patel, P., Y. Sekiguchi, K.H. Oh, S.E. Patterson, M.R. Kolb, P.J. Margetts (2010) Smad3-dependent and -independent pathways are involved in peritoneal membrane injury. Kidney Int *77:* 319–328.

Phanish, M.K., N.A. Wahab, P. Colville-Nash, B.M. Hendry, M.E. Dockrell (2006) The differential role of Smad2 and Smad3 in the regulation of pro-fibrotic TGFbeta1 responses in human proximal-tubule epithelial cells. Biochem J *393:* 601–607.

Poncelet, A.C., H.W. Schnaper, R. Tan, Y. Liu, C.E. Runyan (2007) Cell phenotype-specific down-regulation of Smad3 involves decreased gene activation as well as protein degradation. J Biol Chem *282:* 15534–15540.

Postigo, A.A. (2003) Opposing functions of ZEB proteins in the regulation of the TGFbeta/BMP signaling pathway. EMBO J *22:* 2443–2452.

Qiu, P., X.H. Feng, L. Li (2003) Interaction of Smad3 and SRF-associated complex mediates TGF-beta1 signals to regulate SM22 transcription during myofibroblast differentiation. J Mol Cell Cardiol *35:* 1407–1420.

Qiu, P., R.P. Ritchie, Z. Fu, D. Cao, J. Cumming, J.M. Miano, D.Z. Wang, H.J. Li, L. Li (2005) Myocardin enhances Smad3-mediated transforming growth factor-beta1 signaling in a CArG box-independent manner: Smad-binding element is an important cis element for SM22alpha transcription in vivo. Circ Res *97:* 983–991.

Ramirez, A.M., Z. Shen, J.D. Ritzenthaler, J. Roman (2006) Myofibroblast transdifferentiation in obliterative bronchiolitis: TGF-beta signaling through Smad3-dependent and -independent pathways. Am J Transplant *6:* 2080–2088.

Reisdorf, P., D.A. Lawrence, V. Sivan, E. Klising, M.T. Martin (2001) Alteration of transforming growth factor-beta1 response involves down-regulation of Smad3 signaling in myofibroblasts from skin fibrosis. Am J Pathol *159:* 263–272.

Roberts, A.B., F. Tian, S.D. Byfield, C. Stuelten, A. Ooshima, S. Saika, K.C. Flanders (2006) Smad3 is key to TGF-beta-mediated epithelial-to-mesenchymal transition, fibrosis, tumor suppression and metastasis. Cytokine Growth Factor Rev *17:* 19–27.

Runyan, C.E., T. Hayashida, S. Hubchak, J.F. Curley, H.W. Schnaper (2009) Role of SARA (SMAD anchor for receptor activation) in maintenance of epithelial cell phenotype. J Biol Chem *284(37):* 25181–25189.

Saika, S., S. Kono-Saika, Y. Ohnishi, M. Sato, Y. Muragaki, A. Ooshima, K.C. Flanders, J. Yoo, M. Anzano, C.Y. Liu, W.W. Kao, A.B. Roberts (2004) Smad3 signaling is required for epithelial-mesenchymal transition of lens epithelium after injury. Am J Pathol *164:* 651–663.

Sato, M., Y. Muragaki, S. Saika, A.B. Roberts, A. Ooshima (2003) Targeted disruption of TGF-beta1/Smad3 signaling protects against renal tubulointerstitial fibrosis induced by unilateral ureteral obstruction. J Clin Invest *112:* 1486–1494.

Strutz, F., H. Okada, C.W. Lo, T. Danoff, R.L. Carone, J.E. Tomaszewski, E.G. Neilson (1995) Identification and characterization of a fibroblast marker: FSP1. J Cell Biol *130:* 393–405.

Subramanian, S.V., J.A. Polikandriotis, R.J. Kelm, Jr., J.J. David, C.G. Orosz, A.R. Strauch (2004) Induction of vascular smooth muscle alpha-actin gene transcription in transforming growth factor beta1-activated myofibroblasts mediated by dynamic interplay between the Pur repressor proteins and Sp1/Smad coactivators. Mol Biol Cell *15:* 4532–4543.

Sun, Q., G. Chen, J.W. Streb, X. Long, Y. Yang, C.J. Stoeckert, Jr., J.M. Miano (2006) Defining the mammalian CArGome. Genome Res *16:* 197–207.

Tamiya, S., L. Liu, H.J. Kaplan (2009) Loss of cell-cell contact initiates epithelial-mesenchymal transition and proliferation of retinal pigment epithelial cells. Invest Ophthalmol Vis Sci DOI: 10.1167/iovs.09-4725.

Tan, R., W. He, X. Lin, L.P. Kiss, Y. Liu (2008) Smad ubiquitination regulatory factor-2 in the fibrotic kidney: regulation, target specificity, and functional implication. Am J Physiol Renal Physiol *294:* F1076–F1083.

Tanjore, H., X.C. Xu, V.V. Polosukhin, A.L. Degryse, B. Li, W. Han, T.P. Sherrill, D. Plieth, E.G. Neilson, T.S. Blackwell, W.E. Lawson (2009) Contribution of epithelial-derived fibroblasts to bleomycin-induced lung fibrosis. Am J Respir Crit Care Med *180:* 657–665.

Taura, K., K. Miura, K. Iwaisako, C.H. Osterreicher, Y. Kodama, M. Penz-Osterreicher, D.A. Brenner (2010) Hepatocytes do not undergo epithelial-mesenchymal transition in liver fibrosis in mice. Hepatology *51:* 1027–1036.

Taylor, I.W., J.L. Wrana (2008) SnapShot: The TGFbeta pathway interactome. Cell *133:* 378.e1.

Thuault, S., U. Valcourt, M. Petersen, G. Manfioletti, C.H. Heldin, A. Moustakas (2006) Transforming growth factor-beta employs HMGA2 to elicit epithelial-mesenchymal transition. J Cell Biol *174:* 175–183.

Tian, Y.C., A.O. Phillips (2002) Interaction between the transforming growth factor-beta type II receptor/Smad pathway and beta-catenin during transforming growth factor-beta1-mediated adherens junction disassembly. Am J Pathol *160:* 1619–1628.

Togawa, A., T. Yamamoto, H. Suzuki, H. Fukasawa, N. Ohashi, Y. Fujigaki, K. Kitagawa, T. Hattori, M. Kitagawa, A. Hishida (2003) Ubiquitin-dependent degradation of Smad2 is increased in the glomeruli of rats with anti-thymocyte serum nephritis. Am J Pathol *163:* 1645–1652.

Tomasek, J.J., J. McRae, G.K. Owens, C.J. Haaksma (2005) Regulation of alpha-smooth muscle actin expression in granulation tissue myofibroblasts is dependent on the intronic CArG element and the transforming growth factor-beta1 control element. Am J Pathol *166:* 1343–1351.

Uemura, M., E.S. Swenson, M.D. Gaca, F.J. Giordano, M. Reiss, R.G. Wells (2005) Smad2 and Smad3 play different roles in rat hepatic stellate cell function and alpha-smooth muscle actin organization. Mol Biol Cell *16:* 4214–4224.

Varga, J., D. Abraham (2007) Systemic sclerosis: a prototypic multisystem fibrotic disorder. J Clin Invest *117:* 557–567.

Verrecchia, F., M.L. Chu, A. Mauviel (2001) Identification of novel TGF-beta /Smad gene targets in dermal fibroblasts using a combined cDNA microarray/promoter transactivation approach. J Biol Chem *276:* 17058–17062.

Wang, D., P.S. Chang, Z. Wang, L. Sutherland, J.A. Richardson, E. Small, P.A. Krieg, E.N. Olson (2001) Activation of cardiac gene expression by myocardin, a transcriptional cofactor for serum response factor. Cell *105:* 851–862.

Wang, Z., P. Wade, K.J. Mandell, A. Akyildiz, C.A. Parkos, R.J. Mrsny, A. Nusrat (2007) Raf 1 represses expression of the tight junction protein occludin via activation of the zinc-finger transcription factor slug. Oncogene *26:* 1222–1230.

Wipff, P.J., D.B. Rifkin, J.J. Meister, B. Hinz (2007) Myofibroblast contraction activates latent TGF-beta1 from the extracellular matrix. J Cell Biol *179:* 1311–1323.

Wynn, T.A. (2007) Common and unique mechanisms regulate fibrosis in various fibroproliferative diseases. J Clin Invest *117:* 524–529.

Wynn, T.A. (2008) Cellular and molecular mechanisms of fibrosis. J Pathol *214:* 199–210.

Xu, J., S. Lamouille, R. Derynck (2009) TGF-beta-induced epithelial to mesenchymal transition. Cell Res *19:* 156–172.

Yanagisawa, K., H. Osada, A. Masuda, M. Kondo, T. Saito, Y. Yatabe, K. Takagi, T. Takahashi (1998) Induction of apoptosis by Smad3 and down-regulation of Smad3 expression in response to TGF-beta in human normal lung epithelial cells. Oncogene *17:* 1743–1747.

Yang, X., J.J. Letterio, R.J. Lechleider, L. Chen, R. Hayman, H. Gu, A.B. Roberts, C. Deng (1999) Targeted disruption of SMAD3 results in impaired mucosal immunity and diminished T cell responsiveness to TGF-beta. EMBO J *18:* 1280–1291.

Yu, L., M.C. Hebert, Y.E. Zhang (2002) TGF-beta receptor-activated p38 MAP kinase mediates Smad-independent TGF-beta responses. EMBO J *21:* 3749–3759.

Zeisberg, E.M., O. Tarnavski, M. Zeisberg, A.L. Dorfman, J.R. McMullen, E. Gustafsson, A. Chandraker, X. Yuan, W.T. Pu, A.B. Roberts, E.G. Neilson, M.H. Sayegh, S. Izumo, R. Kalluri (2007a) Endothelial-to-mesenchymal transition contributes to cardiac fibrosis. Nat Med *13:* 952–961.

Zeisberg, E.M., C. Yang, M. Martino, M.B. Duncan, F. Rieder, H. Tanjore, R. Kalluri (2007b) Fibroblasts derive from hepatocytes in liver fibrosis via epithelial to mesenchymal transition. J Biol Chem *282:* 23337–23347.

Zeisberg, M., E.G. Neilson (2009) Biomarkers for epithelial-mesenchymal transitions. J Clin Invest *119:* 1429–1437.

Zhao, Y., D.A. Geverd (2002) Regulation of Smad3 expression in bleomycin-induced pulmonary fibrosis: a negative feedback loop of TGF-beta signaling. Biochem Biophys Res Commun *294:* 319–323.

Zheng, G., J.G. Lyons, T.K. Tan, Y. Wang, T.T. Hsu, D. Min, L. Succar, G.K. Rangan, M. Hu, B.R. Henderson, S.I. Alexander, D.C. Harris (2009) Disruption of E-cadherin by matrix metalloproteinase directly mediates epithelial-mesenchymal transition downstream of transforming growth factor-beta1 in renal tubular epithelial cells. Am J Pathol *175:* 580–591.

Zhu, Y., J.A. Richardson, L.F. Parada, J.M. Graff (1998) Smad3 mutant mice develop metastatic colorectal cancer. Cell *94:* 703–714.

Cells Tissues Organs

Cells Tissues Organs 2011;193:53–63
DOI: 10.1159/000320178

Published online: November 3, 2010

Spatiotemporal Localization of Periostin and Its Potential Role in Epithelial-Mesenchymal Transition during Palatal Fusion

Yukiko Kitase[a] Keisuke Yamashiro[a] Katherine Fu[b] Joy M. Richman[b] Charles F. Shuler[a]

Departments of [a]Oral Biological and Medical Sciences and [b]Oral Health Sciences, Faculty of Dentistry, University of British Columbia, Vancouver, B.C., Canada

Key Words

Periostin · Palatal fusion · Epithelial-mesenchymal transition · Mesenchymal matrix · Epithelial matrix

Abstract

The medial epithelial seam (MES) between the palatal shelves degrades during palatal fusion to achieve the confluence of palatal mesenchyme. Cellular mechanisms underlying the degradation of MES have been proposed, such as apoptosis, epithelial-mesenchymal transition (EMT) and migration of medial edge epithelia (MEE). Extracellular matrix components have been shown to play an important role in EMT in many model systems. Periostin (also known as osteoblast-specific factor-2) is a secreted mesenchymal extracellular matrix component that affects the ability of cells to migrate and/or facilitates EMT during both embryonic development and pathologic conditions. In this study, we evaluated the spatiotemporal expression patterns of periostin during mouse palatal fusion by in situ hybridization and immunofluorescence. Periostin mRNA and protein were present in the palatal mesenchyme, the protein being distributed in a fine fibrillar network and in the basement membrane, but absent from the epithelium. During MES degradation, the protein was strongly expressed in the basement membrane underlying the MES and in some select MEE. Confocal microscopic analysis using an EMT marker, twist1, and an epithelial marker, cytokeratin 14, provided evidence that select MEE were undergoing EMT in association with periostin. Moreover, the major extracellular matrix molecules in basement membrane, laminin and collagen type IV were degraded earlier than periostin. The result is that select MEE establish interactions with periostin in the mesenchymal extracellular matrix, and these new cell-matrix interactions may regulate MEE transdifferentiation during palatal fusion.

Abbreviations used in this paper

CK14	cytokeratin 14
ColIV	collagen type IV
DAPI	4′,6-diamidino-2-phenylindole
E	embryonic day
EMT	epithelial-mesenchymal transition
LN	laminin
MES	medial epithelial seam
MEE	medial edge epithelia
PBS	phosphate-buffered saline
TGF-β	transforming growth factor-β

KARGER

Fax +41 61 306 12 34
E-Mail karger@karger.ch
www.karger.com

Accessible online at:
www.karger.com/cto

Dr. Charles F. Shuler
Department of Oral Biological and Medical Sciences
Faculty of Dentistry, University of British Columbia
2194 Health Sciences Mall, Vancouver, BC V6T 1Z3 (Canada)
Tel. +1 604 822 5773, Fax +1 604 822 4532, E-Mail cshuler@interchange.ubc.ca

Introduction

Formation of the secondary palate is a complex and critical event involving coordinated outgrowth, reorientation, adhesion and fusion of the bilateral palatal shelves. Disturbance in any stage during palatal fusion may result in cleft palate, one of the most common birth defects in humans [Ferguson, 1988]. In the mouse, bilateral palatal shelves arise from the maxillary process of the first branchial arch at embryonic day 12 (E12). At first, the two palatal shelves grow vertically along the sides of the tongue, but at E14.0, they reorient to a horizontal position above the dorsum of the tongue. The medial edge epithelia (MEE) of the opposing palatal shelves then adhere with each other to form a medial epithelial seam (MES). At E14.5, the MES degrades to achieve the confluence of palatal mesenchyme and to complete the process of palatal fusion [Ferguson, 1987; Shuler et al., 1991].

Epithelial-mesenchymal transition (EMT) is considered to be one of the mechanisms involved in the degradation of MES [Fitchett and Hay, 1989; Shuler et al., 1991; Griffith and Hay, 1992]. EMT is a process that involves basal lamina degradation, formation of new cell-extracellular matrix interactions, acquisition of cell motility and loss of intercellular junctions [Boyer et al., 2000]. Previous studies suggest that extracellular matrix components are important determinants to the cellular response to transforming growth factor-β (TGF-β), which is involved in many models of EMT. Epithelial cells cultured on mesenchymal matrix such as fibronectin and collagen type I undergo TGF-β-mediated EMT. These same cells when cultured on matrices containing laminin (LN) and collagen type IV (ColIV) are resistant to EMT and maintain an epithelial phenotype even when stimulated with exogenous TGF-β [Menke et al., 2001; Kim et al., 2006]. TGF-β_3 null mice with cleft palate retain the LN-containing basement membrane that is correlated inversely with the ability of MEE to transdifferentiate [Kaartinen et al., 1997], suggesting that contact of MEE with mesenchymal extracellular matrix during palatal fusion has an important role in promoting TGF-β_3-mediated EMT.

Periostin is a secreted mesenchymal extracellular matrix molecule belonging to the fasciclin family and is expressed in cells undergoing ECM remodeling and/or EMT during both embryonic development [Kruzynska-Frejtag et al., 2001, 2004] and pathologic conditions [Oka et al., 2007; Kikuchi et al., 2008]. Periostin can interact with other ECM scaffold proteins, such as fibronectin, tenascin C, collagen type I, collagen type V and heparin [Sugiura et al., 1995; Takayama et al., 2006; Norris et al., 2007]. It serves as a ligand for select integrins, such as $\alpha V\beta_3$, $\alpha V\beta_5$, $\alpha_6\beta_4$ and β_1 and modulates cell-matrix interactions affecting the ability of cells to adhere, migrate, proliferate, survive and/or undergo EMT [Horiuchi et al., 1999; Gillan et al., 2002; Bao et al., 2004; Baril et al., 2007; Butcher et al., 2007; Li et al., 2010]. Previous studies have shown that periostin facilitates EMT and induces metastatic behavior by upregulating vimentin, fibronectin and matrix metalloproteinase 9 via integrin $\alpha V\beta_5$ in an epithelium-derived tumor cell line [Yan and Shao, 2006]. Periostin has also been reported to promote the migration and proliferation of epithelial cancer cells which was accompanied by inducing vimentin and N-cadherin and downregulating E-cadherin [Hong et al., 2010]. However, it has not been determined whether periostin has a role in the degradation of MES during palatal fusion.

In this study, we evaluated the spatiotemporal expression patterns of periostin by in situ hybridization and immunofluorescence to examine the biological functions of this protein during palatal fusion. Moreover, we performed confocal microscopic analysis to clarify whether MEE associated with periostin were undergoing EMT. Lastly, we investigated temporal changes of basement membrane components to demonstrate cell-mesenchymal matrix contact to enable some select MEE to undergo EMT during palatal fusion.

Materials and Methods

Specimen Preparation

Swiss-Webster and C57BL/6 mice heads were dissected on the indicated gestational days, fixed in 4% paraformaldehyde/phosphate-buffered saline (PBS) at 4°C overnight, washed with PBS, dehydrated through graded ethanol series and embedded in paraffin. Serial frontal sections were prepared along the anterior-posterior axis for in situ hybridization, immunofluorescence and confocal microscopic analysis.

In situ Hybridization

We amplified a 954-bp fragment of mouse periostin from E14.0 palate cDNA using the following primers: forward, 5′-CCA ACC AGC AGA GAA ATC CCT, and reverse, 5′-CTG AGA ACG GCC TTC TCT TGA TC. This fragment was cloned into pGEM-Teasy using TA cloning. The ^{35}S-labelled antisense RNA probe for periostin transcripts was synthesized using the cDNA clone as a template after linearizing with *Xmn*I. The probe contained sequences complementary to those encoding the C-terminal domain of periostin isoform 2. Our probe differs from that used in Kruzynska-Freijtag et al. [2001, 2004] but still recognizes all isoforms. We also cloned other probes that recognized a subset of isoforms including a new isoform A (sequence structure of C-terminal domain: a + c + d + f), but no differences in expression were noted between these and the pan-periostin probe (data not shown). Radioactive in situ hybridization with ^{35}S-labeled probes was carried out as described [Rowe et al., 1992]. After washing, the sections were dehydrated and dipped in photographic emulsion for autoradiography. The slides were exposed for 2–3 weeks. Dark- and bright-field images were captured with a Hitachi camera mounted on a Zeiss Axiophot.

Immunofluorescence

After deparaffinization, rehydration and antigen retrieval using EDTA buffer, 5-μm-thick sections were blocked with 3% bovine serum albumin/PBS for 30 min at room temperature to reduce background staining and incubated with the primary antibody against periostin (1:100, BioVender), LN α-1 (1:100, Santa Cruz), ColIV (1:100, Abcam), twist1 (1:50, Abcam), integrin β_1 (1:100, R&D Systems) and integrin β_5 (1:50, Abcam) at 4°C overnight, followed by 3 rinses in PBS. Frozen sections were used for integrin αV (1:100, Chemicon) and integrin β_3 (1:100, Chemicon). Fluorescence-labeled secondary antibodies (1:100, Invitrogen) were added for 1 h at room temperature. After washing with PBS 3 times, coverslips were mounted with mounting medium including 4′,6-diamidino-2-phenylindole (DAPI; Vector Labs). To confirm the specificity of antibodies, additional slides were incubated without the primary antibodies. No fluorescence staining was found in these sections.

Confocal Microscopic Analysis

Spatial relationships between periostin and MEE were analyzed using confocal laser scanning microscopy. Sections were deparaffinized in xylenes and rehydrated with descending ethanol series. After antigen retrieval, sections were blocked with 3% bovine serum albumin/5% Triton X-100/PBS blocking solution at 37°C for 30 min and incubated with the primary antibody against periostin, twist1, cytokeratin 14 (CK14; 1:100, Abcam) at 4°C overnight and with fluorescence-labeled secondary antibody (1:100, Invitrogen) for 1 h at room temperature, washed with PBS, coverslipped with mounting media including DAPI. All sections were examined with a Nikon Laser Scanning Confocal microscope (C1) that was equipped with an argon (488 nm) and 2 He-Ne lasers (543 and 633 nm). Sections were scanned with a Plan Fluor 40× NA0.75 lens and a Plan Apo VC 60× NA1.4 oil lens as individual images or z-stack images. z-stack series were obtained with 0.2-μm increments to the entire section thickness (20 μm, approximately 100 images in the z-stack). Digital data of frame-mode images were recorded. DeltaViewer 2.1.1 (http://delta.math.sci.osaka-u.ac.jp/DeltaViewer/) and NIH ImageJ (http://rsbweb.nih.gov/ij/) were used for 3D data visualization.

Results

In situ Hybridization Analysis of Periostin mRNA during Palatal Fusion

Periostin transcripts were localized in the palatal mesenchyme with strong signals in the medial tip as well as in the oral side of the palate, but not in the epithelium at E14.0 (fig. 1a–c). After contact of the shelves, intense periostin mRNA expression was observed in the mesenchyme directly adjacent to the MES (fig. 1d–f, j). However, as the degradation of MES proceeded, this distribution of periostin mRNA extended inside the MES at E14.5 and E15.0 (fig. 1g–i, k). Other areas of abundant periostin expression include the dental papillae and tongue as described by others [Kruzynska-Frejtag et al., 2004].

Spatiotemporal Distribution Pattern of Periostin Protein and Integrins during Palatal Fusion

Periostin protein was localized in a distribution that mirrored the expression pattern of periostin mRNA. Fluorescence was mainly localized in the palatal mesenchyme with strong labeling on the oral side while the signal was absent in the ossification center of the maxillary bones (fig. 2a–l). We noted that the far anterior palate and the soft palate showed stronger reactivity compared with other parts (fig. 2a–c, j–l). High magnification images showed that periostin was present in the mesenchyme distributed with a fine fibrillar network architecture and in the basement membrane, but not in the epithelium at E14.0 (fig. 3a, b). However, as palatal fusion proceeded, periostin immunoreactivity was also detected inside the MES at E14.5. Furthermore, there was relatively stronger fluorescence in the basement membrane region of MES undergoing degradation (fig. 3c). There appeared to be active remodeling of periostin in some positions of the MES (fig. 3d). The periostin-containing basement membrane was reorganized during the process of MES degradation, and this distribution was maintained even at late stages (E15.0) of palatal fusion (fig. 3e). During this late period, remodeling of periostin fibrillar networks in the mesenchyme was far advanced, and by E16.0, the periostin-containing basement membrane of MES was barely detectable (fig. 3f). The MEE express select integrins (αV, β_1, β_3 and β_5) (fig. 4a–d), which were reported to be receptors for periostin [Kuhn et al., 2007].

Select MEE Transdifferentiate into Mesenchyme in Association with Periostin

To investigate whether MEE associated with periostin were undergoing EMT, we performed confocal microscopic analysis using an EMT marker, twist1, and an epithelial marker, CK14. Twist1 is a transcription factor that induces EMT by loss of E-cadherin-mediated cell-cell adhesion and induction of mesenchymal markers, such as fibronectin and N-cadherin [Hong et al., 2010]. CK14 is an intermediate filament keratin expressed only in epithelial cells [Schweizer et al., 2006]. To distinguish MEE undergoing EMT from other mesenchymal cells in the region, we used periostin-containing basement

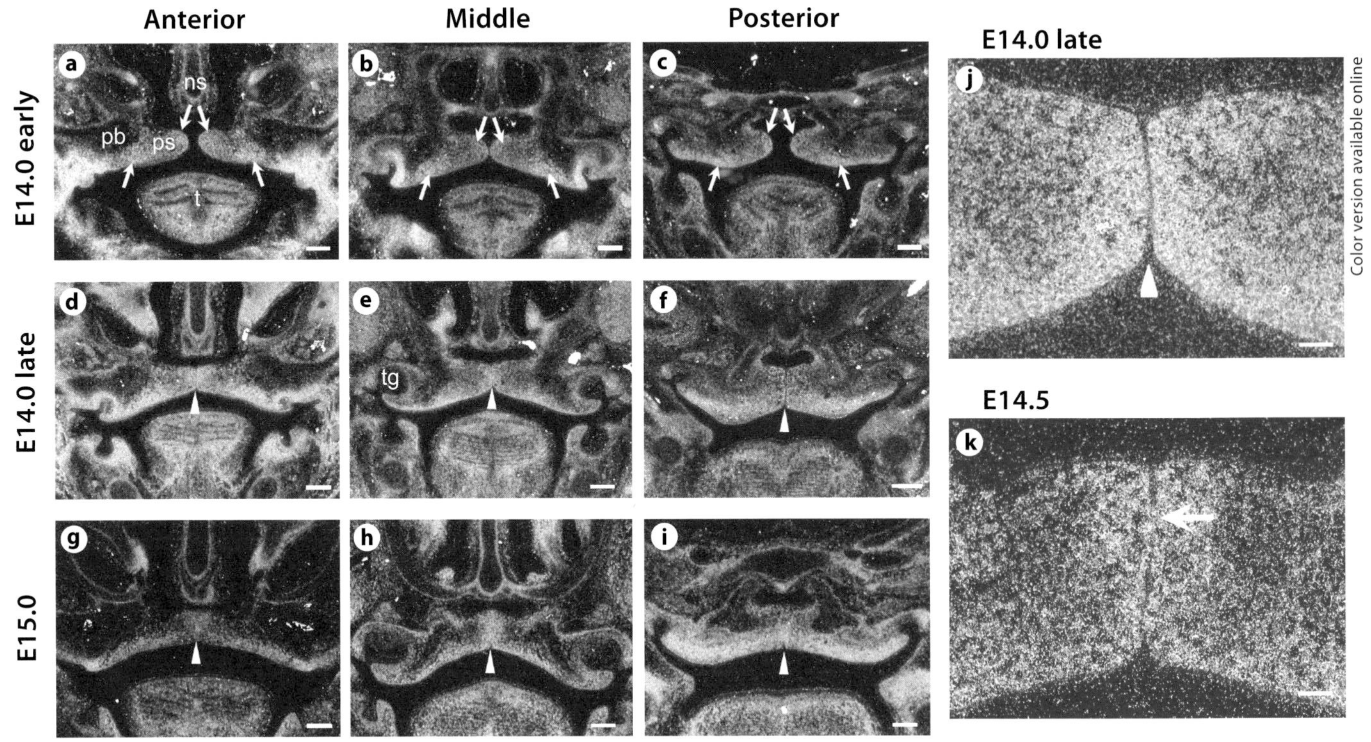

Fig. 1. a–i In situ hybridization analysis of periostin mRNA during palatal fusion. ns = Nasal septum; pb = palatine bone; ps = palatal shelf; t = tongue; tg = tooth germ. Arrows indicate strong signals in the medial tip as well as in the oral side of the palate. Arrowheads indicate MES. **j**, **k** High-magnification images of MES at E14.0 (**j**) and E14.5 (**k**). No signals in MES at E14.0 late. The distribution of periostin mRNA extended inside the MES after E14.5 is indicated by an arrow. Scale bars = 175 μm (**a–i**) and 40 μm (**j**, **k**).

membrane as a marker to separate MES from mesenchyme.

Twist1 was not expressed in MES at E14.0 (data not shown), but as the degradation of MES occurred, select MEE became twist1 positive. As shown in figure 5a–c, the integrity of periostin-containing basement membrane was completely retained. Twist1-positive cells, indicated by the arrowheads (fig. 5a–c), were present between these basement membranes representing MEE undergoing EMT. As the process proceeded, intense labeling of periostin was detected around these twist-positive cells representing transdifferentiation from MEE (fig. 5d–f). We obtained 3D images to show MEE undergoing EMT by demonstrating that they were 3-dimensionally surrounded by the mesenchymal matrix component periostin. Figure 5g–i shows confocal images projected from a z-stack series at three different z-positions extending from the top to the bottom of the cell, represented by an arrowhead. These results further indicate that the twist1-positive cells were located between intact periostin-containing basement membrane. This MEE cell was surrounded by mesenchymal matrix (periostin) at all three z-positions. 3D reconstruction of periostin (fig. 5k) showed that the fine fibrillar architecture of periostin formed inside the MES while no periostin was observed inside MES before MES degradation, as shown in figure 5j.

CK14 showed strong intensity in MEE at E14.0 (data not shown). Figure 6 shows confocal images of MEE projected from a z-stack series at three different z-positions at E14.5. During degradation of MES, CK14 immunoreactivity gradually diminished. Cells marked with a dotted circle in figure 6a were located between periostin-containing basement membrane and they were CK14 negative, indicating that MEE had lost the epithelial phenotype. These cells were surrounded by periostin (fig. 6a). Thus, MEE undergoing EMT exhibited a loss of keratin intermediate filaments while associated with periostin. CK14 labeling in an epithelial island, indicated with two white arrowheads (fig. 6a), was fading out as the z-position was changed (fig. 6b, d). These cells in the epithelial island indicated by the two arrowheads (fig. 6a) were ob-

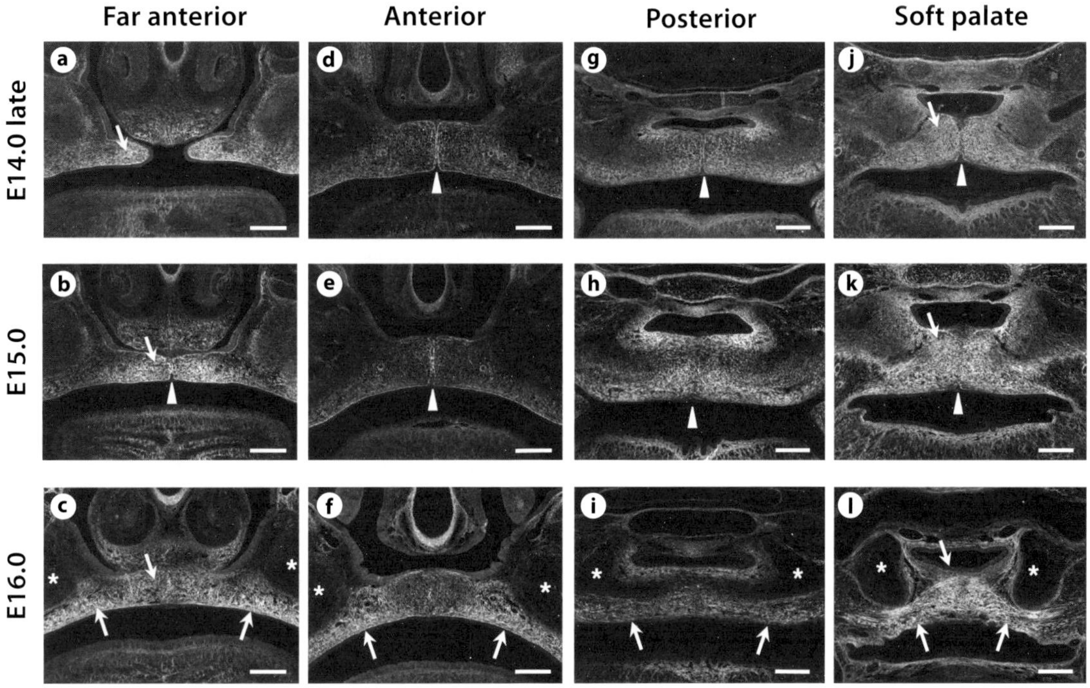

Fig. 2. Fluorescent images of periostin during palate development at E14.0–E16.0. Fluorescence was mainly localized in the palatal mesenchyme with strong labeling in the far anterior and soft palate (arrows) and with absent signal in the ossification center of the maxillary bones (asterisks). Arrowheads indicate MES. Scale bars = 175 μm.

served to have intact nuclear morphology throughout each z-position (fig. 6c, e; online suppl. video 1, www.karger.com/doi/10.1159/000320178), indicating that no signs of apoptosis were present. The cells remained vital, were undergoing EMT, and were also directly associated with the mesenchymal matrix, periostin.

Early Degradation of Epithelial Matrix in Basement Membrane and Newly Established Contact with the Underlying Mesenchymal Matrix, Periostin

Our data revealed prolonged retention of periostin-containing basement membrane underlying the MES during palatal fusion. Therefore, we examined the spatiotemporal relationship between periostin and major epithelial matrix components of basement membrane, LN and ColIV. At E14.0, intact periostin and LN or ColIV-containing basement membrane were observed (fig. 7a, b, fig. 8a, b). However, it was clear that LN in the basement membrane had already started to degrade (fig. 7c, e), as a clear line of basement membrane was no longer present, and that periostin was still completely retained in the same position (fig. 7d, f). Therefore, the MEE established new contacts with the underlying mesenchymal matrix expressing periostin (fig. 7d, f). A similar relationship was found between ColIV (fig. 8a, c) and periostin (fig. 8b, d). MEE in the region were in contact with periostin (fig. 8d, e, i). Moreover, these cells were twist1 positive, indicating that they were in the process of EMT (fig. 8i, j).

Discussion

In this study, we have demonstrated the spatiotemporal localization of periostin during the palatal fusion process. There were no major differences in the distributions of periostin mRNA and protein, suggesting that periostin expression is regulated by transcriptional mechanisms. It has been reported that regulation of palatal fusion may have different mechanisms in the anterior and posterior regions of the palatal shelf. Thus, comparisons of the mid-palatal region during palatal fusion with the anterior and posterior regions were an important objective of our study. The anterior and posterior regions of the palate have been reported to fuse mainly by tissue remodeling, whereas the mid-palate closes mainly by medial elongation of the shelf [Chou et al., 2004; Okano et al., 2006].

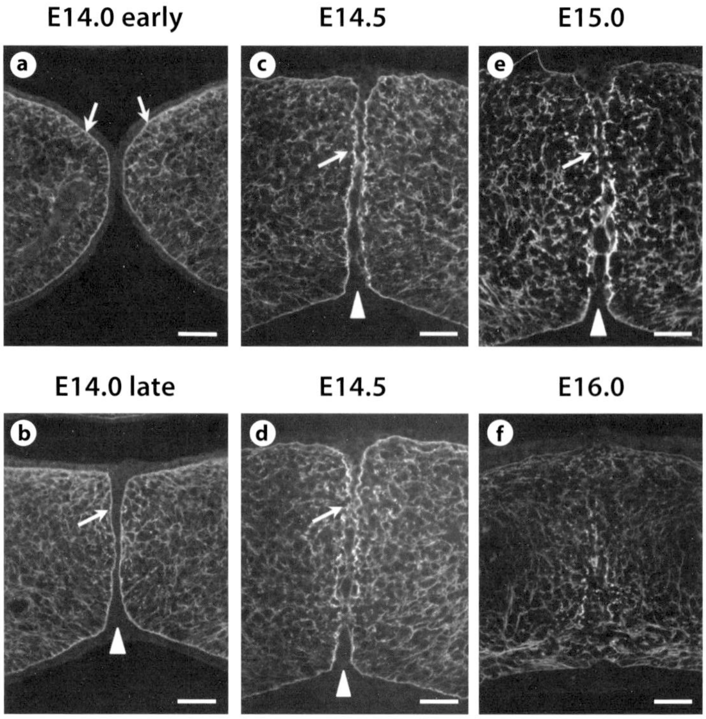

Fig. 3. High-power views of periostin at E14.0 (**a**, **b**), E14.5 (**c**, **d**), E15.0 (**e**) and E16.0 (**f**). The protein showed intense labeling in the basement membrane (arrows) underlying the MES (arrowheads) at E14.5. As seam disruption proceeded, protein was also observed inside the MES. Scale bars = 40 μm.

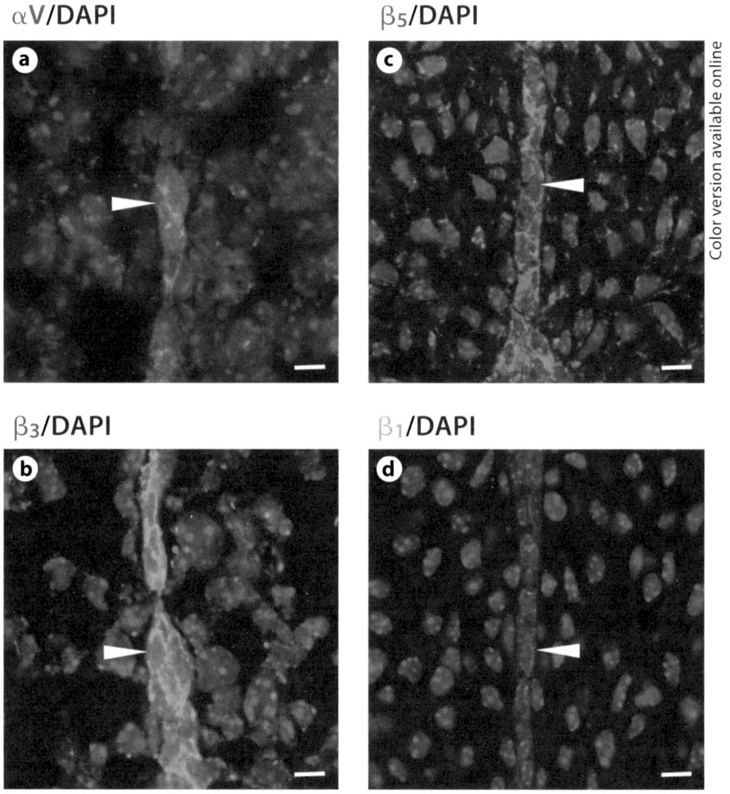

Fig. 4. Double-staining confocal images with integrins and DAPI. Integrin αV (**a**), integrin β_3 (**b**), integrin β_5 (**c**) and integrin β_1 (**d**) at E14.0 late. Frozen sections (**a**, **b**) and paraffin-embedded sections (**c**, **d**) were used. All of the integrins were expressed in MEE (arrowheads). Scale bars = 10 μm. Full-color images are given in the online version of the figure.

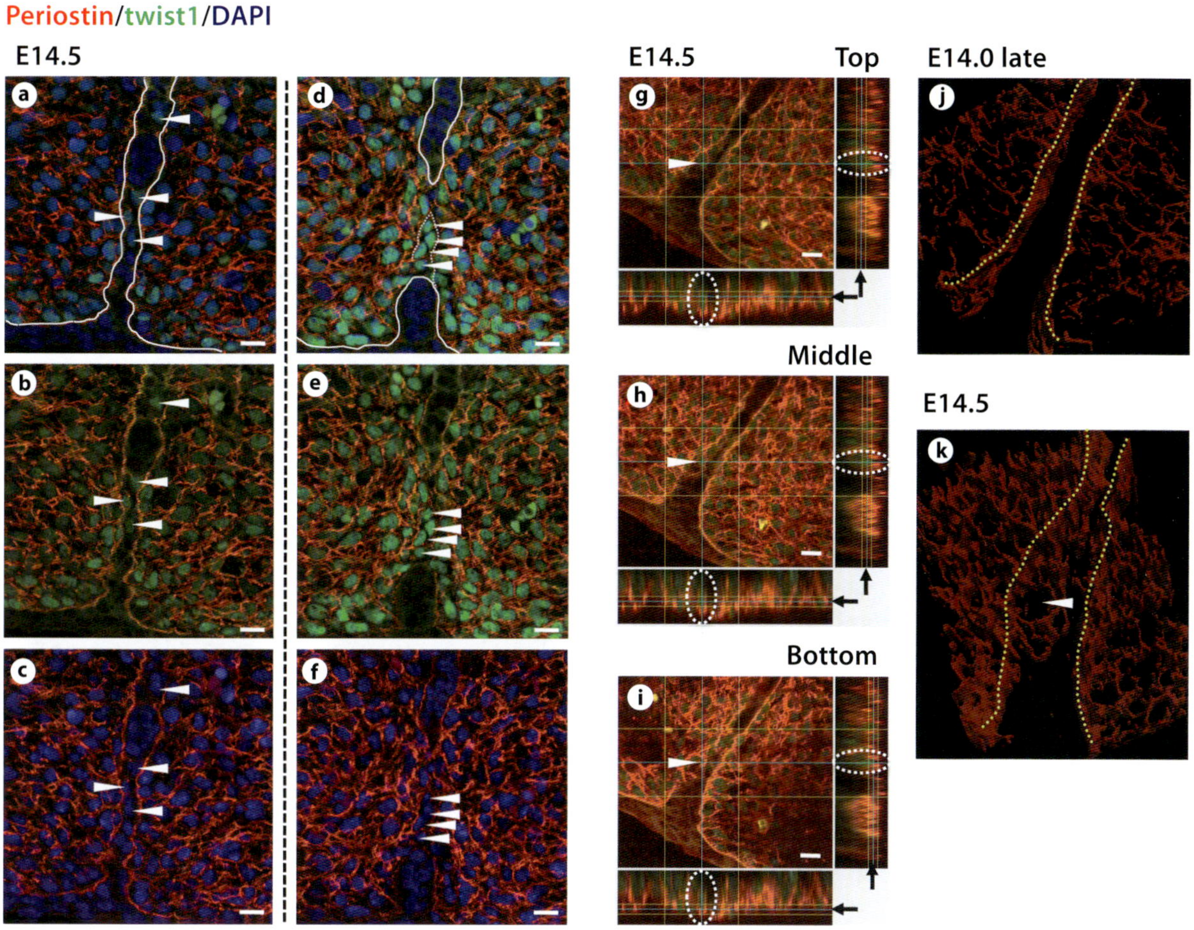

Fig. 5. a–f Triple-staining confocal images with periostin (red), the EMT marker twist1 (green) and DAPI (blue) at E14.5. Lines and arrowheads indicate basement membrane and twist1-positive MEE, respectively. **g–i** z-stack confocal images at 3 different z-positions indicated with arrows, covering from the surface to the bottom of the cell (arrowheads). Periostin is given in red and twist1 in green. Dotted circles indicate the same cell surrounded by periostin. **j** Periostin 3D reconstruction before MES disintegration (E14.0 late). No periostin was observed inside MES. **k** Periostin 3D reconstruction at E14.5. Inside MES, a fibrillar architecture of periostin was formed. The arrowhead indicates the site where the same cells with arrowheads shown in **g** and **h** are located. **j, k** The yellow line represents the basement membrane. Scale bars = 15 μm.

Periostin was present in the mesenchyme with higher levels of expression in the far anterior and posterior region compared with other regions. Since periostin is involved in cell proliferation and migration [Gillan et al., 2002; Kuhn et al., 2007; Hong et al., 2010; Li et al., 2010], regional heterogeneity in the expression of periostin may play a role in the localized remodeling of the palatal shelf.

In contrast to the connective tissue mesenchyme, periostin was absent or diminished from ossification centers. Previous reports show that twist1, a bone differentiation transcription factor, can directly bind to and activate periostin gene expression [Oshima et al., 2002]. In our study, the expression of both twist1 and periostin is highest in undifferentiated mesenchyme. The possibility that periostin controls osteoblast fate is supported in mice with a germline deletion of periostin. In these embryos, ectopic ossification in heart valve mesenchymal cells was observed [Tkatchenko et al., 2009]. This indicates that twist-mediated loss of periostin in select regions of EMT-derived mesenchyme may promote the differentiation of osteoblasts.

Our data showed that strong periostin expression occurred in the mesenchyme immediately adjacent to MES, but not in the epithelium. The protein showed intense labeling in the basement membrane underlying the MES during the seam disruption stage. As seam disruption

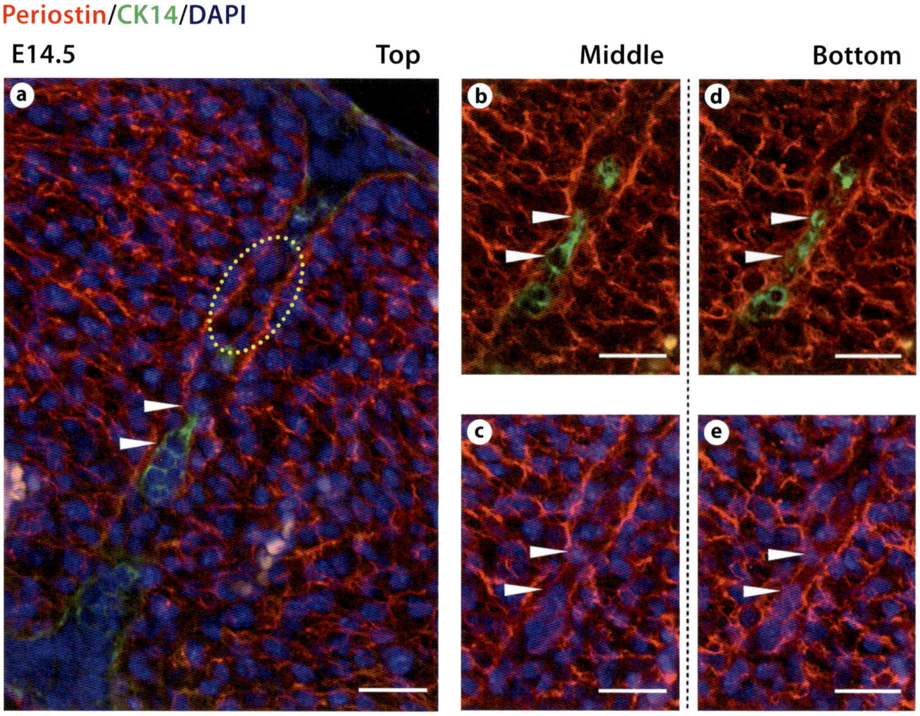

Fig. 6. z-stack confocal images of MEE at 3 different z-positions staining for periostin (red), the epithelial marker CK14 (green) and DAPI (blue) at E14.5. Cells in the yellow dotted circle represent MEE undergoing EMT (CK14 negative). White arrowheads indicate MEE undergoing EMT (diminished CK14). Both were associated with periostin. **b–e** Wide-field images. Scale bars = 25 μm.

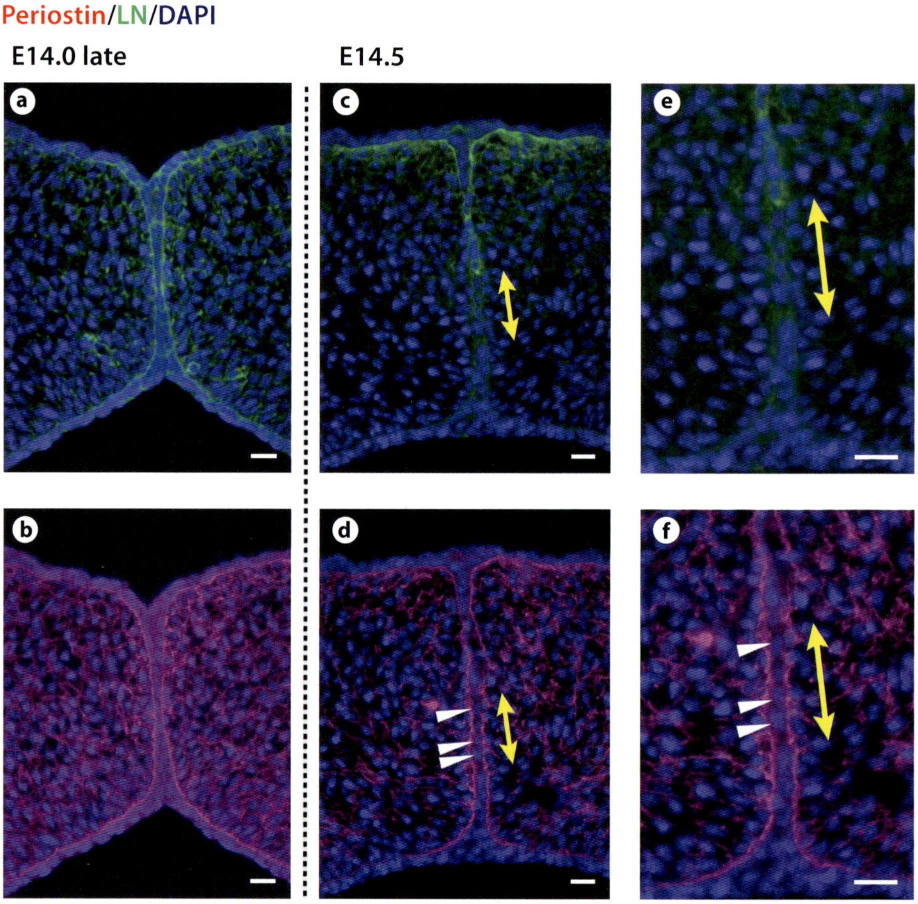

Fig. 7. a–d Triple-staining images with LN, periostin and DAPI at E14.0 and E14.5. **e**, **f** Wide-field images of **c** and **d**, respectively. **c–f** Lines with arrowheads indicate the part where the LN-containing basement membrane has already started to degrade but the periostin-containing basement membrane was still completely retained. **d**, **f** Arrowheads show MEE allowed to establish new contact with periostin. Scale bars = 20 μm.

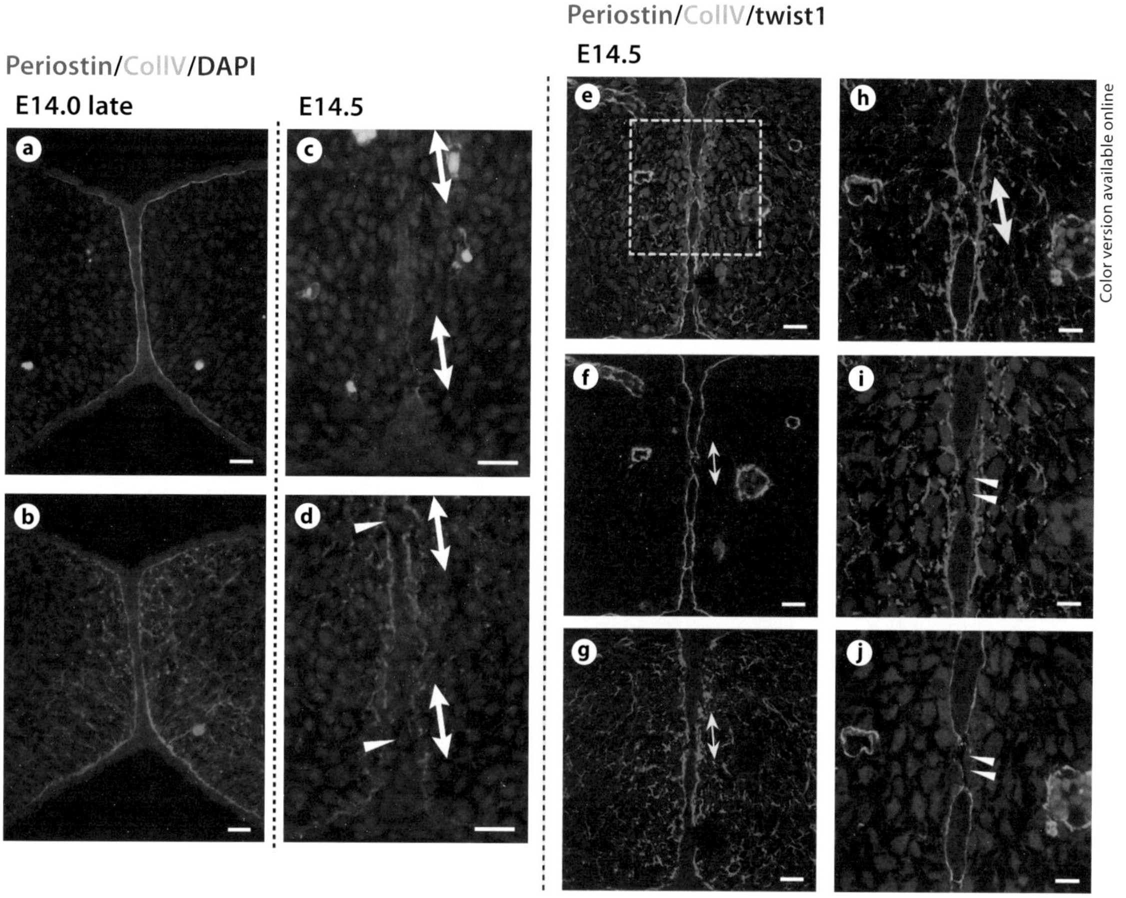

Fig. 8. a–d Triple-staining images with periostin, ColIV and DAPI at E14.0 late and E14.5. ColIV and DAPI (**a**, **c**), periostin and DAPI (**b**, **d**). **c**, **d** Wide-field images. Lines with arrowheads indicate the part where the ColIV-containing basement membrane has already started to degrade but the periostin-containing basement membrane was retained; arrowheads indicate MME. **e–g** Triple-staining confocal images with periostin, ColIV and twist1 at E14.5. Periostin, ColIV and twist1 (**e**), ColIV (**f**) and periostin (**g**). **h–j** High-power images of the rectangle indicated in **e**. Periostin and ColIV (**h**), periostin and twist1 (**i**) and ColIV and twist1 (**j**). Lines with arrowheads (**f–h**) indicate the part where the ColIV-containing basement membrane has already started to degrade. **i**, **j** MEE were associated with periostin and undergoing EMT (arrowheads). Scale bars = 20 μm (**a–g**) and 10 μm (**h–j**). Full-color images are given in the online version of the figure.

proceeded, periostin mRNA and protein were also observed inside the MES. These findings are consistent with previous studies reporting that high levels of periostin mRNA and protein were localized to sites of epithelial-mesenchymal interactions (tooth germs) [Kruzynska-Frejtag et al., 2004]. Periostin is also highly expressed in pathological conditions such as cancer invasion [Fukushima et al., 2008; Kikuchi et al., 2008] and fibrosis [Takayama et al., 2006; Oka et al., 2007]. Periostin is well known to promote cellular motility and facilitate EMT [Gillan et al., 2002; Yan and Shao, 2006; Butcher et al., 2007; Li et al., 2010]. Moreover, periostin is reportedly regulated by several important signaling molecules involved in EMT such as TGF-β_3 [Norris et al., 2009], TGF-β_1 [Horiuchi et al., 1999] and twist [Oshima et al., 2002]. Therefore, periostin may create an EMT-supportive microenvironment enabling MEE to transdifferentiate in order to achieve complete mesenchymal confluence.

Identification of MEE undergoing EMT has used many methods. Several labeling methods such as physical labeling (Dil and CCFSE) [Shuler et al., 1991; Griffith and Hay, 1992], molecular biology-based labeling (vector carrying lacZ) [Martinez-Alvarez et al., 2000] and genetic labeling (Cre-Loxp system) [Martinez-Alvarez et al., 2000] have been used to trace the fate of MEE. Here, we simply took advantage of periostin-containing basement membrane to separate MES from the mesenchyme/mesenchymal cells since the structural integrity of periostin was retained late into the stages of palatal fusion. We demonstrated the association of MEE undergoing EMT (twist1-positive and CK14-negative MEE) with periostin 3-dimensionally. In addition, it was apparent that MEE undergoing EMT (diminished CK14) were also associated with periostin. The presence of strong periostin labeling around a select subset of MEE supports the hypothesis that periostin may play an important role in altering cell response favorable for EMT during palatal fusion. Furthermore, it was noted that MEE undergoing EMT (twist1-positive MEE) were surrounded by intense periostin expression as palatal fusion advanced. Previous work showed that knockdown of twist mRNA using siRNA decreased palatal fusion, and twist mRNA was upregulated by TGF-β_3 [Yu et al., 2008]. These findings suggest that the acquisition of periostin expression in MEE undergoing EMT may contribute to the changed microenvironment and may promote the mesenchymal phenotype induced by TGF-β_3 though twist1.

Basal lamina degradation and new formation of cell-mesenchymal matrix interactions play a role in EMT during palatal fusion [Kaartinen et al., 1997]. Our study revealed that LN and ColIV in the basement membrane were degraded much earlier than the mesenchymal matrix, periostin. In instances where both epithelial-specific and mesenchymal matrices coexisted in the basement membrane, the epithelial phenotype in MEE was maintained. This suggests that integrin engagement with epithelial-specific matrices in the basement membrane has a dominant effect on maintaining epithelial phenotype and suppressing EMT. However, during MES degradation, epithelial-specific matrices were degraded, and new interactions were established with underlying mesenchymal matrix. It was previously reported that selective loss of the basement membrane correlated with EMT occurred during both embryonic development [Fujiwara et al., 2007] and pathologic conditions [Spaderna et al., 2006]. Our data provided evidence for selective loss of epithelial matrix ColIV in the basement membrane underlying MES correlated with MEE transdifferentiation, indicated by expression of the mesenchymal marker twist1. Moreover, we could link the association with the mesenchymal matrix periostin to EMT. It is currently known that periostin serves as a ligand for some members of the integrin family including $\alpha V\beta_3$, $\alpha V\beta_5$ and β_1 [Butcher et al., 2007; Kuhn et al., 2007; Li et al., 2010], which were expressed in MEE. Therefore, interaction between periostin and integrins may occur at epithelial-mesenchymal interfaces after degradation of epithelial-specific matrices in the basement membrane. Focal adhesion kinase, phosphoinositide 3-kinases and integrin-linked kinase are intracellular signaling components of the integrin complex, and all of these are activated by periostin [Bao et al., 2004; Baril et al., 2007]. These kinases function as important regulators of the EMT response [Kang and Svoboda, 2002; Guarino et al., 2007]. Thus, our findings support a hypothesis that periostin alters the MEE response by affecting signaling in MEE through alterations in their engagement of integrins and promotes EMT initiated by TGF-β_3.

In summary, we have described the spatiotemporal distribution of periostin during palatogenesis at the sites of mesenchymal-epithelial interaction during the onset of EMT. The differential patterns of epithelial-specific matrices and mesenchymal matrix during MES degradation suggest novel roles, namely that periostin may play a role in creating the environment favorable for EMT through interactions with integrins.

Acknowledgements

We thank Gregory R. Handrigan and Norihisa Higashihori for their technical assistance with in situ hybridization. Financial support was provided by a research grant (RO1 DE16296) from the National Institute of Dental and Craniofacial Research to C.F.S. and CIHR grants to J.M.R.

References

Bao, S., G. Ouyang, X. Bai, Z. Huang, C. Ma, M. Liu, R. Shao, R.M. Anderson, J.N. Rich, X.F. Wang (2004) Periostin potently promotes metastatic growth of colon cancer by augmenting cell survival via the Akt/PKB pathway. Cancer Cell *5:* 329–339.

Baril, P., R. Gangeswaran, P.C. Mahon, K. Caulee, H.M. Kocher, T. Harada, M. Zhu, H. Kalthoff, T. Crnogorac-Jurcevic, N.R. Lemoine (2007) Periostin promotes invasiveness and resistance of pancreatic cancer cells to hypoxia-induced cell death: role of the beta4 integrin and the PI3K pathway. Oncogene *26:* 2082–2094.

Boyer, B., A.M. Valles, N. Edme (2000) Induction and regulation of epithelial-mesenchymal transitions. Biochem Pharmacol *60:* 1091–1099.

Butcher, J.T., R.A. Norris, S. Hoffman, C.H. Mjaatvedt, R.R. Markwald (2007) Periostin promotes atrioventricular mesenchyme matrix invasion and remodeling mediated by integrin signaling through Rho/PI 3-kinase. Dev Biol *302:* 256–266.

Chou, M.J., T. Kosazuma, T. Takigawa, S. Yamada, S. Takahara, K. Shiota (2004) Palatal shelf movement during palatogenesis: a fate map of the fetal mouse palate cultured in vitro. Anat Embryol (Berl) *208:* 19–25.

Ferguson, M.W. (1987) Palate development: mechanisms and malformations. Ir J Med Sci *156:* 309–315.

Ferguson, M.W. (1988) Palate development. Development *103(suppl):* 41–60.

Fitchett, J.E., E.D. Hay (1989) Medial edge epithelium transforms to mesenchyme after embryonic palatal shelves fuse. Dev Biol *131:* 455–474.

Fujiwara, H., Y. Hayashi, N. Sanzen, R. Kobayashi, C.N. Weber, T. Emoto, S. Futaki, H. Niwa, P. Murray, D. Edgar, K. Sekiguchi (2007) Regulation of mesodermal differentiation of mouse embryonic stem cells by basement membranes. J Biol Chem *282:* 29701–29711.

Fukushima, N., Y. Kikuchi, T. Nishiyama, A. Kudo, M. Fukayama (2008) Periostin deposition in the stroma of invasive and intraductal neoplasms of the pancreas. Mod Pathol *21:* 1044–1053.

Gillan, L., D. Matei, D.A. Fishman, C.S. Gerbin, B.Y. Karlan, D.D. Chang (2002) Periostin secreted by epithelial ovarian carcinoma is a ligand for alpha(V)beta(3) and alpha(V) beta(5) integrins and promotes cell motility. Cancer Res *62:* 5358–5364.

Griffith, C.M., E.D. Hay (1992) Epithelial-mesenchymal transformation during palatal fusion: carboxyfluorescein traces cells at light and electron microscopic levels. Development *116:* 1087–1099.

Guarino, M., B. Rubino, G. Ballabio (2007) The role of epithelial-mesenchymal transition in cancer pathology. Pathology *39:* 305–318.

Hong, L., H. Sun, X. Lv, D. Yang, J. Zhang, Y. Shi (2010) Expression of periostin in the serum of NSCLC and its function on proliferation and migration of human lung adenocarcinoma cell line (A549) in vitro. Mol Biol Rep *37:* 2285–2293.

Horiuchi, K., N. Amizuka, S. Takeshita, H. Takamatsu, M. Katsuura, H. Ozawa, Y. Toyama, L.F. Bonewald, A. Kudo (1999) Identification and characterization of a novel protein, periostin, with restricted expression to periosteum and periodontal ligament and increased expression by transforming growth factor beta. J Bone Miner Res *14:* 1239–1249.

Kaartinen, V., X.M. Cui, N. Heisterkamp, J. Groffen, C.F. Shuler (1997) Transforming growth factor-beta3 regulates transdifferentiation of medial edge epithelium during palatal fusion and associated degradation of the basement membrane. Dev Dyn *209:* 255–260.

Kang, P., K.K. Svoboda (2002) PI-3 kinase activity is required for epithelial-mesenchymal transformation during palate fusion. Dev Dyn *225:* 316–321.

Kikuchi, Y., T.G. Kashima, T. Nishiyama, K. Shimazu, Y. Morishita, M. Shimazaki, I. Kii, H. Horie, H. Nagai, A. Kudo, M. Fukayama (2008) Periostin is expressed in pericryptal fibroblasts and cancer-associated fibroblasts in the colon. J Histochem Cytochem *56:* 753–764.

Kim, K.K., M.C. Kugler, P.J. Wolters, L. Robillard, M.G. Galvez, A.N. Brumwell, D. Sheppard, H.A. Chapman (2006) Alveolar epithelial cell mesenchymal transition develops in vivo during pulmonary fibrosis and is regulated by the extracellular matrix. Proc Natl Acad Sci USA *103:* 13180–13185.

Kruzynska-Frejtag, A., M. Machnicki, R. Rogers, R.R. Markwald, S.J. Conway (2001) Periostin (an osteoblast-specific factor) is expressed within the embryonic mouse heart during valve formation. Mech Dev *103:* 183–188.

Kruzynska-Frejtag, A., J. Wang, M. Maeda, R. Rogers, E. Krug, S. Hoffman, R.R. Markwald, S.J. Conway (2004) Periostin is expressed within the developing teeth at the sites of epithelial-mesenchymal interaction. Dev Dyn *229:* 857–868.

Kuhn, B., F. del Monte, R.J. Hajjar, Y.S. Chang, D. Lebeche, S. Arab, M.T. Keating (2007) Periostin induces proliferation of differentiated cardiomyocytes and promotes cardiac repair. Nat Med *13:* 962–969.

Li, G., R. Jin, R.A. Norris, L. Zhang, S. Yu, F. Wu, R.R. Markwald, A. Nanda, S.J. Conway, S.S. Smyth, D.N. Granger (2010) Periostin mediates vascular smooth muscle cell migration through the integrins alphaνbeta3 and alphaνbeta5 and focal adhesion kinase (FAK) pathway. Atherosclerosis *208:* 358–365.

Martinez-Alvarez, C., C. Tudela, J. Perez-Miguelsanz, S. O'Kane, J. Puerta, M.W. Ferguson (2000) Medial edge epithelial cell fate during palatal fusion. Dev Biol *220:* 343–357.

Menke, A., C. Philippi, R. Vogelmann, B. Seidel, M.P. Lutz, G. Adler, D. Wedlich (2001) Down-regulation of E-cadherin gene expression by collagen type I and type III in pancreatic cancer cell lines. Cancer Res *61:* 3508–3517.

Norris, R.A., B. Damon, V. Mironov, V. Kasyanov, A. Ramamurthi, R. Moreno-Rodriguez, T. Trusk, J.D. Potts, R.L. Goodwin, J. Davis, S. Hoffman, X. Wen, Y. Sugi, C.B. Kern, C.H. Mjaatvedt, D.K. Turner, T. Oka, S.J. Conway, J.D. Molkentin, G. Forgacs, R.R. Markwald (2007) Periostin regulates collagen fibrillogenesis and the biomechanical properties of connective tissues. J Cell Biochem *101:* 695–711.

Norris, R.A., J.D. Potts, M.J. Yost, L. Junor, T. Brooks, H. Tan, S. Hoffman, M.M. Hart, M.J. Kern, B. Damon, R.R. Markwald, R.L. Goodwin (2009) Periostin promotes a fibroblastic lineage pathway in atrioventricular valve progenitor cells. Dev Dyn *238:* 1052–1063.

Oka, T., J. Xu, R.A. Kaiser, J. Melendez, M. Hambleton, M.A. Sargent, A. Lorts, E.W. Brunskill, G.W. Dorn, 2nd, S.J. Conway, B.J. Aronow, J. Robbins, J.D. Molkentin (2007) Genetic manipulation of periostin expression reveals a role in cardiac hypertrophy and ventricular remodeling. Circ Res *101:* 313–321.

Okano, J., S. Suzuki, K. Shiota (2006) Regional heterogeneity in the developing palate: morphological and molecular evidence for normal and abnormal palatogenesis. Congenit Anom (Kyoto) *46:* 49–54.

Oshima, A., H. Tanabe, T. Yan, G.N. Lowe, C.A. Glackin, A. Kudo (2002) A novel mechanism for the regulation of osteoblast differentiation: transcription of periostin, a member of the fasciclin I family, is regulated by the bHLH transcription factor, twist. J Cell Biochem *86:* 792–804.

Rowe, A., J.M. Richman, P.M. Brickell (1992) Development of the spatial pattern of retinoic acid receptor-beta transcripts in embryonic chick facial primordia. Development *114:* 805–813.

Schweizer, J., P.E. Bowden, P.A. Coulombe, L. Langbein, E.B. Lane, T.M. Magin, L. Maltais, M.B. Omary, D.A. Parry, M.A. Rogers, M.W. Wright (2006) New consensus nomenclature for mammalian keratins. J Cell Biol *174:* 169–174.

Shuler, C.F., Y. Guo, A. Majumder, R.Y. Luo (1991) Molecular and morphologic changes during the epithelial-mesenchymal transformation of palatal shelf medial edge epithelium in vitro. Int J Dev Biol *35:* 463–472.

Spaderna, S., O. Schmalhofer, F. Hlubek, G. Berx, A. Eger, S. Merkel, A. Jung, T. Kirchner, T. Brabletz (2006) A transient, EMT-linked loss of basement membranes indicates metastasis and poor survival in colorectal cancer. Gastroenterology *131:* 830–840.

Sugiura, T., H. Takamatsu, A. Kudo, E. Amann (1995) Expression and characterization of murine osteoblast-specific factor 2 (OSF-2) in a baculovirus expression system. Protein Expr Purif *6:* 305–311.

Takayama, G., K. Arima, T. Kanaji, S. Toda, H. Tanaka, S. Shoji, A.N. McKenzie, H. Nagai, T. Hotokebuchi, K. Izuhara (2006) Periostin: a novel component of subepithelial fibrosis of bronchial asthma downstream of IL-4 and IL-13 signals. J Allergy Clin Immunol *118:* 98–104.

Tkatchenko, T.V., R.A. Moreno-Rodriguez, S.J. Conway, J.D. Molkentin, R.R. Markwald, A.V. Tkatchenko (2009) Lack of periostin leads to suppression of Notch1 signaling and calcific aortic valve disease. Physiol Genomics *39:* 160–168.

Yan, W., R. Shao (2006) Transduction of a mesenchyme-specific gene periostin into 293T cells induces cell invasive activity through epithelial-mesenchymal transformation. J Biol Chem *281:* 19700–19708.

Yu, W., H. Kamara, K.K. Svoboda (2008) The role of twist during palate development. Dev Dyn *237:* 2716–2725.

Cells
Tissues
Organs

Cells Tissues Organs 2011;193:64–73
DOI: 10.1159/000320165

Published online: November 3, 2010

Involvement of Dystroglycan in Epithelial-Mesenchymal Transition during Chick Gastrulation

Yukiko Nakaya[a] Erike W. Sukowati[a] Cantas Alev[a, b] Fumie Nakazawa[a] Guojun Sheng[a]

[a]Laboratory for Early Embryogenesis, RIKEN Center for Developmental Biology, and
[b]Vascular Regeneration Research Group, Institute of Biomedical Research and Innovation, Kobe, Japan

Key Words
Gastrulation · Basement membrane · Mesoderm · Epithelial-mesenchymal transition · Dystroglycan

Abstract
Regulated disruption of the basement membrane (BM) is a critical step in many epithelial-mesenchymal transition (EMT) processes. Molecular mechanisms controlling the interaction between the BM and the basal membrane of epithelial cells and its subsequent disruption during EMT are poorly understood. Using chick embryos as a model, we analyzed the molecular complexity of this interaction during gastrulation EMT. Transcriptome data indicated that the BM of the gastrulation stage chick epiblast contains a full range of BM component proteins with unique subtype combinations. Integrins and dystroglycan are 2 major groups of basal membrane proteins involved in BM interaction. We provide evidence that dystroglycan gene expression is restricted to the epiblast during early development and its expression is downregulated in cells undergoing gastrulation EMT. The β-dystroglycan protein is localized to the basolateral membrane in epiblast cells and the basal localization is lost in cells undergoing EMT. Disruption of actin filaments leads to a decrease in the lateral membrane localization of β-dystroglycan and a relative increase in basal membrane localization, whereas disruption of microtubules leads to the loss of BM/basal membrane interaction and basal membrane β-dystroglycan localization. Overall, these data suggest an involvement of dystroglycan, especially the regulation of its expression and localization, in gastrulation EMT.

Introduction

The gastrulation process in amniote (birds and mammals) embryos is one of the earliest models for studying epithelial-mesenchymal transition (EMT) [Hay, 1968]. The epithelial tissue in this EMT process is the epiblast,

Abbreviations used in this paper

BM	basement membrane
DAG1	dystroglycan gene
EG-X	Eyal-Giladi stage X
EMT	epithelial-mesenchymal transition
HH	Hamburger and Hamilton stage

KARGER
Fax +41 61 306 12 34
E-Mail karger@karger.ch
www.karger.com

1422–6405/11/1932–0064$38.00/0

Accessible online at:
www.karger.com/cto

Dr. Guojun Sheng
Laboratory for Early Embryogenesis
RIKEN Center for Developmental Biology
Kobe, Hyogo 650-0047 (Japan)
Tel. +81 78 306 3158, Fax +81 78 306 3146, E-Mail sheng@cdb.riken.jp

the source of all 3 germ layers. The mesenchymal tissue is the mesoderm layer, of which constituent cells undergo, after EMT, extensive migration and differentiation to give rise to the most diverse array of cell types in the animal body [Nakaya and Sheng, 2008]. This EMT takes place during early chick development in a transitory and dynamic structure called 'primitive streak' [Bellairs, 1986; Nakaya and Sheng, 2009].

During gastrulation EMT, primitive streak cells have lost some epithelial characteristics, but are nevertheless linked with the rest of the epiblast through epithelial tight junctions and adherens junctions [Nakaya et al., 2008]. Like many epithelial tissues, the epiblast cells sit on a thin layer of extracellular matrix, the basement membrane (BM). Proper interactions between the BM and the basal membrane of the epiblast cells, together with tight junctions and adherens junctions, are important for the maintenance of epiblast epithelial integrity [Nakaya et al., 2008]. The unique nature of the avian epiblast as a key barrier for the developing embryo and as a continuous sheet of cells under significant tension requires that the integrity of the epiblast be safeguarded even during gastrulation EMT. This is achieved by initiating gastrulation EMT through remodeling of the BM/basal membrane interaction, and at the same time, maintaining tight junctions in streak mesoderm precursors before these cells leave the epiblast. Regulated disruption of the BM/basal membrane interaction and coordination of this step with other EMT-related cell morphological changes are therefore critical for the successful execution of gastrulation EMT [Nakaya et al., 2008].

Molecular mechanisms involved in the regulation of the BM/basal membrane interaction during gastrulation EMT are poorly understood. We have previously shown that integrins and laminins are involved in this interaction during chick gastrulation EMT, and that RhoA activity and microtubule dynamics at the basal cell cortex play an important role in its regulation [Nakaya et al., 2008]. However, it is unclear how microtubule dynamics is linked to membrane receptors such as integrins, or whether other BM and basal membrane molecules are involved in this process.

One potential candidate for such a linker molecule is dystroglycan *(DAG1)*. Dystroglycan was isolated from skeletal muscles as a membrane component of the dystrophin-glycoprotein complex, playing an essential role as a cytolinker that connects muscle BM, sarcolemma and muscle cytoskeleton [Ervasti and Campbell, 1991; Ibraghimov-Beskrovnaya et al., 1992; Ervasti and Campbell, 1993]. Its functions in non-muscle tissues, including Reichert's membrane, kidney, salivary gland and neural epithelia, as well as epithelial tumors in human breast, colon and prostate tissues, have been extensively documented [Williamson et al., 1997; Henry et al., 2001; Muschler et al., 2002; Jing et al., 2004; Sgambato and Brancaccio, 2005; Schroder et al., 2007; Sgambato et al., 2007; Satz et al., 2008; Bao et al., 2009; Giannico et al., 2009].

The *DAG1* gene encodes both α- and β-dystroglycan as posttranslational proteolytic products. α-Dystroglycan, localized extracellularly, is heavily glycosylated and binds to laminin and perlecan in the BM and β-dystroglycan in the basal membrane [Hemler, 1999; Henry and Campbell, 1999; Barresi and Campbell, 2006]. β-Dystroglycan, through the dystrophin-glycoprotein complex, has been reported to interact intracellularly with both actin filaments and microtubules [Campbell, 1995; Henry and Campbell, 1999; Barresi and Campbell, 2006; Ayalon et al., 2008; Cerecedo et al., 2008; Bozzi et al., 2009; Hueston and Suprenant, 2009; Prins et al., 2009]. *DAG1*-null mice were embryonic lethal due to a poor assembly of Reichert's membrane, in addition to gastrulation and mesoderm formation defects [Williamson et al., 1997]. These data indicate that dystroglycan may play an important role in mediating the BM/basal membrane interaction during avian gastrulation.

In this work, we first analyzed the molecular complexity of the chick epiblast BM. We showed that major groups of BM proteins are present in the chick epiblast, and also, that in addition to integrins, dystroglycan is the other major mediator of the BM/basal membrane interaction. Both transcripts and protein products of dystroglycan genes are strongly expressed in the epiblast cells and are downregulated during gastrulation EMT. β-Dystroglycan protein is localized to the basolateral membrane of the epiblast cells. Lateral membrane localization of β-dystroglycan is sensitive to actin depolymerization drug treatment, whereas basal membrane localization is sensitive to microtubule destabilization. These results suggest that β-dystroglycan, through the dystrophin-glycoprotein complex, may be a candidate mediator linking the BM/basal membrane interaction on one hand and microtubule dynamics at the basal epiblast cell cortex on the other.

Materials and Methods

Digoxigenin-labeled antisense in situ probe for chicken *DAG1* gene was made against nucleotides 1–918 of NM_001097540. Standard protocols were followed for RNA in situ hybridization

a

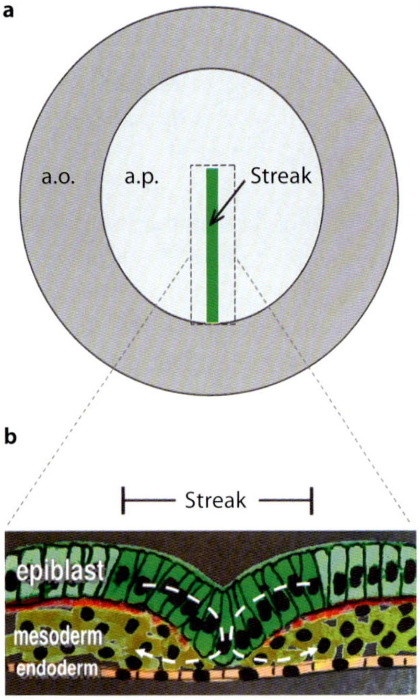

c

BM	Laminin	LAMA1, LAMA5, LAMB1, LAMC1
	Fibronectin	FN1
	HSPG	HSPG2 (perlecan), COL18A1
	Type IV collagen	COL4A2, COL4A4, COL4A5, COL4A6
	Fibulin	FBLN1, FBLN2
	Nidogen	NID1, NID2
	Fibrillin	FBN1, FBN2
Basal membrane	Integrin	ITGA4, ITGA6, ITGAV, ITGB1, ITGB3, ITGB5
	Dystroglycan	DAG1

Fig. 1. Molecular components involved in the interaction between the BM and the basal membrane of epiblast cells during gastrulation EMT. **a**, **b** Schematic diagrams of stage HH4 chick embryos in whole-mount view (**a**) and section view (**b**). a.p. = Area pellucida; a.o. = area opaca. The primitive streak (green) is indicated by the arrow. The dotted rectangle in **a** indicates the tissue region used for transcriptomic analyses, and a section of this region is shown in **b**. **c** Summary of protein groups and specific genes of each group found in the study. Underlined groups (but not individual gene products in the group) have been reported to be expressed with immunohistochemical studies. Laminin *alpha1* (LAMA1) was not detected in our studies, but was reported to be expressed. HSPG = Heparin sulfate proteoglycan.

and after in situ embedding and sectioning with chick embryos [Stern, 1998; Nakazawa et al., 2006]. Mouse anti-β-dystroglycan antibody (NCL-b-DG) was purchased from Novocastra Laboratories (UK), which was made against the C-terminal 15-amino-acid residues of human protein. This region is 100% conserved in the chicken β-dystroglycan protein. The antibody was reported to cross-react with chicken dystroglycan according to the company product datasheet and published literature [Schroder et al., 2007], confirmed by us with Western blot analysis of early embryonic lysates (fig. 4g). Hamburger and Hamilton stage 1 (HH1) and HH3–4 lanes in figure 4g were each loaded with lysate equivalent to a half to one embryo. A 1:100 dilution of this antibody was used for frozen section immunofluorescence staining analysis. Rabbit anti-laminin antibody was purchased from Sigma (No. L9393), and a 1:100 dilution was used for frozen section staining. The following secondary antibodies were used: Alexa Fluor 488 for mouse IgG and Alexa Fluor 594 for rabbit IgG (both from Molecular Probes). Nocodazole (No. M1404) and cytochalasin D (No. C8273) were purchased from Sigma. Stocks (1,000× the final concentration in DMSO) were diluted in freshly collected thin albumen. Embryos were grown at 38.5°C in a new culture setting, with the endoderm side up and with indirect contact with the albumen that contained either the above-mentioned chemicals or control 0.1% DMSO through the vitelline membrane. Fertilized hens' eggs were purchased from Shiroyama farm (Kanagawa, Japan). An Affymetrix Chicken Genome Array-based transcriptome screen was carried out using dissected tissues from stage HH4 embryos. Details of the screen have been published elsewhere [Alev et al., 2010].

Results

During chick gastrulation EMT, lateral epiblast cells move toward the primitive streak, undergo morphological changes and ingress to become mesoderm cells (fig. 1a, b). In a screen for genes expressed in and surrounding the primitive streak at HH4 [Alev et al., 2010],

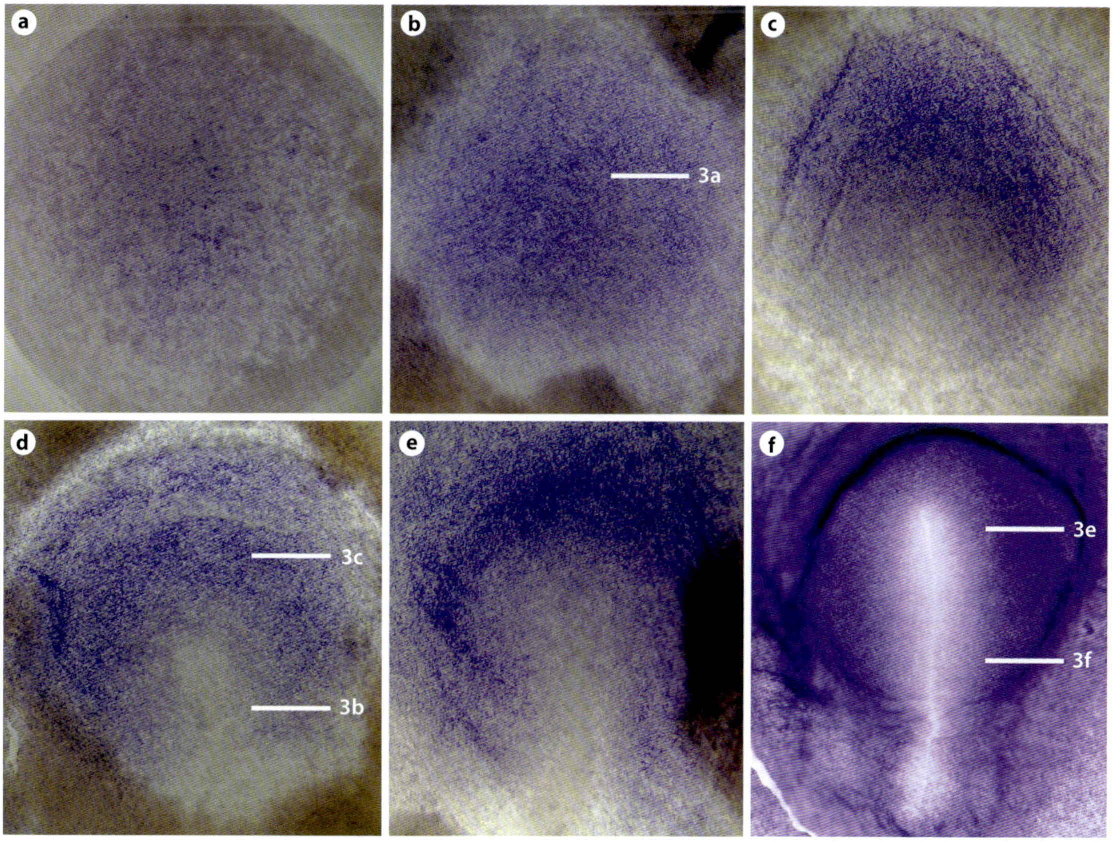

Fig. 2. Expression pattern of *DAG1* during early chick development. *DAG1* expression from unincubated to HH4 stages were analyzed by whole-mount RNA in situ analysis. Unincubated (stage EG-X) (**a**); late-stage HH1 (**b**); stage HH2 (**c**); stage HH3 (**d**); stage HH3+ (**e**); stage HH4 (**f**). White lines indicate levels of sections shown in figure 3.

we found many genes encoding BM proteins. A systematic search revealed that all major groups of BM proteins are present in the chick epiblast BM. These groups include laminins, fibronectin, heparan sulfate proteoglycans, type IV collagens, fibulins, nidogens and fibrillins (fig. 1c).

Similar to what has been reported in many mammalian systems [LeBleu et al., 2007], the chick epiblast BM has its unique signature of subtype specificity for each of the BM protein groups (fig. 1c). For example, only 3 chicken laminin genes *(alpha5, beta1* and *gamma1)* were found to be expressed during gastrulation EMT, in agreement with what has been reported for gastrulation stage mouse embryos which express laminins *alpha1, alpha5, beta1* and *gamma1* [Miner et al., 2004; Miner and Yurchenco, 2004]. Chicken laminin *alpha1* was reported to be expressed in gastrulation stage epiblast cells [Zagris et al., 2000]. However, the level of expression may be very low and we could not detect the expression of laminin *alpha1* in our transcriptome screen or by RNA in situ analysis. Although subtype specificity is often difficult to discern from immunostaining, the presence of laminin and several other BM components at protein group levels has been reported for gastrulation stage chick embryos [Sanders, 1979, 1984; Raddatz et al., 1991; Soulintzi and Zagris, 2007; Nakaya et al., 2008; Nakaya and Sheng, 2009].

Among genes encoding membrane proteins that have been reported to interact with BM components, we found 6 integrin genes *(alpha4, alpha6, alphaV, beta1, beta3* and *beta5)* and a dystroglycan *(DAG1)* gene. Integrins are well-known to mediate cell/matrix interactions [Hynes, 2002; Li et al., 2003; Berrier and Yamada, 2007], and we have previously reported that integrins *alpha6* and *beta1* are involved during gastrulation EMT in chick embryos [Nakaya et al., 2008]. Roles of dystro-

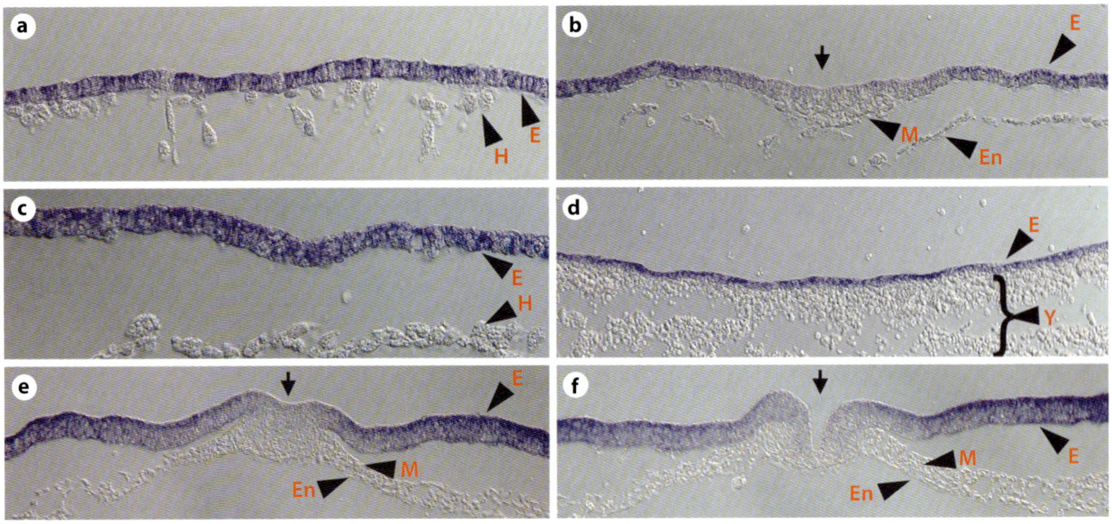

Fig. 3. Epiblast-specific expression of *DAG1*. Levels of the sections are shown in figure 2. Arrows = Streak midline; arrowheads = tissue layers; E = epiblast or ectoderm; H = hypoblast; M = mesoderm; En = endoderm; Y = yolk. Late-stage HH1 (**a**); streak level at stage HH3 (**b**); anterior to the streak at stage HH3 (**c**); area opaca at stage HH3 (**d**); anterior streak region at stage HH4 (**e**); mid-streak region at stage HH4 (**f**).

glycan during early development in maintaining epiblast cell integrity and in gastrulation EMT are not well understood. As a potential linker molecule connecting the BM, basal membrane and basal cortex of the epiblast cells, we decided to investigate the expression and protein localization of dystroglycan during chick early development in more detail.

To know whether dystroglycan expression is restricted to the region surrounding the primitive streak or broadly associated with the epiblast, we generated a digoxigenin-labeled anti-sense RNA probe (see Materials and Methods) and analyzed an expression pattern of *DAG1* in embryos from Eyal-Giladi stage X (EG-X) to HH4. At stage EG-X (freshly laid eggs), the epiblast has just become a single-celled layer from the earlier multilayered blastoderm; and at stage HH4 (full primitive streak stage), all epiblast cells except for those located within the primitive streak undergoing gastrulation EMT have well-formed BM in electron microscopy or immunohistochemical studies. *DAG1* was detected weakly at stage EG-X (fig. 2a). After approximately 8 h of development, by the end of stage HH1, robust *DAG1* expression was seen throughout the area pellucida (fig. 2b). Sectioning of stained embryos revealed that *DAG1* expression is restricted to the epiblast and is negative in hypoblast cells (fig. 3a). A very small percentage of epiblast cells do not express *DAG1* at this stage (fig. 3a), possibly representing primordial germ cells that are being formed from the epiblast. When the streak starts to form at HH2 (fig. 2c), strong *DAG1* expression was detected in all epiblast cells except for those in the primitive streak where *DAG1* was very weak. This pattern persists at stages HH3 (fig. 2d, e, 3b, c) and HH4 (fig. 2f, 3e, f). Section analysis revealed that epiblast cells in the area opaca, with squamous epithelial morphology, are also positive for *DAG1* (fig. 3d). Our RNA in situ analysis indicated a gradual decrease in *DAG1* expression levels in epiblast cells approaching the primitive streak and a sharp decrease as cells enter the primitive streak (fig. 3b, e, f). At the stages investigated, neither the mesoderm nor the endoderm cells are positive for *DAG1* expression. Although the endoderm layer also adopts an epithelial morphology, the lack of *DAG1* expression is consistent with the fact that the endoderm lacks a noticeable BM at these early stages of development.

The decrease in *DAG1* expression when epiblast cells enter the primitive streak is reminiscent of the loss of BM markers when epiblast cells initiate EMT changes [Nakaya et al., 2008]. If dystroglycan, especially β-dystroglycan, plays a role in gastrulation EMT, its subcellular distribution in epiblast cells should be dynamically regulated. To investigate this, we used a monoclonal antibody specific for β-dystroglycan (see Materials and Methods) and analyzed its subcellular localization in the epiblast

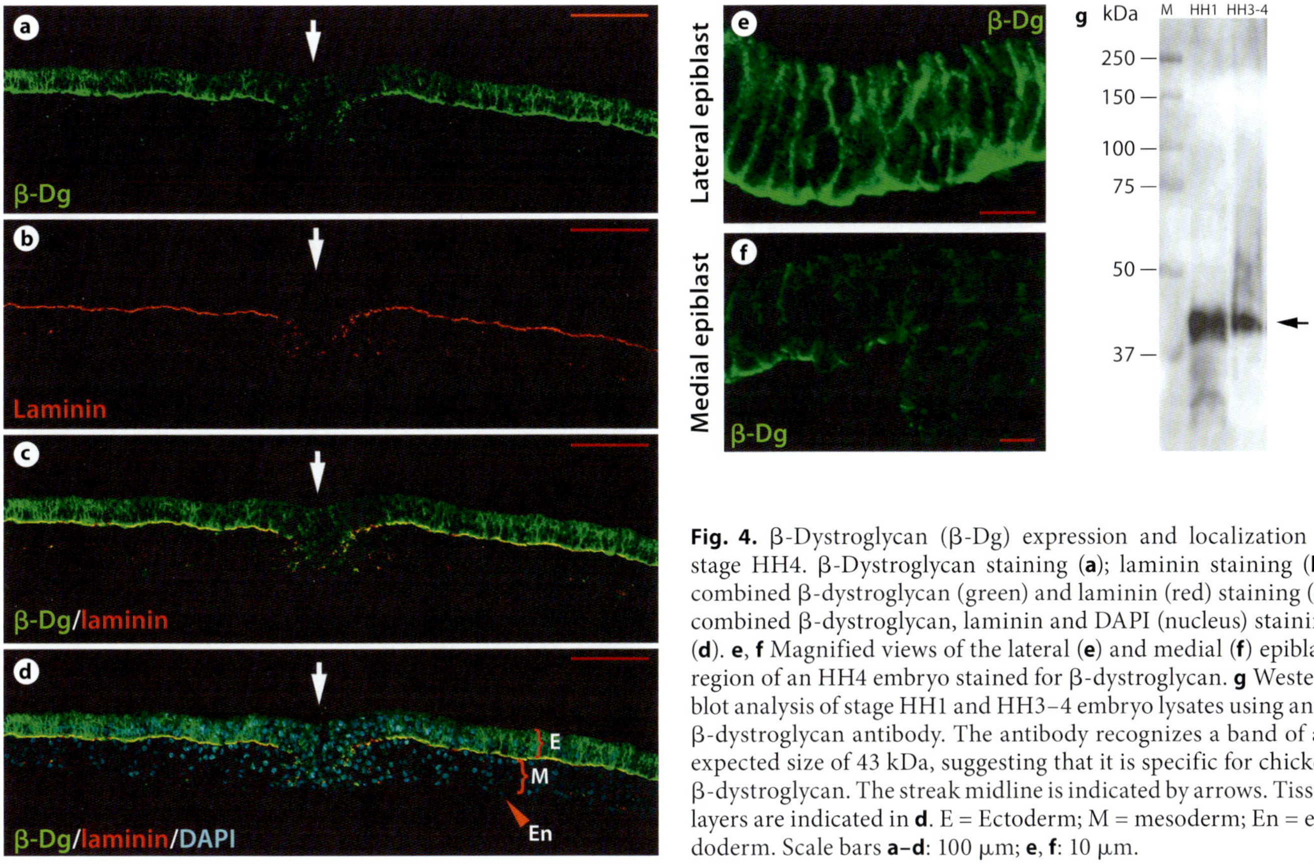

Fig. 4. β-Dystroglycan (β-Dg) expression and localization at stage HH4. β-Dystroglycan staining (**a**); laminin staining (**b**); combined β-dystroglycan (green) and laminin (red) staining (**c**); combined β-dystroglycan, laminin and DAPI (nucleus) staining (**d**). **e**, **f** Magnified views of the lateral (**e**) and medial (**f**) epiblast region of an HH4 embryo stained for β-dystroglycan. **g** Western blot analysis of stage HH1 and HH3–4 embryo lysates using anti-β-dystroglycan antibody. The antibody recognizes a band of an expected size of 43 kDa, suggesting that it is specific for chicken β-dystroglycan. The streak midline is indicated by arrows. Tissue layers are indicated in **d**. E = Ectoderm; M = mesoderm; En = endoderm. Scale bars **a–d**: 100 μm; **e**, **f**: 10 μm.

during chick gastrulation. In agreement with our RNA expression analysis, section immunofluorescence staining showed that β-dystroglycan protein expression is restricted to the epiblast (fig. 4a). A few prominent features of β-dystroglycan localization were also revealed. In most epiblast cells, β-dystroglycans are localized to the basolateral membrane (fig. 4a, e). Those cells close to the streak have relatively stronger basal signals compared with the lateral signals, although the overall β-dystroglycan signal intensity appeared to decrease as cells approach the streak. When epiblast cells enter the primitive streak, the overall β-dystroglycan level decreases sharply (fig. 4a, f), with the basal membrane localization lost completely and the lateral membrane localization only weakly detectable. Coimmunofluorescence analysis indicated that the loss of basal membrane β-dystroglycan localization coincides with the loss of the BM marker laminin (fig. 4b–d). Confirming a previous report [Schroder et al., 2007], the β-dystroglycan antibody used in this work, generated against a peptide in human β-dystroglycan that is 100% conserved in chicken β-dystroglycan, recognized a band of expected size (43 kDa) in Western blot with stage HH1 and HH3–4 embryonic lysates (fig. 4g), suggesting that this antibody also specifically recognizes β-dystroglycan in chicken tissues.

The dystrophin-glycoprotein complex has been reported to interact with both actin filaments and microtubules (see Introduction). Our previous studies suggested that microtubule dynamics in the basal compartment of the epiblast cells has a more prominent role in regulating the BM/basal membrane interaction [Nakaya et al., 2008]. We then asked whether basolateral localization of β-dystroglycan is affected by chemicals that disrupt either actin filaments (cytochalasin D) or microtubules (nocodazole). Embryos were grown to stage HH4 and were treated for 3 h with either 5 μg/ml cytochalasin D or 10 μg/ml nocodazole, followed by fixation and section staining for β-dystroglycan and laminin expression. Control treatment with 0.1% DMSO did not affect β-dystroglycan expression or localization (n = 6; fig. 5a–h). As previously reported [Nakaya et al., 2008], cytochalasin D treatment did not have a prominent effect on laminin ex-

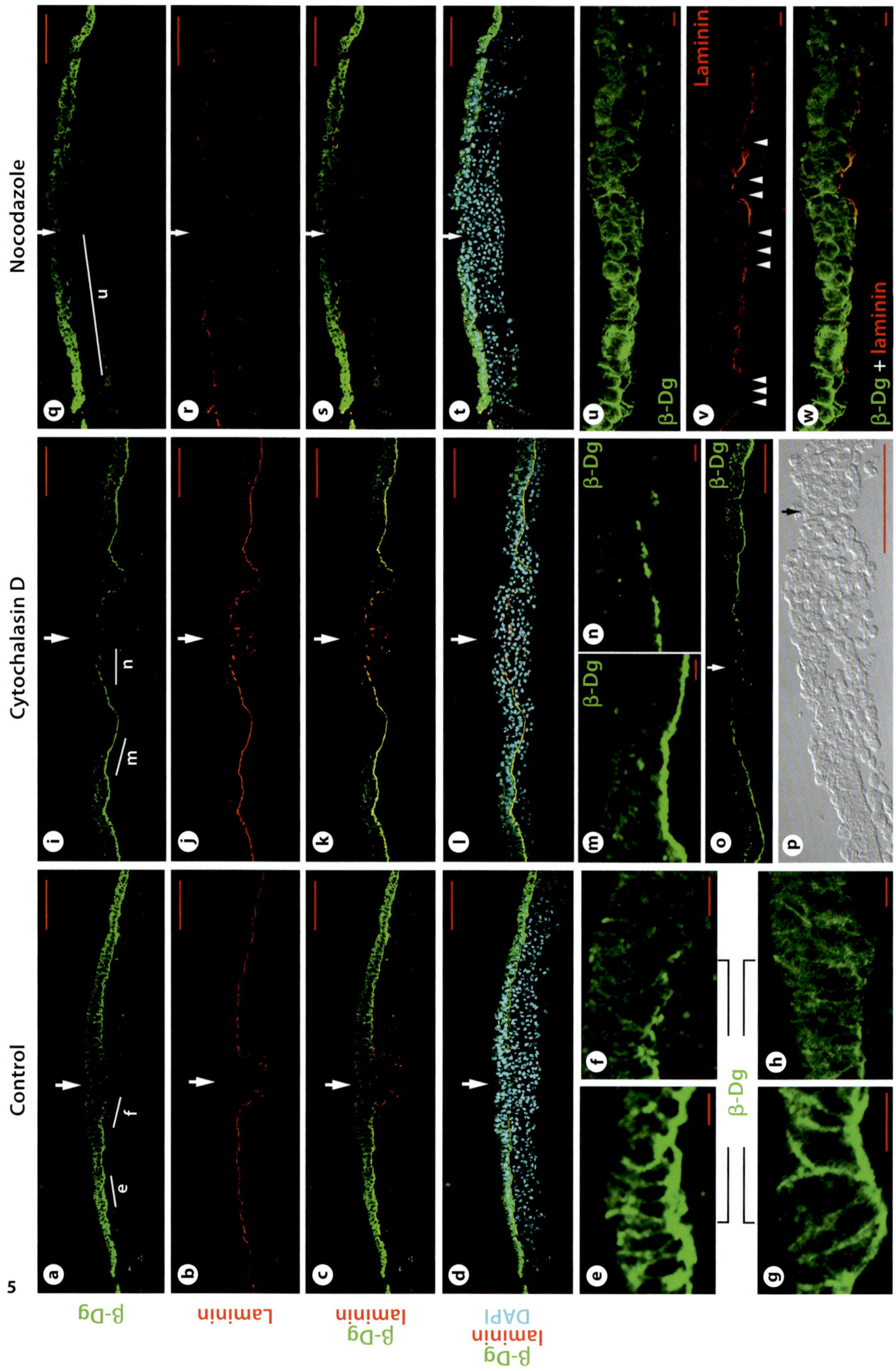
5
Control
Cytochalasin D
Nocodazole
β-Dg
Laminin
β-Dg
laminin
β-Dg
laminin
DAPI
β-Dg
Laminin
β-Dg + laminin

pression (n = 7; fig. 5j), although the apical membrane of the epiblast cells became rough after treatment (fig. 5p). Nocodazole treatment led to a premature breakdown of the BM in lateral epiblast cells (n = 7; fig. 5r, v). Interestingly, both chemicals had a clear effect on β-dystroglycan subcellular localization (fig. 5i, m–o for cytochalasin D treatment, and fig. 5q, u for nocodazole treatment), although the overall intensity of protein expression signals was not greatly affected by either chemical treatment. In cytochalasin-D-treated embryos, a dramatic reduction in β-dystroglycan was observed in the lateral membrane, whereas its basal membrane localization remained robust in lateral epiblast cells (fig. 5m) and seemed to increase in epiblast cells closer to the streak (fig. 5n), suggesting a redistribution of β-dystroglycan localization. In the medial streak region where BM breakdown normally occurs, no basal β-dystroglycan localization was observed (fig. 5i, m–o). In embryos treated with nocodazole, basal localization of β-dystroglycan disappeared in regions of the lateral epiblast with ectopic BM breakdown (fig. 5q, u). Under close examination, the cause for this may likely be the disruption of the BM/basal membrane interaction by nocodazole (fig. 5v, arrowheads), leading to rounding up of the basolateral membrane (fig. 5q–t, u–w) which in normal epiblast cells adopts a columnar epithelial morphology (fig. 5e–h). β-Dystroglycan signals could still be detected in these rounded-up cells (fig. 5v, w). In regions of the epiblast where the BM is still present, many epiblast cells exhibited a rounded-up morphology, suggesting that the effect of nocodazole on BM/basal membrane interaction may be more immediate than its effect on BM breakdown.

Fig. 5. Effect of cytochalasin D and nocodazole on β-dystroglycan (β-Dg) localization. Arrows indicate the streak midline. Control DMSO treatment (**a–h**); cytochalasin D treatment (**i–p**); nocodazole treatment (**q–w**). Panels **a–d** (control), **i–l** (cytochalasin D) and **q–t** (nocodazole) show different fluorescent stainings (as indicated on the left) of the same section at mid-streak level in respective treatment. Regions with magnified views in **a** (for **e**, **f**), **i** (for **m**, **n**) and **q** (for **u**) are indicated by white lines. **g**, **h** Additional examples from a different section of lateral (**g**) and medial (**h**) epiblast dystroglycan staining in control treatment. **o** Additional example of β-dystroglycan localization after cytochalasin D treatment. **p** Overall morphology in bright field view of epiblast cells after cytochalasin D treatment. Apical membrane protrusion is obvious and the basal membrane is largely normal. **u–w** Magnified views of a region in **q**. Rounding up of the basolateral membrane is correlated with a loss of the BM marker laminin (arrowheads). Rounded-up cells still have β-dystroglycan localization on the nonapical side. Scale bars **a–d**, **i–l**, **o–t:** 100 μm; **e–h**, **m**, **n**, **u–w**: 10 μm.

Taken together, our data suggest that during chick gastrulation EMT, dystroglycan expression is tightly correlated spatially and temporally with the regulation of BM/basal membrane interaction. Future functional analyses will reveal whether dystroglycan is directly involved in this regulation and how this regulation is linked to the integrin-mediated BM/basal membrane interaction.

Discussion

In this work, we present evidence that dystroglycan is involved in gastrulation EMT during avian development. In addition to the dystroglycan studied here, our transcriptome data indicated the presence of other members of the dystrophin-glycoprotein complex (including ε-sarcoglycan, dystrophin, α- and β-dystrobrevins, and β_2-syntrophin), supporting our hypothesis that dystroglycan-mediated BM/basal membrane interaction is active during chick gastrulation EMT. Our studies showed that dystroglycan is expressed from the onset of epiblast epithelialization, suggesting its involvement in either the assembly of young BM or the establishment of epithelial polarity. During gastrulation EMT, when the BM beneath medial epiblast cells needs to be broken down in preparation for ingression, dystroglycan RNA expression is strongly downregulated and the basal localization of β-dystroglycan is lost.

Although dystroglycan has been widely associated with the epithelial integrity and BM/basal membrane interaction, its exact function in EMT is not well understood. Mice with *DAG1* null mutation die early during embryonic development due to disruption of Reichert's membrane [Williamson et al., 1997]. The epiblast of *DAG1*-null embryos was reported to be positive for BM markers, although gastrulation appeared to be disrupted and no mesoderm cells formed [Williamson et al., 1997], suggesting a direct involvement of dystroglycan in gastrulation EMT. Studies using mouse embryoid bodies revealed that dystroglycan is also important for epiblast cell survival [Li et al., 2002]. However, approximately half of the mouse embryos with epiblast-specific *DAG1* null mutation could still develop to term [Satz et al., 2008], suggesting that at least in these embryos, mesoderm cells could be generated normally. In several other studies, loss of dystroglycan function was shown to have no obvious effect under normal development on the maintenance of epithelial BM or epithelial cell polarity [Mirouse et al., 2009; Esser et al., 2010], although epithelial integrity under stress conditions was compromised [Mirouse et al.,

2009]. Therefore, it is unclear whether the association we have observed in dystroglycan expression and localization with gastrulation EMT necessarily reflects a direct role of dystroglycan in this process, or if so, which molecular/cellular aspect(s) of gastrulation EMT it is essential for.

One possible clue may come from its subcellular localization. β-Dystroglycan was detected in our studies in both basal and lateral membranes. The basal membrane localization of β-dystroglycan most likely reflects its role in BM/basal membrane interaction, whereas the lateral membrane localization may reflect its involvement in epithelial cell-cell interaction, an aspect which has not received much investigation. More importantly, a dynamic balance of lateral and basal membrane localization of β-dystroglycan was observed in our studies. The lateral membrane localization is sensitive to cytochalasin D treatment, whereas the basal membrane localization is not. One possible explanation is that there is an active F-actin-dependent dynamic redistribution of β-dystroglycan from the basal to the lateral membrane. Another possible explanation is that the basal membrane localization is more dependent on microtubule dynamics than on F-actin. Although the latter explanation is more consistent with our previous observation (also confirmed in this study) that the BM/basal membrane interaction is more sensitive to nocodazole than to cytochalasin D treatment, both hypotheses deserve to be tested in future investigations. Functional analysis of β-dystroglycan during gastrulation EMT may eventually help us understand its role in disease-related EMTs.

Acknowledgements

We would like to thank Michael Henry and Erik Thompson for their encouragement in this study.

References

Alev, C., Y. Wu, T. Kasukawa, L.M. Jakt, H.R. Ueda, G. Sheng (2010) Transcriptomic landscape of the primitive streak. Development *137:* 2863–2874.

Ayalon, G., J.Q. Davis, P.B. Scotland, V. Bennett (2008) An ankyrin-based mechanism for functional organization of dystrophin and dystroglycan. Cell *135:* 1189–1200.

Bao, X., M. Kobayashi, S. Hatakeyama, K. Angata, D. Gullberg, J. Nakayama, M.N. Fukuda, M. Fukuda (2009) Tumor suppressor function of laminin-binding alpha-dystroglycan requires a distinct beta3-N-acetylglucosaminyltransferase. Proc Natl Acad Sci USA *106:* 12109–12114.

Barresi, R., K.P. Campbell (2006) Dystroglycan: from biosynthesis to pathogenesis of human disease. J Cell Sci *119:* 199–207.

Bellairs, R. (1986) The primitive streak. Anat Embryol (Berl) *174:* 1–14.

Berrier, A.L., K.M. Yamada (2007) Cell-matrix adhesion. J Cell Physiol *213:* 565–573.

Bozzi, M., S. Morlacchi, M.G. Bigotti, F. Sciandra, A. Brancaccio (2009) Functional diversity of dystroglycan. Matrix Biol *28:* 179–187.

Campbell, K.P. (1995) Three muscular dystrophies: loss of cytoskeleton-extracellular matrix linkage. Cell *80:* 675–679.

Cerecedo, D., B. Cisneros, R. Suarez-Sanchez, E. Hernandez-Gonzalez, I. Galvan (2008) Beta-dystroglycan modulates the interplay between actin and microtubules in human-adhered platelets. Br J Haematol *141:* 517–528.

Ervasti, J.M., K.P. Campbell (1991) Membrane organization of the dystrophin-glycoprotein complex. Cell *66:* 1121–1131.

Ervasti, J.M., K.P. Campbell (1993) A role for the dystrophin-glycoprotein complex as a transmembrane linker between laminin and actin. J Cell Biol *122:* 809–823.

Esser, A.K., M.B. Cohen, M.D. Henry (2010) Dystroglycan is not required for maintenance of the luminal epithelial basement membrane or cell polarity in the mouse prostate. Prostate *70:* 777–787.

Giannico, G., H. Yang, E.G. Neilson, A.B. Fogo (2009) Dystroglycan in the diagnosis of FSGS. Clin J Am Soc Nephrol *4:* 1747–1753.

Hay, E.D. (1968) Organization and fine structure of epithelium and mesenchyme in the developing chick embryo; in Fleischmajer, R., R.E. Billingham (eds): Epithelial-Mesenchymal Interactions; 18th Hahnemann Symposium. Baltimore, Williams & Wilkins, pp 31–55.

Hemler, M.E. (1999) Dystroglycan versatility. Cell *97:* 543–546.

Henry, M.D., K.P. Campbell (1999) Dystroglycan inside and out. Curr Opin Cell Biol *11:* 602–607.

Henry, M.D., M.B. Cohen, K.P. Campbell (2001) Reduced expression of dystroglycan in breast and prostate cancer. Hum Pathol *32:* 791–795.

Hueston, J.L., K.A. Suprenant (2009) Loss of dystrophin and the microtubule-binding protein ELP-1 causes progressive paralysis and death of adult *C. elegans*. Dev Dyn *238:* 1878–1886.

Hynes, R.O. (2002) Integrins: bidirectional, allosteric signaling machines. Cell *110:* 673–687.

Ibraghimov-Beskrovnaya, O., J.M. Ervasti, C.J. Leveille, C.A. Slaughter, S.W. Sernett, K.P. Campbell (1992) Primary structure of dystrophin-associated glycoproteins linking dystrophin to the extracellular matrix. Nature *355:* 696–702.

Jing, J., C.F. Lien, S. Sharma, J. Rice, P.A. Brennan, D.C. Gorecki (2004) Aberrant expression, processing and degradation of dystroglycan in squamous cell carcinomas. Eur J Cancer *40:* 2143–2151.

LeBleu, V.S., B. Macdonald, R. Kalluri (2007) Structure and function of basement membranes. Exp Biol Med (Maywood) *232:* 1121–1129.

Li, S., D. Edgar, R. Fassler, W. Wadsworth, P.D. Yurchenco (2003) The role of laminin in embryonic cell polarization and tissue organization. Dev Cell *4:* 613–624.

Li, S., D. Harrison, S. Carbonetto, R. Fassler, N. Smyth, D. Edgar, P.D. Yurchenco (2002) Matrix assembly, regulation, and survival functions of laminin and its receptors in embryonic stem cell differentiation. J Cell Biol *157:* 1279–1290.

Miner, J.H., C. Li, J.L. Mudd, G. Go, A.E. Sutherland (2004) Compositional and structural requirements for laminin and basement membranes during mouse embryo implantation and gastrulation. Development *131:* 2247–2256.

Miner, J.H., P.D. Yurchenco (2004) Laminin functions in tissue morphogenesis. Annu Rev Cell Dev Biol *20:* 255–284.
Mirouse, V., C.P. Christoforou, C. Fritsch, D. St Johnston, R.P. Ray (2009) Dystroglycan and perlecan provide a basal cue required for epithelial polarity during energetic stress. Dev Cell *16:* 83–92.
Muschler, J., D. Levy, R. Boudreau, M. Henry, K. Campbell, M.J. Bissell (2002) A role for dystroglycan in epithelial polarization: loss of function in breast tumor cells. Cancer Res *62:* 7102–7109.
Nakaya, Y., G. Sheng (2008) Epithelial to mesenchymal transition during gastrulation: an embryological view. Dev Growth Differ *50:* 755–766.
Nakaya, Y., G. Sheng (2009) An amicable separation: Chick's way of doing EMT. Cell Adh Migr *3:* 160–163.
Nakaya, Y., E.W. Sukowati, Y. Wu, G. Sheng (2008) RhoA and microtubule dynamics control cell-basement membrane interaction in EMT during gastrulation. Nat Cell Biol *10:* 765–775.
Nakazawa, F., H. Nagai, M. Shin, G. Sheng (2006) Negative regulation of primitive hematopoiesis by the FGF signaling pathway. Blood *108:* 3335–3343.
Prins, K.W., J.L. Humston, A. Mehta, V. Tate, E. Ralston, J.M. Ervasti (2009) Dystrophin is a microtubule-associated protein. J Cell Biol *186:* 363–369.
Raddatz, E., F. Monnet-Tschudi, C. Verdan, P. Kucera (1991) Fibronectin distribution in the chick embryo during formation of the blastula. Anat Embryol (Berl) *183:* 57–65.
Sanders, E.J. (1979) Development of the basal lamina and extracellular materials in the early chick embryo. Cell Tissue Res *198:* 527–537.
Sanders, E.J. (1984) Labelling of basement membrane constituents in the living chick embryo during gastrulation. J Embryol Exp Morphol *79:* 113–123.
Satz, J.S., R. Barresi, M. Durbeej, T. Willer, A. Turner, S.A. Moore, K.P. Campbell (2008) Brain and eye malformations resembling Walker-Warburg syndrome are recapitulated in mice by dystroglycan deletion in the epiblast. J Neurosci *28:* 10567–10575.
Schroder, J.E., M.R. Tegeler, U. Grosshans, E. Porten, M. Blank, J. Lee, C. Esapa, D.J. Blake, S. Kroger (2007) Dystroglycan regulates structure, proliferation and differentiation of neuroepithelial cells in the developing vertebrate CNS. Dev Biol *307:* 62–78.
Sgambato, A., A. Brancaccio (2005) The dystroglycan complex: from biology to cancer. J Cell Physiol *205:* 163–169.
Sgambato, A., B. De Paola, M. Migaldi, M. Di Salvatore, A. Rettino, G. Rossi, B. Faraglia, A. Boninsegna, A. Maiorana, A. Cittadini (2007) Dystroglycan expression is reduced during prostate tumorigenesis and is regulated by androgens in prostate cancer cells. J Cell Physiol *213:* 528–539.
Soulintzi, N., N. Zagris (2007) Spatial and temporal expression of perlecan in the early chick embryo. Cells Tissues Organs *186:* 243–256.
Stern, C.D. (1998) Detection of multiple gene products simultaneously by in situ hybridization and immunohistochemistry in whole mounts of avian embryos. Curr Top Dev Biol *36:* 223–243.
Williamson, R.A., M.D. Henry, K.J. Daniels, R.F. Hrstka, J.C. Lee, Y. Sunada, O. Ibraghimov-Beskrovnaya, K.P. Campbell (1997) Dystroglycan is essential for early embryonic development: disruption of Reichert's membrane in Dag1-null mice. Hum Mol Genet *6:* 831–841.
Zagris, N., A.E. Chung, V. Stavridis (2000) Differential expression of laminin genes in early chick embryo. Int J Dev Biol *44:* 815–818.

Cells Tissues Organs

Cells Tissues Organs 2011;193:74–84
DOI: 10.1159/000320359

Published online: November 2, 2010

Angiotensin II and Its Role in Tubular Epithelial to Mesenchymal Transition Associated with Chronic Kidney Disease

W.C. Burns M.C. Thomas

Danielle Alberti Memorial Centre for Diabetes Complications, Baker IDI Heart and Diabetes Institute, Melbourne, Vic., Australia

Key Words

Angiotensin II · Epithelial to mesenchymal transition · Chronic kidney disease · Renal fibrosis · Renin-angiotensin system

Abstract

Activation of the intra-renal renin-angiotensin system (RAS) and the subsequent generation of angiotensin II (Ang II) are important mediators of haemodynamic changes in both health and disease. However, the effects of locally produced Ang II are not limited to haemodynamic actions. Ang II is also an important stimulus for tubular hypertrophy with the induction of growth factors, including transforming growth factor (TGF)-β_1 and connective tissue growth factor. In this article, we explore the direct pro-fibrotic effects of Ang II and its role in inducing tubular epithelial to mesenchymal transition (EMT, also known as type 2 EMT), a known mediator of renal fibrogenesis. There is accumulating evidence that Ang II is able to induce EMT by both TGF-dependent and TGF-independent actions, both in vitro and in vivo. Moreover, blockade of the RAS has synergistic renoprotective effects across a number of causally different forms of renal disease. There is hope that targeted combinations to offset angiotensin-converting enzyme escape in the setting of RAS blockade will eventually achieve the long-term efficacy that has been expected for so long.

The Renin-Angiotensin System

Activation of the intra-renal renin-angiotensin system (RAS) and the subsequent generation of angiotensin II (Ang II) are important mediators of haemodynamic changes in both health and disease. This is especially the case in the kidney, where genetic overactivity of the RAS

Abbreviations used in this paper

ACE	angiotensin-converting enzyme
AGEs	advanced glycation endproducts
Ang II	angiotensin II
AT1	angiotensin type 1 receptor
CKD	chronic kidney disease
CTGF	connective tissue growth factor
ECM	extracellular matrix
EMT	epithelial to mesenchymal transition
ERK1/2	extracellular signal-regulated kinase 1/2
MAPK	mitogen-activated protein kinase
RAGE	receptor for advanced glycation end products
RAS	renin-angiotensin system
RhoA	Ras homolog gene family, member A
ROCK	RhoA kinase
ROS	reactive oxygen species
α-SMA	α-smooth muscle actin
TGF-β_1	transforming growth factor-β
UUO	unilateral ureteral obstruction

KARGER

Fax +41 61 306 12 34
E-Mail karger@karger.ch
www.karger.com

1422–6405/11/1932–0074$38.00/0

Accessible online at:
www.karger.com/cto

Dr. Wendy C. Burns
Danielle Alberti Memorial Centre for Diabetic Complications
Baker IDI Heart and Diabetes Institute, PO Box 6492
Melbourne, VIC 8008 (Australia)
Tel. +61 3 8532 1277, Fax +61 3 8532 1480, E-Mail wendy.burns@bakeridi.edu.au

results in accelerated progression of diabetic nephropathy [Kelly et al., 1998]. Equally, patients homozygous for the D allele of the angiotensin-converting enzyme (ACE) gene, which results in increased ACE activity, have increased rates of renal damage [Fujisawa et al., 1998]. This association is of particular clinical relevance, as blockade of the RAS with ACE inhibitors or angiotensin type 1 (AT1) receptor antagonists [Zatz et al., 1986] is able to protect against kidney damage.

The means by which activation of the RAS is able to promote renal injury is an active field of ongoing investigation. Certainly, the effects of locally produced Ang II are not limited to haemodynamic actions such as promoting systemic and intra-glomerular hypertension. Ang II is also an important stimulus for tubular hypertrophy with the induction of growth factors, including transforming growth factor (TGF)-β_1 and epidermal growth factor. In this article, we explore the direct pro-fibrotic effects of Ang II and its role in inducing tubular epithelial to mesenchymal transition (EMT, also known as type 2 EMT), a known mediator of renal fibrogenesis.

RAS – An Overview

The RAS is a well-characterized circulatory and tissue hormonal system. Renin is released from the juxtaglomerular cells of the kidney [Wolf et al., 1996] in response to reduced renal perfusion pressure, reduced salt transport to the distal tubule or increased renal sympathetic tone. Its subsequent physiological effects are determined by a series of proteolytic steps. The first step requires renin to cleave its substrate angiotensinogen to form the decapeptide angiotensin I. The 2 terminal amino acids are subsequently split by the dipeptide carboxypeptidase, ACE, to form the octapeptide, Ang II [Erdos, 1976; Lavoie et al., 2003]. As well as the classical pathway for the formation of Ang II, other proteolytic enzymes and pathways are also capable of generating Ang II in vitro. These include a variety of non-renin angiotensinases including tonin, cathepsin G, tissue plasminogen activator, elastase as well as chymase, a specific enzyme present particularly in mast cells and in the heart [Husain et al., 2003]. The importance of these alternative pathways in vivo remains to be established. Nonetheless, evidence is accumulating in humans that, under certain conditions, chymase can be responsible for Ang II production [Kokkonen et al., 2003].

Ang II has a variety of biological actions spanning the diverse roles of the RAS in the homeostasis of many organ systems. In the cardiovascular system, the RAS is important in both blood pressure regulation and sodium and volume homeostasis. Ang II fulfils these roles both as a direct vasoconstrictor as well as stimulating aldosterone production and renal sodium and water transport. It also stimulates thirst and the release of vasopressin [Zimmerman et al., 2002]. Ang II facilitates the sympathetic nervous system both by central actions and by stimulating the presynaptic release of noradrenaline [English et al., 1999]. However, Ang II is more than just a vasoconstrictor and has trophic effects independent of its haemodynamic actions. More recently, the role of Ang II in cell differentiation and in modulating growth and hypertrophy has been recognized [Wolf, 2001]. Ang II is a potent pro-oxidant, partly as a result of stimulation of NAD(P)H oxidase [Seshiah et al., 2002; Touyz et al., 2002]. It also acts as a pro-inflammatory, pro-fibrotic and pro-thrombotic agent, with direct effects in the kidney including activation of nuclear factor-κB, increased synthesis and release of pro-fibrotic mediators, angiogenic cytokines and pro-inflammatory chemokines, like monocyte chemotactic protein-1 [Sadoshima, 2000].

Most of the actions of Ang II are mediated via activation of specific angiotensin receptors situated on the cell surface. In humans, there are 2 distinct angiotensin receptors, AT1 and AT2 [Ruiz-Ortega et al., 2003]. Both are members of the 7 transmembrane-spanning G-protein-coupled class of receptors with distinctive intracellular signalling pathways. In addition to signalling, these receptors also play a role in angiotensin metabolism. Receptor-coupled Ang II is internalized into the cells where it is either recycled or degraded by lysosomal enzymes. Recent evidence suggests Ang II may directly interact with chromatin and other intracellular targets, which may partly mediate some of its physiological actions.

The Intra-Renal RAS

Ang II is produced locally in many tissues, including the kidney [Navar et al., 1996; Klahr et al., 1998]. Activity of this so-called 'local' or 'tissue' RAS may be regulated independently to the systemic RAS [Dzau, 1988]. Inside the kidney, in the renal interstitium, Ang II levels are 1,000-fold higher than in plasma [Nishiyama et al., 2002]. Most of the angiotensinogen synthesis within the kidney is localized to the proximal tubular cells. Therefore, these tubular cells ultimately constitute the source for intra-tubular and interstitial Ang II. In addition, the proximal tubule has a key role in the conversion of angiotensin I to

Ang II which occurs via ACE on the proximal tubule cell brush border [Navar et al., 1996]. Taken together, these findings point to the proximal tubule as the key mediator of the intra-renal RAS.

The primary role of the intra-renal RAS appears to be homeostatic, particularly in states of effective or absolute volume depletion. In addition, activation of the renal RAS provides an important compensatory mechanism to maintain renal function in the response to nephron loss. Ang II modulates glomerular filtration by influencing both afferent and efferent arterial tone and by direct effects on mesangial cell contraction to modulate the glomerular ultra-filtration coefficient. Ang II also influences glomerular permselectivity both by its effects on glomerular pressure as well as by a direct action on the glomerular sieving coefficient. In addition, Ang II stimulates renal salt retention via direct effects on the proximal tubule and stimulation of aldosterone secretion. While in the short term these responses are invaluable, they are at the expense of capillary hypertension in the remaining glomeruli. Ultimately, activation of the intra-renal RAS becomes counter-productive resulting in progressive nephron 'burnout', placing even more 'pressure' on the remaining nephron mass. The same phenomenon also occurs in the renal tubule as compensatory changes induced by Ang II lead to tubular damage, tubular drop-out and interstitial fibrosis. Tubular EMT may be regarded in much the same light as hyperfiltration, as a form of metastable adaptation which may be expedient in allowing cells threatened by a hostile environment to escape cell death [Song, 2007], but at the cost of phenotypic change.

Ang II and Renal Fibrogenesis

Ang II has been directly implicated in tubulointerstitial injury and fibrosis and acts as a local growth factor, directly influencing tubulointerstitial changes [Ruiz-Ortega et al., 1997; Border et al., 1998; Mezzano et al., 2001], possibly via its regulation of cell growth and extracellular matrix (ECM) synthesis and degradation [Wolf et al., 1993; Egido, 1996; Ruiz-Ortega et al., 1997]. A chronic infusion of Ang II results in glomerular and tubulointerstitial injury in the kidney [Johnson et al., 1992; Kagami et al., 1994; Yoo et al., 1998]. Similarly, in vitro treatment with Ang II stimulates matrix biosynthesis via activation of the AT1 receptor leading to the production of a cascade of pro-fibrogenic cytokines and growth factors including TGF-β_1, vascular endothelial growth factor and platelet-derived growth factor [Kagami et al., 1994; Wolf et al., 1997]. Ang II may also influence a range of other pathogenic mediators such as protein kinase C [Arendshorst et al., 1999; Nagahama et al., 2000] and the nuclear transcription factor, nuclear factor-κB [Ruiz-Ortega et al., 2000]. In rat mesangial cells, glucose-induced TGF-β_1 secretion is abrogated by AT1 receptor blockade [Singh et al., 1999]. Similarly, inhibition of the RAS in experimental diabetes is associated with reduced renal cytokine expression, particularly in the tubulointerstitium. However, the pro-fibrogenic effects of Ang II are not limited to the stimulation of ECM production. Ang II may also act to inhibit matrix metalloproteinase activity leading to increased matrix accumulation [Singh et al., 1999]. Again, reduced matrix degradation in diabetic nephropathy may be restored by blockade of the RAS, implying a key role [McLennan et al., 2002].

A causal relationship between RAS activation and renal fibrogenesis is also supported by studies in which blockade of the RAS has been shown to reduce renal interstitial fibrosis in experimental models. For example, in neonatal dogs with partial urethral obstruction [Shirazi et al., 2007], in the obstructed kidney of mice after unilateral ureteral obstruction (UUO) [Schanstra et al., 2002], bromoethylamine induced renal fibrosis [Garber et al., 1998], and in rats with subtotal nephrectomy [Gilbert et al., 1999], ACE inhibition reduced the severity of renal damage. Similarly, treatment with AT1 receptor antagonists attenuated tubulointerstitial fibrosis experimental models of diabetic nephropathy [Bolos et al., 2003], UUO [Ishidoya et al., 1995; Shirazi et al., 2007], subtotal (5/6) nephrectomy [Yu et al., 2000] and chronic cyclosporin nephropathy [Pichler et al., 1995].

Tubular EMT in Renal Disease

Progressive tubular interstitial fibrosis, resulting from both an increase in the synthesis and a decrease in the breakdown of ECM proteins, is thought to represent a 'common pathway' for chronic kidney disease (CKD), ultimately leading to the irreversible loss of renal function. Activation of the RAS may be considered one common mediator of renal fibrosis, as Ang II is increased in a causally diverse range of experimental models of progressive renal disease including subtotal nephrectomy [Gilbert et al., 1999], anti-Thy1 glomerulonephritis [Hisada et al., 1999], anti-glomerular basement membrane nephritis [Lafayette, 2000], membranous nephropathy [Zoja et al., 1997] and glomerulosclerosis [Pagtalunan et al., 2000]. Another common mediator appears to be the interstitial myofibroblast [Yang et al., 2001; Liu, 2004], which is the major source of excessive matrix production in CKD. In chronic nephropathies including chronic allograft nephropathy, glomerulonephritis, spontaneous lupus nephritis and diabetic kidney disease [Oldfield et al., 2001; Rastaldi et al., 2002; Kalluri et al., 2003], there is a marked accumulation of interstitial fibroblasts. In each of these conditions, the accumulation of myofibroblasts is closely correlated with the degree of interstitial damage and the risk of progression of renal disease. Although the role of myofibroblasts is well documented, there remains considerable controversy as to their origin, particularly in the setting of progressive kidney diseases. Some of these cells are clearly derived from the activation and proliferation of resident renal fibroblasts and pericytes, which migrate to the interstitium due to chemokines released in response to injury. A small number are also derived from circulating bone marrow precursors. In addition, the transition of endothelial cells and tubular epithelial cells into myofibroblasts (endothelial to mesenchymal transition and EMT, respectively) also contributes to the interstitial burden of prosclerotic cells, and ultimately, to renal fibrogenesis [Strutz et al., 1996; Oldfield et al., 2001; Iwano et al., 2002; Li et al., 2009]. Again, the relative contribution of each component continues to be hotly debated. However, proof-of-concept studies have demonstrated that tubular epithelial selective changes can themselves induce progressive kidney disease in experimental animals [Cheng et al., 2006], suggesting that tubular EMT has a direct and specific role in renal fibrosis. Moreover, labelling studies have demonstrated that up to one third of interstitial myofibroblasts may be of tubular origin in the UUO model of renal fibrosis [Iwano et al., 2002]. However, even if no tubular cell enters the interstitium, it is likely that phenotypic changes associated with EMT effect a range of tubular functions including the ability to sense and respond to the flow/shear stress, to synthesize and maintain the tubular basement membrane, the re-absorption of salt protein and other filtered components, as well as to signal other parts of the nephron, including the glomerulus.

Ang II and Tubular EMT

Although Ang II has a range of pro-fibrotic actions, its effects on tubular EMT have only been recently described. Certainly, Ang II induces the expression of mesenchymal markers in experimental models of renal fibrosis. For example, increased expression of α-smooth muscle actin (α-SMA) in the obstructed kidney of rats [Ishidoya et al., 1995; Morrissey et al., 1999] and mice [Yang et al., 2002] is attenuated by treatment with an AT2 receptor blocker, PD123319 [Morrissey et al., 1999], an AT1 receptor antagonist, SC-51316, or the ACE inhibitor, enalapril [Ishidoya et al., 1995]. More direct support for the involvement of Ang II in the induction of tubular EMT has been provided by a number of experimental studies, which used a chronic infusion of Ang II. One study showed that Ang II infusion resulted in tubular injury associated with de novo expression of α-SMA and vimentin in renal interstitial cells [Johnson et al., 1992]. A separate study demonstrated that Ang II infusion led to the expression of vimentin protein in proximal tubules which was absent in control animals [Bravo et al., 2003]. Although these studies did not examine other markers of EMT, including changes in cellular morphology to a mesenchymal phenotype or loss of epithelial markers such as E-cadherin, they did show the induction of α-SMA or vimentin which are considered to be key events in tubular EMT [Yang et al., 2001].

More recently, Ang II has been shown to induce tubular EMT in cell culture models [Chen et al., 2006; Carvajal et al., 2008; Rodrigues-Diez et al., 2008; Burns et al., 2010]. For example, we have demonstrated that Ang II induces EMT in a rat proximal tubular cell line (NRK52-E) as defined by changes in cellular morphology from the typical cobblestone pattern of the epithelial cell in culture to elongated, spindle-shaped mesenchymal cells (fig. 1a). This transition was associated with a reduction in E-cadherin protein and de novo synthesis of α-SMA protein expression (fig. 1a).

(For figure see next page.)
Fig. 1. NRK52-E cells were pre-incubated in control media or in the presence of the TGF-β type 1 receptor inhibitor (TβR1) SB431542 (2 μM) for 30 min prior to the addition of Ang II (1 nM) for 3 days. **a** Phase contrast microscopy was used to demonstrate changes in cellular morphology between control and treatment groups (left column). The arrow indicates the enlarged, spindle-shaped cells characteristic of the mesenchymal phenotype. In contrast, control cells have the cobblestone appearance of epithelial cells in culture. Confocal fluorescent microscopy demonstrates de novo expression of α-SMA (middle column) and a reduction in E-cadherin expression (right column). α-SMA and E-cadherin proteins are shown in green. The α-SMA-stained cells were counterstained with propidium iodide (red) to demonstrate the nuclei. Scale bars = 20 μm. **b** Real-time RT-PCR demonstrated altered gene expression of the α-SMA compared with untreated control cells. **c** Protein expression of α-SMA as quantified by in-cell Western blot analysis. The in-cell Western was adapted from Counihan et al. [2006]. The control group was arbitrarily assigned a value of 1. Each bar represents the mean ± SEM for 6 samples per group. [a] $p < 0.05$ versus control; [b] $p < 0.05$ versus Ang II.

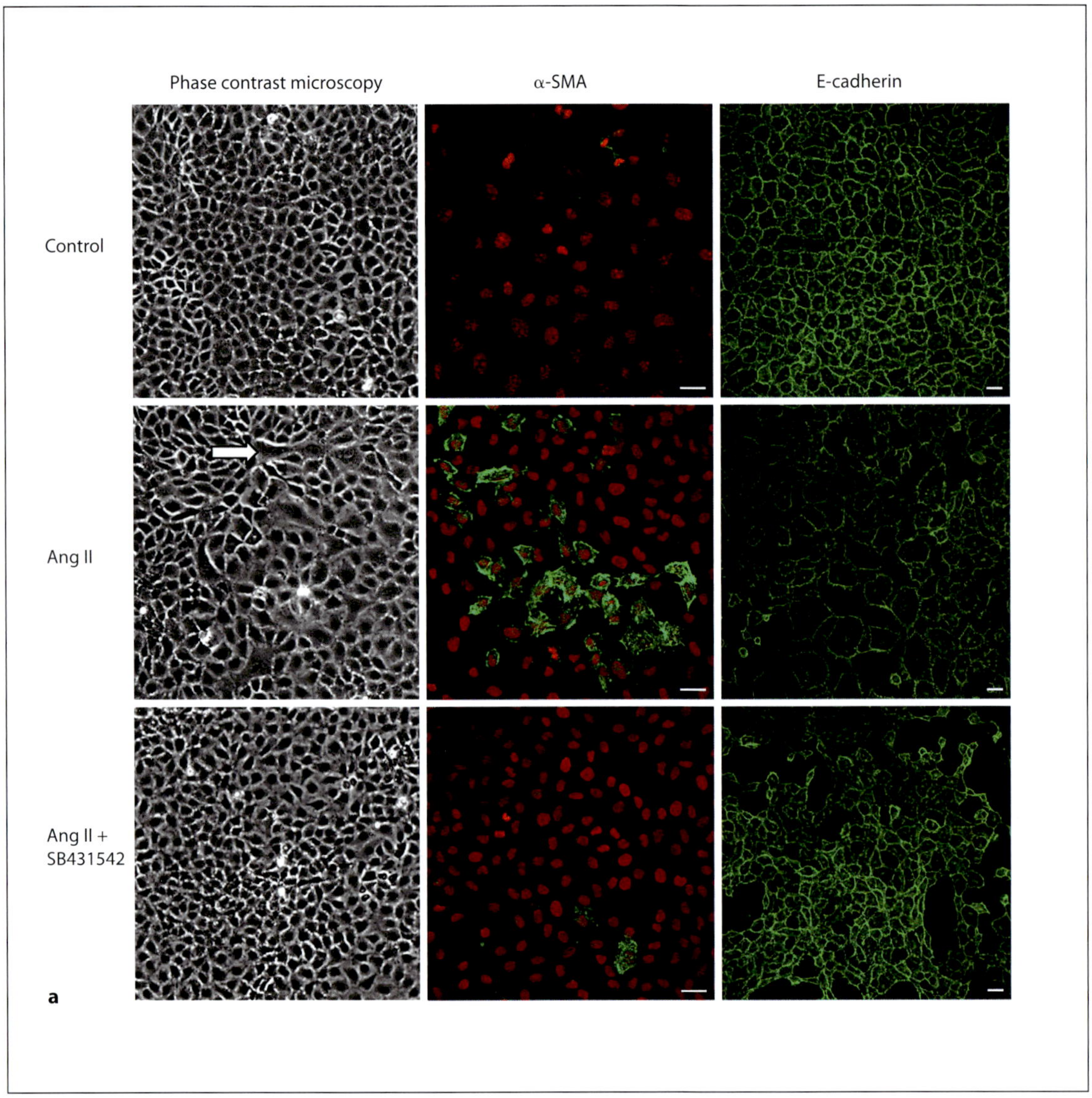

Phase contrast microscopy
α-SMA
E-cadherin
Control
Ang II
Ang II +
SB431542
a

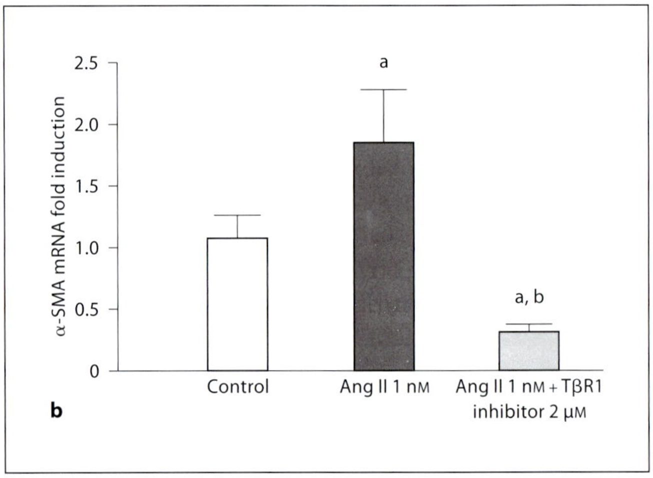

α-SMA mRNA fold induction
2.5
2.0
1.5
1.0
0.5
0
a
a, b
Control
Ang II 1 nM
Ang II 1 nM + TβR1
inhibitor 2 μM
b

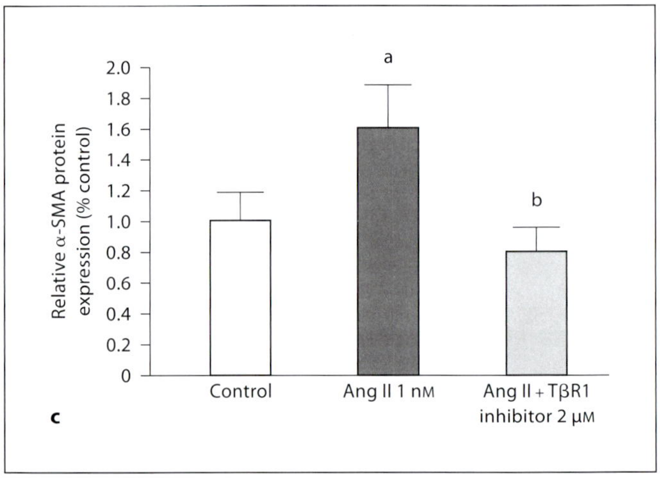

Relative α-SMA protein
expression (% control)
2.0
1.8
1.6
1.4
1.2
1.0
0.8
0.6
0.4
0.2
0
a
b
Control
Ang II 1 nM
Ang II + TβR1
inhibitor 2 μM
c

TGF and Ang-II-Dependent EMT

A number of factors have been suggested as potential initiators of EMT in different in vitro and in vivo models or settings. With a few key exceptions, each of these mediators require the induction of TGF-β_1 to complete the process of EMT [Yang et al., 2001; Lan, 2003; Liu, 2004]. Ang II is a potent stimulus for TGF-β_1 production in kidney cells in vitro [Border et al., 1997] and in vivo [Border et al., 1998]. The expression of TGF-β_1 is induced by Ang II at sites of ECM accumulation and renal injury [Wolf et al., 1993]. Ang II induces TGF-β_1 via an AT1 receptor-mediated pathway [Wolf et al., 1993], such that AT1 receptor blockade inhibits TGF-β_1 expression in Thy 1.1 nephritis [Peters et al., 1998] and other experimental models including cyclosporin nephropathy [Shihab et al., 1997], Heymann nephritis [Zoja et al., 1997] and spontaneously hypertensive rats [Ohta et al., 1994]. Treatment with an AT1 receptor antagonist also reduces urinary TGF-β_1 levels in type 2 diabetic patients with advanced kidney disease [Song et al., 2006].

There are also strong data linking Ang II and EMT. For example, exposure to elevated levels of Ang II leads to altered expression of genes associated with EMT including α-SMA, E-cadherin and TGF-β_1 [Carvajal et al., 2008]. At least in vitro, this EMT appears to occur via both TGF-β_1-dependent and -independent pathways [Carvajal et al., 2008]. For example, either a TGF-β_1-neutralizing antibody or the TGF-β type 1 receptor inhibitor, SB431542, is able to attenuate Ang-II-induced vimentin expression and changes in cellular morphology observed after 2 days in HK-2 cells [Carvajal et al., 2008] and Ang-II-induced changes in α-SMA and E-cadherin expression and cellular morphology at 3 days in NRK52-E cells (fig. 1). However, this protective effect is not observed at earlier time points suggesting that early changes induced by Ang II involve the activation of other pathways, including Smad2/3, extracellular signal-regulated kinase (ERK)1/2, p38- and mitogen-activated protein kinase (MAPK) [Carvajal et al., 2008]. Notably, this pattern is similar to that seen with EMT induced by advanced glycation end products (AGEs), whereby AGEs can activate Smad2/3 in renal cells at an early time point (5–30 min), prior to TGF-β_1 synthesis at 24 h via a receptor for AGEs (RAGE) and ERK/p38 MAPK-dependent pathway [Esteban et al., 2004]. Like Ang II, AGEs can also induce EMT and activate Smads at 24 h via the classic TGF-β_1-dependent pathway [Oldfield et al., 2001; Esteban et al., 2004].

The precise mechanism by which Ang II initiates and augments TGF-β signalling is a matter of ongoing research. Certainly, the expression of TGF-β isoforms is stimulated by Ang II, most likely via AT1-dependent activation of ERK1/2. However, in tubular cells, metabolites of Ang II, including Ang 1–7, may also promote EMT via activation of the Mas-1 receptor [Burns et al., 2010]. Finally, activation of many G-protein-coupled receptors may also trigger the transactivation of the TGF-β receptor [Burch et al., 2010]. Whether activation of the Mas-1 or AT receptors (both of which are G-protein-coupled receptors) also stimulates the TGF-β receptors is unclear. However, both can transactivate epidermal growth factor signalling, which is known itself to transactivate the TGF-β receptors.

Connective Tissue Growth Factor and Ang-II-Dependent EMT

Connective tissue growth factor (CTGF) is a downstream mediator of the actions of TGF-β_1 and its ability to induce EMT. In vitro studies have shown that treatment with Ang II also leads to increased CTGF expression in mouse tubular epithelial cells (MCT) [Ruiz-Ortega et al., 2003], human proximal tubule cells (HK-2) [Bolos et al., 2003], rat mesangial cells [Ruiz-Ortega et al., 2003] and human renal fibroblasts [Hussain et al., 2008] by both TGF-β_1-dependent [Ruiz-Ortega et al., 2003] and TGF-β_1-independent pathways [Rodriguez-Vita et al., 2005]. These findings are supported by in vivo studies in which CTGF expression is upregulated in the tubuli, glomeruli and renal arteries of Ang-II-infused rats [Ruiz-Ortega et al., 2003]. Both Ang II levels and CTGF gene expression are increased in the renal cortex and medullary tissues of aldosterone/salt-treated hypertensive rats [Fan et al., 2006]. Furthermore, the reduction in Ang II levels via ACE inhibition also decreases renal CTGF expression and fibrosis in the UUO model [Esteban et al., 2004] and in rats with immune complex nephritis [Ruiz-Ortega et al., 2003].

Ang II appears to directly induce CTGF expression via an AT1 receptor-mediated pathway [Ruiz-Ortega et al., 2003]. Blockade of the AT1 receptor attenuates increased CTGF expression in diabetes [Bolos et al., 2003], in the obstructed kidney of rats after UUO [Esteban et al., 2004], in mesangioproliferative glomerulonephritis [Liu et al., 2007], in aldosterone/salt-treated hypertensive rats [Fan et al., 2006] and in Ang-II-infused rats [Ruiz-Ortega et al., 2003]. By contrast, treatment with an AT2 receptor antagonist did not reduce CTGF expression or renal fibrosis [Ruiz-Ortega et al., 2003; Esteban et al., 2004].

Ang-II-induced EMT in human proximal tubular cells is also associated with increased expression of CTGF [Chen et al., 2006; Carvajal et al., 2008] which could subsequently be prevented by MAPK and Ras homolog gene family member A (RhoA) kinase (ROCK) inhibitors [Carvajal et al., 2008]. Similarly, blockade of either RhoA or its downstream target, ROCK, has been shown to inhibit EMT induced by TGF-β_1 [Bhowmick et al., 2001]. In a separate study, CTGF was shown to be an integral component of Ang-II-induced EMT as the CTGF blockade attenuated this process [Chen et al., 2006].

Oxidative Stress and Ang-II-Dependent EMT

Oxidative stress that leads to the formation of reactive oxygen species (ROS) is recognized as a key component in the development of progressive kidney disease. ROS are directly cytotoxic and upregulate inflammation and fibrosis. In addition, there is accumulating evidence that ROS is also able to promote EMT, possibly as a key downstream mediator of TGF-β_1 [Rhyu et al., 2005; Bondi et al., 2010]. Oxidative stress is increased in a range of kidney diseases. For example, in the obstructed kidney of experimental rats after UUO, superoxide dismutase activity is decreased and the production of hydroxyl radicals and O_2- are increased [Manucha et al., 2005]. Interestingly, pre-treatment with an AT1 receptor blocker reduced ROS and increased superoxide dismutase activity in the obstructed kidney, suggesting that Ang II has an important role in ROS generation in this setting [Manucha et al., 2005]. The induction of oxidative stress by Ang II may play a role in Ang-II-induced EMT. Certainly, NADPH oxidase is directly activated by Ang II following activation of the AT1 receptor [Griendling et al., 2000]. Inhibition of ROS with antioxidants blocked EMT in these cells [Rhyu et al., 2005]. In so far as the activation of ROS and NADP are partially independent of TGF-β_1, it is likely that the induction of ROS represents one important way in which common mediators of EMT (such as TGF-β_1, Ang II, AGEs) synergize to augment and sustain phenotypic transition of tubular cells.

RhoA Signalling and Ang-II-Dependent EMT

RhoA is a GTPase that is required for cytoskeletal reorganization, including the formation of stress fibres, as well as the induction of genes and other pathways required for mesenchymal phenotypic transition [Masszi et al., 2003]. RhoA activates ROCK (p160), a serine/threonine-specific protein kinase, which triggers a downstream cascade that results in the wholesale re-organization of the actin cytoskeleton of the cell and the instability of adherens junctions [Bhowmick et al., 2001; Bolos et al., 2003]. ROCK also phosphorylates other target proteins to regulate a number of different cellular functions, including kinase activity, contractile function, contraction proliferation, cell division and remodelling. The RhoA/ROCK pathway plays a major role in EMT. TGF-β_1 and CTGF induce RhoA and ROCK phosphorylation [Kolosionek et al., 2009]. Ang II is a potent activator of the Rho/ROCK pathway. Moreover, blockade of either RhoA or its downstream target, ROCK, inhibits EMT induced by Ang II [Carvajal et al., 2008].

AGEs and Ang-II-Dependent EMT

AGEs are another common mediator of progressive kidney disease. All forms of CKD are associated with high circulating and tissue levels of AGEs, which have a range of pathological effects in the kidney and in particular in the proximal tubule cells, the main site for processing and re-absorption of AGEs [Asano et al., 2002]. AGE-modified proteins are able to directly induce EMT via the induction and activation of RAGE and subsequently via activation of TGF-β_1 [Oldfield et al., 2001], as well as downstream signalling through Smad2/3 [Esteban et al., 2004]. More recently, it has been appreciated that AGEs are able to stimulate EMT, independently of TGF-β_1, possibly via activation of ERK1/2 MAPK-dependent signalling [Esteban et al., 2004], following activation of RAGE [Oldfield et al., 2001; Esteban et al., 2004]. Interactions between the RAS and the AGE/RAGE axis has been demonstrated in a number of studies using both cell culture and experimental models. For example, in experimental animal studies, the formation and accumulation of serum and tissue AGEs is observed following an Ang II infusion [Thomas et al., 2005]. Equally, blockade of the RAS is able to reduce AGE accumulation, particularly in the kidney [Lassila et al., 2004]. Indeed, many of their activities may overlap. For example, Fan and colleagues [2001] examined the effect of AGEs on the induction of collagen synthesis in NRK52-E cells. While they found that AGEs increased collagen production in both a dose- and time-dependent manner, this effect could be inhibited by the ACE inhibitor captopril. It was suggested that blockade of the RAS may have reduced the expression of RAGE and the activity of its downstream mediators

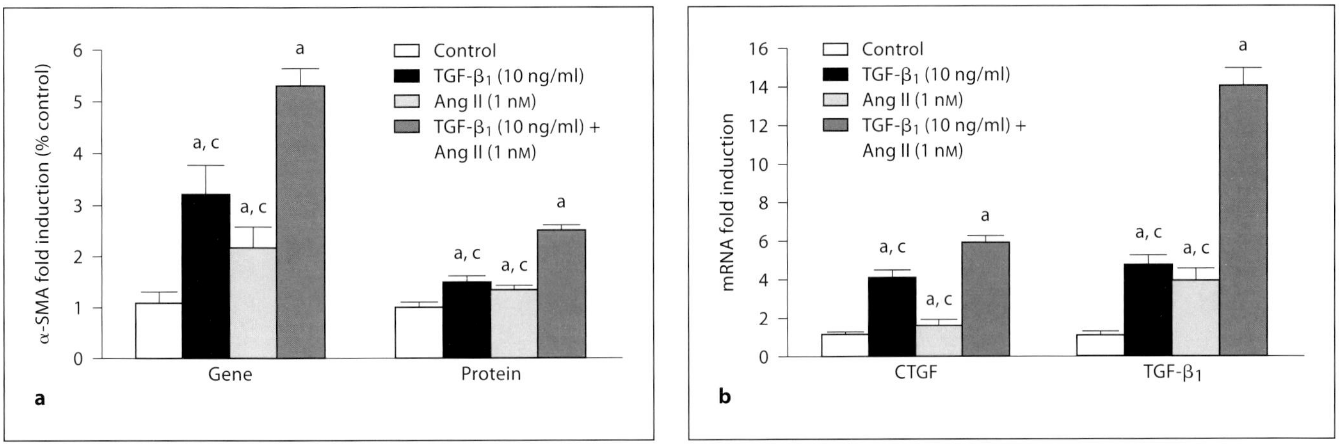

Fig. 2. NRK52-E cells were incubated in control media or in the presence of recombinant human TGF-β_1 (10 ng/ml), Ang II (1 nM) or the combination of recombinant human TGF-β_1 and Ang II (1 nM) for 3 days. **a** α-SMA gene and protein expression as measured by real-time RT-PCR and in-cell Western analysis, respectively. **b** Gene expression of the pro-fibrotic growth factors CTGF and TGF-β_1 compared with untreated control cells. The control group was arbitrarily assigned a value of 1. Each bar represents the mean ± SEM for 6 samples per group. [a] $p < 0.05$ versus control; [c] $p < 0.05$ versus Ang II + TGF-β_1.

including JAK2-STAT1/STAT3 [Fan et al., 2001]. The overlapping activities of the RAS and AGEs are further illustrated by the comparable effects of inhibition of AGE formation and blockade of the RAS in experimental diabetes [Forbes et al., 2002]. Finally, inhibition of advanced glycation may also prevent renal injury in an Ang-II-dependent model. For example, renal injury can be attenuated following treatment with an inhibitor of AGE formation, ALT-946, in a renin-overexpressing diabetic rat [Wilkinson-Berka et al., 2002]. Equally, we have shown that renal damage associated with an angiotensin infusion can be attenuated with the AGE inhibitor pyridoxamine [Thomas et al., 2005].

Synergism in the Development and Progression of EMT

The RAS is not the only mediator of EMT in the kidney. In chronic renal disease it is likely that a number of different components contribute to the accumulation of myofibroblasts and subsequent interstitial fibrosis. The majority of these mediators result in the induction of TGF-β_1 and the activation of common downstream pathways. Consequently, a number of different initiators of EMT are able to act in a synergistic manner to promote the development and progression of this phenotypic transition. For example, Ang II increases the ability of TGF-β_1 to induce EMT, such that combining Ang II (1 M) and TGF-β_1 (10 ng/ml) results in enhanced morphological changes of EMT and had an additive effect on increasing the gene expression of α-SMA and CTGF, but led to a synergistic increase in TGF-β_1 gene expression (fig. 2). Another example of this is provided by Yang and colleagues [2002] who demonstrated that Ang II (1 nM to 1 μM) treatment alone was not sufficient to induce α-SMA expression in human proximal tubular epithelial cells, but when used in combination with TGF-β_1 (0.5 ng/ml), Ang II potentiated the ability of TGF-β_1 to induce α-SMA and EMT.

A number of different actions appear to contribute to the observed synergism between Ang II and other mediators of EMT. Certainly, the induction of TGF-β_1 and CTGF expression by Ang II (as detailed above) appears to be important. In addition, the RAS is also able to enhance the downstream TGF-β_1 signaling cascade as well as adding alternative inputs to it through transactivation of the TGF receptor. This synergism has important implications in disease states, in which different pathogenic stimuli may result in the same phenomenon, or combine to accelerate pathological lesions. Equally, RAS blockade may exert beneficial effects across a diverse range of conditions.

The Future of RAS Blockade

The strong association between adverse outcomes and escape afforded from RAS blockade provides a strong rationale for specifically targeting escape as part of any vasculo-protective strategy. Yet, despite the use of ACE inhibitors in adequate doses to achieve maximal suppression of circulating ACE activity, their ability to suppress plasma Ang II and aldosterone levels in the clinical setting is weak, variable and unsustained, often only lasting for a few hours after each dose, with levels rapidly returning to pre-treatment levels. Indeed, there is little correlation between ACE inhibition and achieved Ang II and aldosterone levels. This negative feedback phenomenon is known as ACE escape and is intrinsically antagonistic to the therapeutic desire to suppress Ang-II-mediated tissue damage. Indeed, it may be counterproductive. In a third to a half of all patients treated with ACE inhibitors, there is a paradoxical elevation in aldosterone concentrations after 12 months of treatment. While there is no doubt that conventional RAS blockade has important organ-protective benefits for many individuals, it is increasingly apparent that better blockade can be achieved by rational therapies that seek to target feedback in the RAS and with this synergism achieve superior prevention of renal complications. Escape has been attributed to renin production, which is exponentially increased in response to ACE inhibition, AT1 receptor blockade and especially their combination. Consequently, the development of selective renin inhibitors, such as aliskiren, now offers a practical alternative means to offset compensatory mechanisms that allow the body to overcome, or 'escape' from, treatment effects. It is likely that in the future such targeted combinations will eventually achieve the long-term efficacy that has been expected of RAS blockade for so long.

References

Arendshorst, W.J., K. Brannstrom, X. Ruan (1999) Actions of angiotensin II on the renal microvasculature. J Am Soc Nephrol *10(suppl 11):* S149–S161.

Asano, M., Y. Fujita, Y. Ueda, D. Suzuki, T. Miyata, H. Sakai, A. Saito (2002) Renal proximal tubular metabolism of protein-linked pentosidine, an advanced glycation end product. Nephron *91:* 688–694.

Bhowmick, N.A., M. Ghiassi, A. Bakin, M. Aakre, C.A. Lundquist, M.E. Engel, C.L. Arteaga, H.L. Moses (2001) Transforming growth factor-beta1 mediates epithelial to mesenchymal transdifferentiation through a RhoA-dependent mechanism. Mol Biol Cell *12:* 27–36.

Bolos, V., H. Peinado, M.A. Perez-Moreno, M.F. Fraga, M. Esteller, A. Cano (2003) The transcription factor Slug represses E-cadherin expression and induces epithelial to mesenchymal transitions: a comparison with Snail and E47 repressors. J Cell Sci *116:* 499–511.

Bondi, C.D., N. Manickam, D.Y. Lee, K. Block, Y. Gorin, H.E. Abboud, J.L. Barnes (2010) NAD(P)H oxidase mediates TGF-beta1-induced activation of kidney myofibroblasts. J Am Soc Nephrol *21:* 93–102.

Border, W., A.N.A. Noble (1997) TGF-beta in kidney fibrosis: a target for gene therapy. Kidney Int *51:* 1388–1396.

Border, W., A.N.A. Noble (1998) Interactions of transforming growth factor-beta and angiotensin II in renal fibrosis. Hypertension *31:* 181–188.

Bravo, J., Y. Quiroz, H. Pons, G. Parra, J. Herrera-Acosta, R.J. Johnson, B. Rodriguez-Iturbe (2003) Vimentin and heat shock protein expression are induced in the kidney by angiotensin and by nitric oxide inhibition. Kidney Int Suppl *86:* S46–S51.

Burch, M.L., M.L. Ballinger, S.N. Yang, R. Getachew, C. Itman, K. Loveland, N. Osman, P.J. Little (2010) Thrombin stimulation of proteoglycan synthesis in vascular smooth muscle is mediated by PAR-1 transactivation of the transforming growth factor beta type I receptor. J Biol Chem *285:* 26798–26805.

Burns, W.C., E. Velkoska, R.G. Dean, L.M. Burrell, M.C. Thomas (2010) Angiotensin II mediates epithelial-to-mesenchymal transformation in tubular cells by Ang1-7/Mas-1 dependent pathways. Am J Physiol Renal Physiol, Epub ahead of print.

Carvajal, G., J. Rodriguez-Vita, R. Rodrigues-Diez, E. Sanchez-Lopez, M. Ruperez, C. Cartier, V. Esteban, A. Ortiz, J. Egido, S.A. Mezzano, M. Ruiz-Ortega (2008) Angiotensin II activates the Smad pathway during epithelial mesenchymal transdifferentiation. Kidney Int *74:* 585–595.

Chen, L., B.C. Liu, X.L. Zhang, J.D. Zhang, H. Liu, M.X. Li (2006) Influence of connective tissue growth factor antisense oligonucleotide on angiotensin II-induced epithelial mesenchymal transition in HK2 cells. Acta Pharmacol Sin *27:* 1029–1036.

Cheng, S., A.S. Pollock, R. Mahimkar, J.L. Olson, D.H. Lovett (2006) Matrix metalloproteinase 2 and basement membrane integrity: a unifying mechanism for progressive renal injury. FASEB J *20:* 1898–1900.

Counihan, N.A., L.M. Daniel, J. Chojnacki, D.A. Anderson (2006) Infrared fluorescent immunofocus assay (IR-FIFA) for the quantitation of non-cytopathic and minimally cytopathic viruses. J Virol Methods *133:* 62–69.

Dzau, V.J. (1988) Circulating versus local renin-angiotensin system in cardiovascular homeostasis. Circulation *77:* I4–I13.

Egido, J. (1996) Vasoactive hormones and renal sclerosis. Kidney Int *49:* 578–597.

English, V., L. Cassis (1999) Facilitation of sympathetic neurotransmission contributes to angiotensin regulation of body weight. J Neural Transm *106:* 631–644.

Erdos, E.G. (1976) Conversion of angiotensin I to angiotensin II. Am J Med *60:* 749–759.

Esteban, V., O. Lorenzo, M. Ruperez, Y. Suzuki, S. Mezzano, J. Blanco, M. Kretzler, T. Sugaya, J. Egido, M. Ruiz-Ortega (2004) Angiotensin II, via AT1 and AT2 receptors and NF-kappaB pathway, regulates the inflammatory response in unilateral ureteral obstruction. J Am Soc Nephrol *15:* 1514–1529.

Fan, Y.Y., R. Baba, Y. Nagai, A. Miyatake, N. Hosomi, S. Kimura, G.P. Sun, M. Kohno, M. Fujita, Y. Abe, A. Nishiyama (2006) Augmentation of intrarenal angiotensin II levels in uninephrectomized aldosterone/salt-treated hypertensive rats; renoprotective effects of an ultrahigh dose of olmesartan. Hypertens Res *29:* 169–178.

Fan, J.M., X.R. Huang, Y.Y. Ng, D.J. Nikolic-Paterson, W. Mu, R.C. Atkins, H.Y. Lan (2001) Interleukin-1 induces tubular epithelial-myofibroblast transdifferentiation through a transforming growth factor-beta1-dependent mechanism in vitro. Am J Kidney Dis *37:* 820–831.

Forbes, J.M., M.E. Cooper, V. Thallas, W.C. Burns, M.C. Thomas, G.C. Brammar, F. Lee, S.L. Grant, L.M. Burrell, G. Jerums, T.M. Osicka (2002) Reduction of the accumulation of advanced glycation end products by ACE inhibition in experimental diabetic nephropathy. Diabetes *51:* 3274–3282.

Fujisawa, T., H. Ikegami, Y. Kawaguchi, Y. Hamada, H. Ueda, M. Shintani, M. Fukuda, T. Ogihara (1998) Meta-analysis of association of insertion/deletion polymorphism of angiotensin I-converting enzyme gene with diabetic nephropathy and retinopathy. Diabetologia *41:* 47–53.

Garber, S.L., Y. Mirochnik, S.S. Desai, J.A. Arruda, G. Dunea (1998) Angiotensin-converting enzyme inhibition reduces the effect of bromoethylamine-induced papillary necrosis and renal fibrosis. J Am Soc Nephrol *9:* 1052–1059.

Gilbert, R.E., L.L. Wu, D.J. Kelly, A. Cox, J.L. Wilkinson-Berka, C.I. Johnston, M.E. Cooper (1999) Pathological expression of renin and angiotensin II in the renal tubule after subtotal nephrectomy. Implications for the pathogenesis of tubulointerstitial fibrosis. Am J Pathol *155:* 429–440.

Griendling, K.K., D. Sorescu, M. Ushio-Fukai (2000) NAD(P)H oxidase: role in cardiovascular biology and disease. Circ Res *86:* 494–501.

Hisada, Y., T. Sugaya, M. Yamanouchi, H. Uchida, H. Fujimura, H. Sakurai, A. Fukamizu, K. Murakami (1999) Angiotensin II plays a pathogenic role in immune-mediated renal injury in mice. J Clin Invest *103:* 627–635.

Husain, A., M. Li, R.M. Graham (2003) Do studies with ACE N- and C-domain-selective inhibitors provide evidence for a non-ACE, non-chymase angiotensin II-forming pathway? Circ Res *93:* 91–93.

Hussain, A., A.W. Wyatt, K. Wang, M. Bhandaru, R. Biswas, D. Avram, M. Foller, R. Rexhepaj, B. Friedrich, S. Ullrich, G. Muller, D. Kuhl, T. Risler, F. Lang (2008) SGK1-dependent upregulation of connective tissue growth factor by angiotensin II. Kidney Blood Press Res *31:* 80–86.

Ishidoya, S., J. Morrissey, R. McCracken, A. Reyes, S. Klahr (1995) Angiotensin II receptor antagonist ameliorates renal tubulointerstitial fibrosis caused by unilateral ureteral obstruction. Kidney Int *47:* 1285–1294.

Iwano, M., D. Plieth, T.M. Danoff, C. Xue, H. Okada, E.G. Neilson (2002) Evidence that fibroblasts derive from epithelium during tissue fibrosis. J Clin Invest *110:* 341–350.

Johnson, R.J., C.E. Alpers, A. Yoshimura, D. Lombardi, P. Pritzl, J. Floege, S.M. Schwartz (1992) Renal injury from angiotensin II-mediated hypertension. Hypertension *19:* 464–474.

Kagami, S., W.A. Border, D.E. Miller, N.A. Noble (1994) Angiotensin II stimulates extracellular matrix protein synthesis through induction of transforming growth factor-beta expression in rat glomerular mesangial cells. J Clin Invest *93:* 2431–2437.

Kalluri, R.E., G. Neilson (2003) Epithelial-mesenchymal transition and its implications for fibrosis. J Clin Invest *112:* 1776–1784.

Kelly, D.J., J.L. Wilkinson-Berka, T.J. Allen, M.E. Cooper, S.L. Skinner (1998) A new model of diabetic nephropathy with progressive renal impairment in the transgenic (mRen-2)27 rat (TGR). Kidney Int *54:* 343–352.

Klahr, S., J. Morrissey (1998) Angiotensin II and gene expression in the kidney. Am J Kidney Dis *31:* 171–176.

Kokkonen, J.O., K.A. Lindstedt, P.T. Kovanen (2003). Role for chymase in heart failure: angiotensin II-dependent or -independent mechanisms? Circulation *107:* 2522–2524.

Kolosionek, E., R. Savai, H.A. Ghofrani, N. Weissmann, A. Guenther, F. Grimminger, W. Seeger, G.A. Banat, R.T. Schermuly, S.S. Pullamsetti (2009) Expression and activity of phosphodiesterase isoforms during epithelial mesenchymal transition: the role of phosphodiesterase 4. Mol Biol Cell *20:* 4751–4765.

Lafayette, R.A. (2000) How does knocking out angiotensin II activity reduce renal injury in mice? Am J Kidney Dis *35:* 166–172.

Lan, H.Y. (2003) Tubular epithelial-myofibroblast transdifferentiation mechanisms in proximal tubule cells. Curr Opin Nephrol Hypertens *12:* 25–29.

Lassila, M., M.E. Cooper, K. Jandeleit-Dahm (2004) Antiproteinuric effect of RAS blockade: new mechanisms. Curr Hypertens Rep *6:* 383–392.

Lavoie, J. L.C., D. Sigmund (2003) Minireview: overview of the renin-angiotensin system – an endocrine and paracrine system. Endocrinology *144:* 2179–2183.

Li, J., X. Qu, J.F. Bertram (2009) Endothelial-myofibroblast transition contributes to the early development of diabetic renal interstitial fibrosis in streptozotocin-induced diabetic mice. Am J Pathol *175:* 1380–1388.

Liu, N., S. Shimizu, T. Ito-Ihara, K. Takagi, T. Kita, T. Ono (2007) Angiotensin II receptor blockade ameliorates mesangioproliferative glomerulonephritis in rats through suppression of CTGF and PAI-1, independently of the coagulation system. Nephron Exp Nephrol *105:* e65–e74.

Liu, Y. (2004) Epithelial to mesenchymal transition in renal fibrogenesis: pathologic significance, molecular mechanism, and therapeutic intervention. J Am Soc Nephrol *15:* 1–12.

Manucha, W., L. Carrizo, C. Ruete, H. Molina, P. Valles (2005) Angiotensin II type I antagonist on oxidative stress and heat shock protein 70 (HSP 70) expression in obstructive nephropathy. Cell Mol Biol (Noisy-le-grand) *51:* 547–555.

Masszi, A., C. Di Ciano, G. Sirokmany, W.T. Arthur, O.D. Rotstein, J. Wang, C.A. McCulloch, L. Rosivall, I. Mucsi, A. Kapus (2003) Central role for Rho in TGF-beta1-induced alpha-smooth muscle actin expression during epithelial-mesenchymal transition. Am J Physiol Renal Physiol *284:* F911–F924.

McLennan, S.V., D.J. Kelly, A.J. Cox, Z. Cao, J.G. Lyons, D.K. Yue, R.E. Gilbert (2002) Decreased matrix degradation in diabetic nephropathy: effects of ACE inhibition on the expression and activities of matrix metalloproteinases. Diabetologia *45:* 268–275.

Mezzano, S.A., M. Ruiz-Ortega, J. Egido (2001) Angiotensin II and renal fibrosis. Hypertension *38:* 635–638.

Morrissey, J., J.S. Klahr (1999) Effect of AT2 receptor blockade on the pathogenesis of renal fibrosis. Am J Physiol *276:* F39–F45.

Nagahama, T., K. Hayashi, Y. Ozawa, T. Takenaka, T. Saruta (2000) Role of protein kinase C in angiotensin II-induced constriction of renal microvessels. Kidney Int *57:* 215–223.

Navar, L.G., E.W. Inscho, S.A. Majid, J.D. Imig, L.M. Harrison-Bernard, K.D. Mitchell (1996) Paracrine regulation of the renal microcirculation. Physiol Rev *76:* 425–536.

Nishiyama, A., D.M. Seth, L.G. Navar (2002) Renal interstitial fluid concentrations of angiotensins I and II in anesthetized rats. Hypertension *39:* 129–134.

Ohta, K., S. Kim, A. Hamaguchi, T. Yukimura, K. Miura, K. Takaori, H. Iwao (1994) Role of angiotensin II in extracellular matrix and transforming growth factor-beta 1 expression in hypertensive rats. Eur J Pharmacol *269:* 115–119.

Oldfield, M.D., L.A. Bach, J.M. Forbes, D. Nikolic-Paterson, A. McRobert, V. Thallas, R.C. Atkins, T. Osicka, G. Jerums, M.E. Cooper (2001) Advanced glycation end products cause epithelial-myofibroblast transdifferentiation via the receptor for advanced glycation end products (RAGE). J Clin Invest *108:* 1853–1863.

Pagtalunan, M.E., J.L. Olson, T.W. Meyer (2000) Contribution of angiotensin II to late renal injury after acute ischemia. J Am Soc Nephrol *11:* 1278–1286.

Peters, H., W.A. Border, N.A. Noble (1998) Targeting TGF-beta overexpression in renal disease: maximizing the antifibrotic action of angiotensin II blockade. Kidney Int *54:* 1570–1580.

Pichler, R.H., N. Franceschini, B.A. Young, C. Hugo, T.F. Andoh, E.A. Burdmann, S.J. Shankland, C.E. Alpers, W.M. Bennett, W.G. Couser, et al. (1995) Pathogenesis of cyclosporine nephropathy: roles of angiotensin II and osteopontin. J Am Soc Nephrol *6:* 1186–1196.

Rastaldi, M.P., F. Ferrario, L. Giardino, G. Dell'Antonio, C. Grillo, P. Grillo, F. Strutz, G.A. Muller, G. Colasanti, G. D'Amico (2002) Epithelial-mesenchymal transition of tubular epithelial cells in human renal biopsies. Kidney Int *62:* 137–146.

Rhyu, D.Y., Y. Yang, H. Ha, G.T. Lee, J.S. Song, S.T. Uh, H.B. Lee (2005) Role of reactive oxygen species in TGF-beta1-induced mitogen-activated protein kinase activation and epithelial-mesenchymal transition in renal tubular epithelial cells. J Am Soc Nephrol *16:* 667–675.

Rodrigues-Diez, R., G. Carvajal-Gonzalez, E. Sanchez-Lopez, J. Rodriguez-Vita, R. Rodrigues Diez, R. Selgas, A. Ortiz, J. Egido, S. Mezzano, M. Ruiz-Ortega (2008) Pharmacological modulation of epithelial mesenchymal transition caused by angiotensin II. Role of ROCK and MAPK pathways. Pharm Res *25:* 2447–2461.

Rodriguez-Vita, J., E. Sanchez-Lopez, V. Esteban, M. Ruperez, J. Egido, M. Ruiz-Ortega (2005) Angiotensin II activates the Smad pathway in vascular smooth muscle cells by a transforming growth factor-beta-independent mechanism. Circulation *111:* 2509–2517.

Ruiz-Ortega, M., M.J. Egido (1997) Angiotensin II modulates cell growth-related events and synthesis of matrix proteins in renal interstitial fibroblasts. Kidney Int *52:* 1497–1510.

Ruiz-Ortega, M., O. Lorenzo, M. Ruperez, S. Konig, B. Wittig, J. Egido (2000) Angiotensin II activates nuclear transcription factor kappaB through AT(1) and AT(2) in vascular smooth muscle cells: molecular mechanisms. Circ Res *86:* 1266–1272.

Ruiz-Ortega, M., M. Ruperez, V. Esteban, J. Egido (2003) Molecular mechanisms of angiotensin II-induced vascular injury. Curr Hypertens Rep *5:* 73–79.

Sadoshima, J. (2000) Cytokine actions of angiotensin II. Circ Res *86:* 1187–1189.

Schanstra, J.P., E. Neau, P. Drogoz, M.A. Arevalo Gomez, J.M. Lopez Novoa, D. Calise, C. Pecher, M. Bader, J.P. Girolami, J.L. Bascands (2002) In vivo bradykinin B2 receptor activation reduces renal fibrosis. J Clin Invest *110:* 371–379.

Seshiah, P.N., D.S. Weber, P. Rocic, L. Valppu, Y. Taniyama, K.K. Griendling (2002) Angiotensin II stimulation of NAD(P)H oxidase activity: upstream mediators. Circ Res *91:* 406–413.

Shihab, F.S., W.M. Bennett, A.M. Tanner, T.F. Andoh (1997) Angiotensin II blockade decreases TGF-beta1 and matrix proteins in cyclosporine nephropathy. Kidney Int *52:* 660–673.

Shirazi, M., A. Noorafshan, M.A. Bahri, N. Tanideh (2007) Captopril reduces interstitial renal fibrosis and preserves more normal renal tubules in neonatal dogs with partial urethral obstruction: a preliminary study. Urol Int *78:* 173–177.

Singh, R., N. Alavi, A.K. Singh, D.J. Leehey (1999) Role of angiotensin II in glucose-induced inhibition of mesangial matrix degradation. Diabetes *48:* 2066–2073.

Song, J. (2007) EMT or apoptosis: a decision for TGF-beta. Cell Res *17:* 289–290.

Song, J.H., S.H. Cha, H.J. Lee, S.W. Lee, G.H. Park, M.J. Kim (2006) Effect of low-dose dual blockade of renin-angiotensin system on urinary TGF-beta in type 2 diabetic patients with advanced kidney disease. Nephrol Dial Transplant *21:* 683–689.

Strutz, F., G.A. Muller, E.G. Neilson (1996) Transdifferentiation: a new angle on renal fibrosis. Exp Nephrol *4:* 267–270.

Thomas, M.C., C. Tikellis, W.M. Burns, K. Bialkowski, Z. Cao, M.T. Coughlan, K. Jandeleit-Dahm, M.E. Cooper, J.M. Forbes (2005). Interactions between renin angiotensin system and advanced glycation in the kidney. J Am Soc Nephrol *16:* 2976–2984.

Touyz, R.M., X. Chen, F. Tabet, G. Yao, G. He, M.T. Quinn, P.J. Pagano, E.L. Schiffrin (2002) Expression of a functionally active gp91phox-containing neutrophil-type NAD(P)H oxidase in smooth muscle cells from human resistance arteries: regulation by angiotensin II. Circ Res *90:* 1205–1213.

Wilkinson-Berka, J.L., D.J. Kelly, S.M. Koerner, K. Jaworski, B. Davis, V. Thallas, M.E. Cooper (2002) ALT-946 and aminoguanidine, inhibitors of advanced glycation, improve severe nephropathy in the diabetic transgenic (mREN-2)27 rat. Diabetes *51:* 3283–3289.

Wolf, G. (2001) Angiotensin II as a renal growth factor. Contrib Nephrol 92–110.

Wolf, G., E. Mueller, R.A. Stahl, F.N. Ziyadeh (1993) Angiotensin II-induced hypertrophy of cultured murine proximal tubular cells is mediated by endogenous transforming growth factor-beta. J Clin Invest *92:* 1366–1372.

Wolf, G.E., G. Neilson (1996) From converting enzyme inhibition to angiotensin II receptor blockade: new insight on angiotensin II receptor subtypes in the kidney. Exp Nephrol *4(suppl 1):* 8–19.

Wolf, G.F., N. Ziyadeh (1997) Renal tubular hypertrophy induced by angiotensin II. Semin Nephrol *17:* 448–454.

Yang, J., C. Dai, Y. Liu (2002) Hepatocyte growth factor gene therapy and angiotensin II blockade synergistically attenuate renal interstitial fibrosis in mice. J Am Soc Nephrol *13:* 2464–2477.

Yang, J., J.Y. Liu (2001) Dissection of key events in tubular epithelial to myofibroblast transition and its implications in renal interstitial fibrosis. Am J Pathol *159:* 1465–1475.

Yoo, K.H., B.A. Thornhill, J.T. Wolstenholme, R.L. Chevalier (1998) Tissue-specific regulation of growth factors and clusterin by angiotensin II. Am J Hypertens *11:* 715–722.

Yu, X.Q., L.L. Wu, X.R. Huang, N. Yang, R.E. Gilbert, M.E. Cooper, R.J. Johnson, K.N. Lai, H.Y. Lan (2000) Osteopontin expression in progressive renal injury in remnant kidney: role of angiotensin II. Kidney Int *58:* 1469–1480.

Zatz, R., B.R. Dunn, T.W. Meyer, S. Anderson, H.G. Rennke, B.M. Brenner (1986) Prevention of diabetic glomerulopathy by pharmacological amelioration of glomerular capillary hypertension. J Clin Invest *77:* 1925–1930.

Zimmerman, M.C., E. Lazartigues, J.A. Lang, P. Sinnayah, I.M. Ahmad, D.R. Spitz, R.L. Davisson (2002) Superoxide mediates the actions of angiotensin II in the central nervous system. Circ Res *91:* 1038–1045.

Zoja, C., R. Donadelli, D. Corna, D. Testa, D. Facchinetti, R. Maffi, E. Luzzana, V. Colosio, T. Bertani, G. Remuzzi (1997) The renoprotective properties of angiotensin-converting enzyme inhibitors in a chronic model of membranous nephropathy are solely due to the inhibition of angiotensin II: evidence based on comparative studies with a receptor antagonist. Am J Kidney Dis *29:* 254–264.

Cells
Tissues
Organs

Cells Tissues Organs 2011;193:85–97
DOI: 10.1159/000320360

Published online: November 3, 2010

Growth Factors in Induction of Epithelial-Mesenchymal Transition and Metastasis

Nur Akmarina B.M. Said[a, b] Elizabeth D. Williams[a]

[a]Centre for Cancer Research, Monash Institute of Medical Research, Monash University, Melbourne, Vic., Australia;
[b]University of Malaya, Kuala Lumpur, Malaysia

Key Words
Epithelial-mesenchymal transition · Growth factor · Cancer

Abstract
Epithelial to mesenchymal transition (EMT) has gained widespread acceptance over recent years as a mechanism by which normally sessile epithelial tumour cells can move away from the primary tumour and metastasize. This review article examines the role of a number of growth factors in inducing EMT, and the reverse process mesenchymal to epithelial transition. Unique and common intracellular signalling pathways are highlighted. A comprehensive understanding of the regulation of EMT will be critical in manipulating this process to develop novel anti-metastasis therapies.

Introduction

Epithelial to mesenchymal transition (EMT) is a process well recognized in embryological development. During the gastrulation process in the early stage of embryogenesis, EMT gives rise to the formation of migratory mesenchymes from pre-gastrulation blastula cells with epithelial morphology to generate mesoderm and endoderm in the majority of metazoans [Nakaya and Sheng, 2008; Nakaya et al., 2011].

Abbreviations used in this paper

ECM	extracellular matrix
EMT	epithelial to mesenchymal transition
EGF	epidermal growth factor
EGFR	epidermal growth factor receptor
FGF	fibroblast growth factor
FGFR	fibroblast growth factor receptor
GSK3β	glycogen synthase kinase-3β
Hey1	hairy/enhancer-of-split-related transcriptional repressor
HGF	hepatocyte growth factor
HH	hedgehog
Id	inhibitor of differentiation
IGF	insulin-like growth factor
IGF-IR	insulin-like growth factor-I receptor
ILK	integrin-linked kinase
LEF	lymphoid enhancer-binding factor
MET	mesenchymal to epithelial transition
MMP	matrix metalloproteinase
MAPK	mitogen-activated protein kinase
PDGF	platelet-derived growth factor
PI3K	phosphatidylinositol 3-kinase
PTCH	patched
STAT3	signal transducer and activator of transcription 3
TCF	T-cell factor
TGF-β	transforming growth factor-β
TGF-βR	transforming growth factor-β receptor

N.A.B.M.S. and E.D.W. contributed equally to this article.

KARGER

Fax +41 61 306 12 34
E-Mail karger@karger.ch
www.karger.com

1422–6405/11/1932–0085$38.00/0

Accessible online at:
www.karger.com/cto

Dr. Elizabeth D. Williams, Cancer Metastasis Laboratory, Centre for Cancer Research
Monash Institute of Medical Research, Monash University
Monash Medical Centre, 246 Clayton Rd., Clayton VIC 3168 (Australia)
Tel. +61 3 9594 7164, Fax +61 3 9594 7252
E-Mail Elizabeth.Williams@med.monash.edu.au

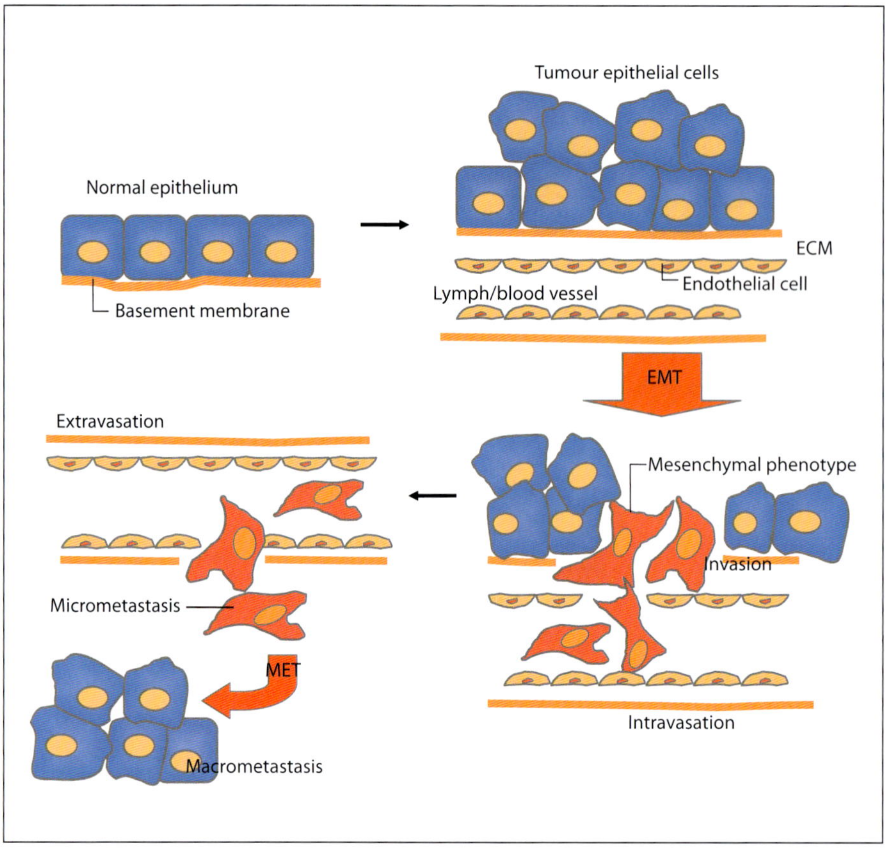

Fig. 1. Schematic representation of epithelial cells undergoing EMT and MET. In EMT, the loss of epithelial differentiation and acquisition of mesenchymal phenotype endow the tumour cells with tumour migratory and invasive capabilities to invade the basement membranes and intravasate into circulation. The reverse process, MET, is implicated in secondary tumour growth where the mesenchymal-like cells re-adopt several epithelial properties to enable colonization at secondary sites.

This transition, which occurs as a result of interplay between a number of growth factors and polypeptides, is also observed in tissue injury and carcinoma metastasis [Kalluri and Weinberg, 2009]. In metastasis, the loss of tumour epithelial cell differentiation and acquisition of mesenchymal phenotype bestow the cell with motile and invasive capabilities to travel to distant sites (fig. 1). Epithelial cells are characterized by apicobasal polarity and lateral adherence to their neighbours. The adhesion sites to extracellular matrix (ECM) are focused to the basal lamina, and cytokeratins are the main intermediate filaments. In contrast, mesenchymal cells display front-back polarity while migrating with only focal adhesions to their neighbours and to ECM, and have vimentin as a major intermediate filament.

Epithelial cells are maintained mostly by cell-to-cell junctions, which contribute to the rigidity of cell-cell lateral adherence. The junctions involved in maintaining epithelial cell integrity include tight, adherens and gap junctions as well as desmosomes. Following the induction of signalling by various growth factors, changes in expression of these intracellular junction molecules occur via a number of pathways. The consequent decrease in intercellular adhesion leads to detachment of cancer cells from the tumour mass. This, together with upregulated mesenchymal genes, contributes to the malignant phenotype of carcinoma cells.

In this review, growth factor pathways that promote the phenotypic transition are discussed with respect to each growth factor and other critical mediators. However, it is important to note that individual growth factors do not work in isolation – there is extensive cross-talk of pathways as well as autocrine stimulation, and the effect of a given inducer on EMT is context dependent.

Molecular Mechanisms of EMT

The association of a growth factor with its cognate receptor tyrosine kinase promotes signal transduction through the recruitment of downstream kinases, such as mitogen-activated protein kinase (MAPK), Src and phosphatidylinositol 3-kinase (PI3K), to either directly

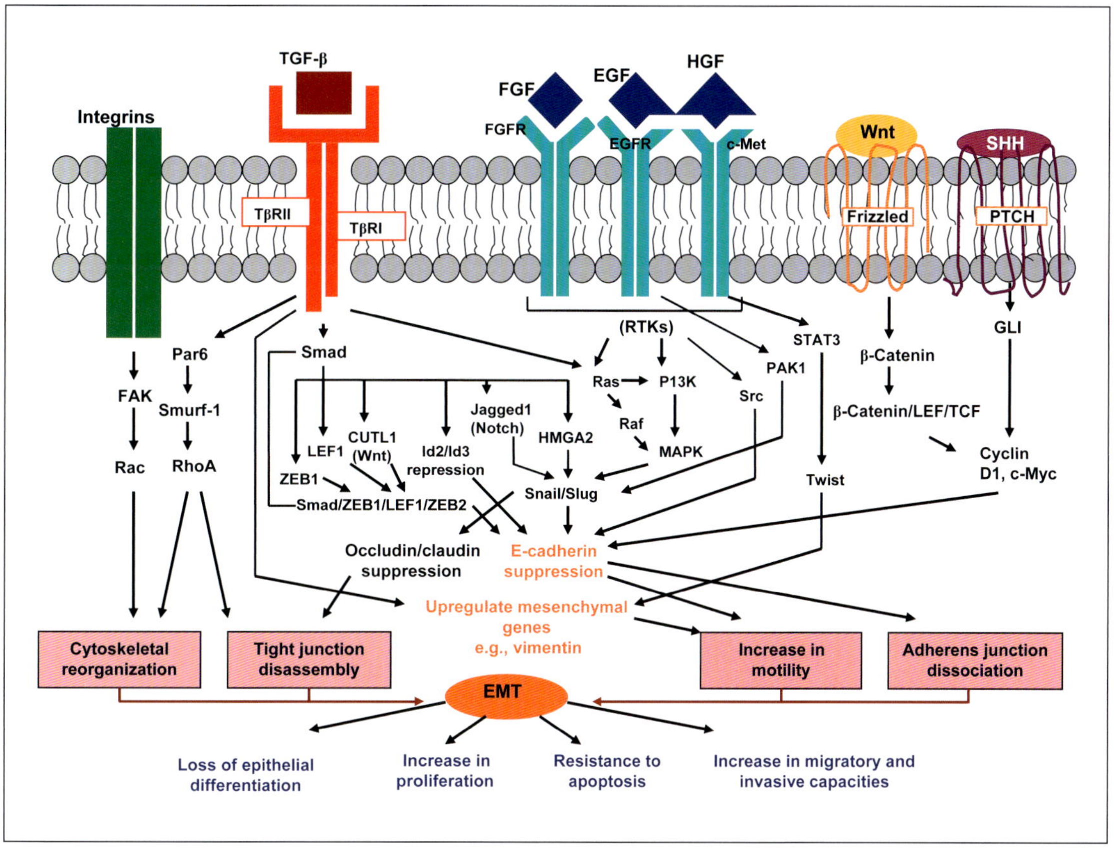

Fig. 2. Intracellular signal transduction pathways that induce EMT and the resulting morphological and cellular characteristics. The activation of receptor tyrosine kinase (RTKs), TGF-βR, Wnt/β-catenin, sonic HH (SHH) and integrin signalling pathways target the signal transduction molecules to transcriptionally regulate genes involved in this transition, including the epithelial junction components E-cadherin, occludin and claudin, as well as mesenchymal genes such as vimentin. The compromised intercellular adherence, gain in motility and cytoskeletal reorganization lead to the establishment of EMT. Apart from the hierarchical signalling pathways depicted in the figure, there are also autocrine/paracrine crosstalks among the growth factors (further discussed in the text). EMT may contribute to cellular processes that favour tumour progression including sustained growth and survival through increase in proliferation and resistance to apoptosis, as well as through increase in migratory and invasive capacities to metastasize. TβRI = TGF-β type I receptor; TβRII = TGF-β type II receptor; PTCH = patched; FAK = focal adhesion kinase; HMGA2 = high mobility group A2; PAK1 = p21-activated kinase-1.

affect the epithelial integrity or target downstream transcriptional regulators such as Snail, Slug or Twist to regulate epithelial/mesenchymal gene expression. EMT signalling pathways have many common endpoints and the adherens junction protein E-cadherin is a central target [Thiery and Sleeman, 2006] (fig. 2). Loss of E-cadherin function is associated with passive dissemination of carcinoma cells and increased cell invasiveness [Thiery, 2002]. EMT also involves other inducers such as matrix metalloproteinases (MMPs) and urokinase plasminogen activator which, like growth factors, may be secreted by either the tumour cells themselves or by the surrounding tumour stromal cells. These molecules degrade the components of basal lamina leading to invasion of the migrating cancer cells into reactive stroma and subsequently lymphatic vessels and systemic circulation.

Transforming Growth Factor-β

In normal cells and in early-stage carcinogenesis of certain carcinomas, transforming growth factor-β (TGF-β) plays a role in inhibition of cell cycle progression and/or apoptosis. However, in late-stage carcinoma, this soluble factor can promote tumour invasion and metastasis

[Tian and Schiemann, 2009; Allington and Schiemann, 2011]. It has also been shown that in addition to the tumour suppressor and pro-oncogenic role of TGF-β, loss of carcinoma cell responsiveness to TGF-β stimulation can promote metastasis through the recruitment of prometastatic myeloid-derived suppressor cell populations to the tumour microenvironment that enhance angiogenesis and provide matrix-degrading enzymes [Bierie and Moses, 2010].

TGF-β may be produced by the tumour stroma and act in a paracrine manner or be secreted by the tumour cells and act in an autocrine manner. Being a major inducer of EMT, TGF-β has many targets and is able to regulate the activation of other signalling pathways besides establishing a hierarchical gene network. Certain pathways activated by TGF-β, including MAPK and Notch, may induce TGF-β secretion and activity themselves, resulting in amplification of EMT [Moustakas and Heldin, 2007].

TGF-β receptor (TGF-βR) stimulation activates the Ras-MAPK and Smad-dependent pathways. The TGF-β/Ras/MAPK pathway targets multiple zinc finger-containing proteins, in particular Snail and Slug, which in turn inhibit E-cadherin gene expression to disrupt the adherens junction formed by E-cadherin/β-catenin complexes. This pathway of Snail induction has been blocked by a dominant-negative form of H-Ras, whereas oncogenic H-Ras has been shown to induce Snail promoter activity [Peinado et al., 2003]. TGF-β has also been shown to interact with occludin, to mediate tight junction dissolution during EMT, through the action of the Snail-Smad3/4 complex [Vincent et al., 2009]. Smad-dependent pathway activation occurs via TGF-β type I and type II receptors. Following ligand binding, the type II receptor transphosphorylates the type I receptor which in turn phosphorylates cytoplasmic Smad proteins – Smad2 and Smad3. Activated Smad2/3 then forms a complex with Smad4 and enters the nucleus to further complex with transcription factors and regulate the expression of genes that control cell proliferation, differentiation and cell migration [Moustakas and Heldin, 2007]. Smad4 is an essential component in this process, as its knockdown potently inhibited TGF-β-induced EMT. Furthermore, the frequency of breast cancer-bone metastasis is inhibited by 75% following the knockdown of Smad4 [Deckers et al., 2006].

The Smad complex, upon entry into the nucleus, can activate a 2-handed zinc finger-containing protein that binds consensus E-box sequences, ZEB1 [Verschueren et al., 1999] and lymphoid-enhancer binding factor (LEF)-1. Besides inducing their expression, the Smad complex can form another complex with these proteins, together with ZEB2 (SIP1), to repress the E-cadherin gene. The expression of ZEB2 in human epithelial cells resulted in morphological transition from an epithelial to a mesenchymal phenotype, as well as in repression of several junctional proteins and their mRNA levels that are directly mediated by ZEB2 [Vandewalle et al., 2005]. Transcriptomic analysis showed that the Smad complex may also induce high mobility group A2 to further induce expression of Twist, Slug and Snail [Thuault et al., 2006].

The Smad complex can also induce Jagged1, which activates the Notch pathway, and CUTL1, a homeobox transcription factor which induces expression of the Wnt5 pathway [Moustakas and Heldin, 2007]. CUTL1 is reported to be associated with increased invasiveness and migration as it activates a transcriptional programme directed to genes that regulate cell motility, invasion and ECM composition [Michl et al., 2005]. The Smad complex also contributes to the repression of the inhibitor of differentiation (Id)2/Id3 gene, whose function is to inhibit basic helix-loop-helix proteins such as E12/E47, leading to subsequent E-cadherin downregulation and EMT. In mouse embryos, E12/E47 is involved in the maintenance of the mesenchymal state [Perez-Moreno et al., 2001]. While TGF-β/Smad signalling represses Id genes, bone morphogenetic proteins/Smad signalling induces Id expression in epithelial cells, and this opposing regulation is essential for proliferative and differentiation purpose [Kowanetz et al., 2004]. Moustakas and Heldin [2007] proposed that cells that undergo EMT reduce their Id levels, but upon arrival at the metastatic site, the cells increase their Id levels to support proliferation and survival.

Alternatively, TGF-βR signals towards Par6 phosphorylation, which functions as a scaffold for polarity-regulating protein such as Rho, atypical protein kinase C and PAR3. Par6 is demonstrated to interact with TGF-βR and is a substrate of the TGF-β type II receptor [Ozdamar, 2005]. The interaction between TGF-βR and Par6 leads to activation of Smurf-1, an E3-ubiquitin ligase which ubiquitylates RhoA and controls the degradation. Smurf-1 and RhoA ubiquitination are necessary for tight junction disassembly and cell adhesion inhibition [Christiansen and Rajasekaran, 2006]. Inhibition of TGF-β-induced EMT in epithelial cells expressing dominant negative mutant RhoA suggests that TGF-β activates RhoA-dependent signalling pathways [Bhowmick et al., 2000].

TGF-β_1 has been shown to work synergistically with epidermal growth factor (EGF) to regulate ECM degradation through the upregulation of MMPs and collagenolysis [Wilkins-Port and Higgins, 2007]. In lung adenocarcinoma cells, TGF-β autocrine activation could be elicited by the ECM molecule collagen I, through PI3K/ERK signalling [Shintani et al., 2008]. TGF-β has been found to be the key gene in a pathway analysis of 7 gene sets associated with platinum resistance in ovarian cancer, as well as the key gene in networks of ECM-related genes that were expressed higher in resistant ovarian carcinoma and tamoxifen-resistant breast cancer, with fibronectin being overlapped in both gene sets [Helleman et al., 2010]. As fibronectin is a putative target of miR-200c, a microRNA that belongs to the miR-200 family that is responsible for the maintenance of the epithelial phenotype and is implicated in TGF-β-induced EMT, the authors postulated that EMT contributes to therapy resistance through a signalling pathway involving TGF-β-induced ECM alterations [Helleman et al., 2010].

Novel TGF-β targets involved in EMT are still being discovered. In gene expression profiling studies, it was found that TGF-β stimulated the expression of a cytokine called 'interleukin-like EMT inducer'. Interleukin-like EMT inducer independently induces EMT, invasive growth of carcinomas and metastasis in various cancer models, probably through stimulating secretion of chemokines from the carcinoma cells [Waerner et al., 2006]. Another inducer of TGF-β signalling, protein tyrosine phosphatase Pez, was first found to be regulating EMT in zebrafish embryos [Wyatt et al., 2007], and Pez loss-of-function mutations have been predicted to be associated with colorectal cancers [Wyatt and Khew-Goodall, 2008]. Transfection of Madin-Darby canine kidney cells with Pez causes the cells to undergo EMT with downregulation of several miR-200 family members (miR-200a, miR-200b, miR-200c, miR-141 and miR-429) and miR-205 [Gregory et al., 2008]. Ectopic expression of miR-200a and miR-200b was able to induce mesenchymal to epithelial transition (MET), and these microRNAs regulate the expression of ZEB1 and ZEB2. Besides the transcriptional repression of ZEB1 and ZEB2, the miR-200 family has been reported to indirectly increase histone H3 acetylation at the E-cadherin promoter, thereby inhibiting EMT [Tryndyak et al., 2010]. It has also been proposed that reduced miR-200c during tumour progression could mediate apoptosis resistance associated with EMT, and Schickel et al. [2010] showed that miR-200 sensitized cells to CD95-mediated apoptosis by targeting Fas-associated phosphatase-1. Another microRNA, miR-155, has been demonstrated to be regulated by the TGF-β/Smad pathway to target RhoA, causing tight junction dissolution and leading to EMT [Kong et al., 2008b].

A transcriptome profiling study in BRI-JM01 mammary tumour epithelial cells undergoing a TGF-β-induced EMT revealed clusterin to be the most highly upregulated gene. Antibodies targeting secreted clusterin inhibit TGF-β-induced EMT but do not affect proliferation of cells, suggesting that this effect does not lie within the TGF-β growth-inhibitory pathways [Lenferink et al., 2010]. Antibodies against clusterin might be the ideal strategy for treatment of invasion and metastasis of cancer since it inhibited TGF-β-induced EMT but not TGF-β-induced growth arrest [Miyazono, 2009]. In fact, another approach in inhibiting clusterin with an antisense compound against clusterin (custirsen, OGX-011) has undergone a phase I and phase II trial in prostate cancer (in combination with docetaxel, gemcitabine-cisplatin or mitoxantrone) following its ability to enhance the cytotoxicity of these agents [Miyake et al., 2006; Chi et al., 2008].

Epidermal Growth Factor

The EGF receptor (EGFR) is not only stimulated by EGF, but also by other ligands such as TGF-β. While TGF-β promotes shedding of EGF-like ligands for EGF signalling activation, the activation of c-Src by TGF-β_1 is EGFR dependent and required for cell survival, demonstrating the interplay between the 2 growth factors [Murillo et al., 2005]. The autocrine loop of TGF-β has also been suggested to confer resistance to EMT-related apoptosis in hepatocytes through the increase in EGFR ligand expression [Del Castillo et al., 2006].

EGF is reported to increase cell motility, enhancing the activity of secreted MMP-2 and MMP-9, Erk and integrin-linked kinase (ILK) [Hugo et al., 2007]. Several studies have shown that activation of EGFR signalling causes the disruption of desmosomal and/or adherens junctions leading to dissociation of cancer cells [Mimeault and Batra, 2007]. The latter has been associated with the downregulation of caveolin-1 and induction of Snail [Lu et al., 2003]. EGF has been shown to signal p21-activated kinase-1 to phosphorylate Snail, thus causing Snail accumulation in the nucleus and subsequent repression of target genes [Thiery and Sleeman, 2006]. EGF has also been found to induce phosphorylation and nuclear localization of the transcription factor signal transducer and activator of transcription 3 (STAT3), which can then transactivate the Twist promoter [Lo et al., 2007]. In ovarian cancer cell lines, EGF-induced EMT occurs concomitantly with JAK2/STAT3 activation and these pathways crosstalk with interleukin-6 receptor signalling [Colomiere et al., 2009].

EGFR inhibition by EGFR tyrosine kinase inhibitor PKI166 or EGFR blocking antibody C225 in oral squamous cell carcinoma cells caused transition from a fibroblastoid morphology to a more epithelial phenotype [Lorch et al., 2004]. Similarly, inhibition of EGFR in inflammatory breast cancer cells by erlotinib reversed the mesenchymal phenotype of inflammatory breast cancer cells to epithelial phenotype in 3D culture and in a xenograft model [Zhang et al., 2009]. A constitutively active mutant EGFR variant III has been associated with EMT, and when transfected into an epithelial ovarian cell line, resulted in the disruption of adherens and desmosomal junctions, a switch of E-cadherin to N-cadherin and an increase in vimentin expression [Zeineldin et al., 2006]. However, a immunohistochemical analysis investigating the association of EMT status with EGFR genotype found expression of a significantly higher epithelial phenotype in tumours harbouring an EGFR mutation [Deng et al., 2009]. EMT has been implicated in reduced sensitivity of tumour cells to EGFR inhibitors. Despite induction of EMT by EGFR, mesenchymal-like tumour cells are able to attenuate their dependence on EGFR signalling. It has been found that these cells, apart from expressing low levels of EGFR family ligands, exhibit aberrant platelet-derived growth factor (PDGF) receptor and fibroblast growth factor (FGF) receptor (FGFR) expression as an alternative to maintain proliferation and survival [Thomson et al., 2008]. In mesenchymal bladder cancer cells, increased sensitivity to EGFR inhibitors was observed following stable expression of miR-200 [Adam et al., 2009]. A novel mechanism of miRNA regulation by EGFR has been reported by Cowden Dahl et al. [2009], where transcriptional repression of miR-125 by EGFR-mediated PEA3 activity (an ETS family transcription factor) leads to AT-rich interactive domain 3B accumulation and EMT.

Hepatocyte Growth Factor

Hepatocyte growth factor (HGF) is involved in proliferation, migration, differentiation and survival of many cell types and it activates c-Met, a receptor tyrosine kinase. High levels of expression of HGF and its receptor are associated with invasive human breast cancer and metastasis and have been considered as a possible indicator of earlier recurrence as well as of shortened survival in breast cancer patients [Thiery, 2002]. Amplification of Met and FGFR2 induce EMT in gastric cancer [Katoh, 2005], and activating mutations of this receptor have also been described in metastatic head and neck squamous cell carcinoma and papillary renal carcinoma [Thiery, 2002]. Upon binding of HGF to c-Met, phosphorylation of 2 adjacent tyrosines (Y14 and Y15) in the cytoplasmic domain of Met is induced. Y14 and Y15 recruit Scr homology 2 domain-containing proteins, including adaptor proteins (such as Grb2, Shc, Gab and Cbl) and effector proteins (such as P13K, Src, PLCγ, Shp2 and STAT3) – which all work to promote EMT [Thiery, 2002]. Generally, the Scr homology 2 domain is thought to activate small GTP-binding proteins, such as Ras, Rho and Rac. In Madin-Darby canine kidney cells, HGF-dependent activation of Cdc42 occurs concomitantly with filopodia and lamellipodia formation and leads to the activation of PAK and translocation of Rho-dependent Rho kinase to membrane ruffles. While p21-activated kinase-1 is essential for Actin reorganization, cell spreading and dissociation, Rho kinase is involved in the formation of focal adhesions and stress fibres, indicating the importance of Rho GTPases and their effectors in HGF-induced EMT [Royal et al., 2000].

HGF-induced EMT is associated with Snail activity as demonstrated by the inhibition of HGF-induced cell scattering via short hairpin RNA-mediated ablation of Snail expression. In this context, the activity of Snail is induced by the recruitment of early growth response factor-1 [Grotegut et al., 2006]. Some studies suggest that the MAPK/early growth response factor-1 pathway can induce EMT even in the absence of functional Y14 and Y15 docking sites [Tulasne et al., 1999]. Another molecular player involved in HGF-induced EMT, Numb, has been suggested to play a role in metastasis by delaying EMT through its regulation of E-cadherin localization and interaction with the Par polarity complex. Depletion of Numb by short hairpin RNA demonstrated increased sensitivity to HGF-induced cell scattering, reduced cell-cell adhesion and increased cell migration [Wang et al., 2009].

Fibroblast Growth Factor

In the rat bladder cancer NBT-II cell system, genetic manipulation to generate cells with an autocrine loop for FGF-1 or FGF-2 resulted in cells that were highly invasive and tumorigenic and displayed a mesenchymal phenotype. In this case, FGF signalling primarily targets urokinase plasminogen activator receptor and later targets E-cadherin and leucocyte common antigen-related protein-tyrosine phosphatase [Billottet et al., 2004]. Treatment of NBT-II cells with FGF-1 showed that the immediate genes to be upregulated included Notch-1, MMP-13 and urokinase plasminogen activator receptor, while late genes modulated included genes responsible for loss of epithelial phenotype and maintenance of mesenchymal phenotypes [Billottet et al., 2008]. FGF-1-induced EMT has also been shown to involve $\alpha_2\beta_1$-integrin, the major collagen-binding receptor [Valles et al., 1996].

FGF works in a similar fashion as HGF to induce EMT. FGFR1 signalling targets Snail through the MAPK pathway [Thiery, 2003]. The FGFR2b is present in normal epithelia and contributes to the differentiation and maintenance of epithelial phenotype while mesenchymal cells typically express the FGFR2c isoform. Indeed, class switch from FGFR2b to FGFR2c often occurs during EMT of prostate and bladder cancer [Katoh and Katoh, 2009], and in the latter, a low expression level of FGFR2b is associated with loss of E-cadherin [Thiery, 2002].

Platelet-Derived Growth Factor

Through the action of TGF-β and the oncogenic Ras pathway, the PDGF ligands (PDGF-A) and PDGF receptor subunits are upregulated resulting in the increase in secretion and autocrine regulation of PDGF. In hepatocytes expressing hyperactive Ha-Ras (which adopt an invasive and metastatic phenotype), hepatocytes expressing dominant negative PDGFα receptor display a decrease in TGF-β-induced migration in vitro and suppression of tumour in vivo [Gotzmann et al., 2006].

PC3 cells expressing high levels of PDGF-D resulted in loss of E-cadherin and zonula occludens-1 and in gain of vimentin as well as in rapid tumour growth in severe combined immunodeficient mice [Kong et al., 2008a]. This acquisition of an EMT phenotype is partly a result of repression of miR-200 and of upregulation of ZEB1, ZEB2 and Slug expression [Kong et al., 2009]. PDGF signalling targets PI3K as well as nuclear β-catenin accumulation [Fischer et al., 2007]. This has been shown to be mediated by PDGF-dependent phosphorylation of p68, which blocks phosphorylation of β-catenin by glycogen synthase kinase-3β (GSK3β) and displaces Axin from β-catenin [Yang et al., 2006].

Insulin-Like Growth Factor

In NBT-II cells, insulin-like growth factor (IGF)-II mediates EMT through nuclear relocation of β-catenin, E-cadherin intracellular sequestration and degradation as well as transcriptionally inducing β-catenin/T-cell factor (TCF)-3 target genes [Morali et al., 2001]. In the human breast cancer cell line MCF-7, transfection with an antisense construct to the IGF-I receptor increased cell migration and decreased adhesion and cellular aggregation accompanied by a significant (50%) decrease in expression of E-cadherin [Pennisi et al., 2002]. IGF-I stimulation in prostate cancer cells has been suggested to cause aberrant expression of ZEB1 [Graham et al., 2008].

Overexpression of constitutively activated IGF-I receptor (IGF-IR) has been shown to induce an EMT which is mediated by nuclear factor-κB and Snail [Kim et al., 2007]. Using a doxycycline-inducible mouse model of IGF-IR-initiated breast cancer, downregulation of IGF-IR resulted in tumour size-dependent regression to an undetectable state. However, spontaneously recurrent tumours are independent of IGF-IR expression, and this was associated with an EMT and upregulation of transcriptional repressors of E-cadherin [Jones et al., 2009].

Wnt Signalling Pathway

The activation of the Wnt signalling pathway through the Frizzled receptor and low-density lipoprotein receptor-related proteins 5/6 co-receptor results in inhibition of intracellular β-catenin degradation and its nuclear accumulation through downregulation of GSK3β (which would otherwise phosphorylate β-catenin and Snail). Nuclear β-catenin forms a complex with LEF/TCF to enhance the expression of tumorigenic gene products such as cyclin D1, c-Myc, Snail and Slug [Katoh, 2006]. Activating mutations of β-catenin might contribute to its stabilization and nuclear translocation [Hajra and Fearon, 2002]. The β-catenin/TCF complex has been shown to signal Axin-2 to stabilize Snail as Axin-2 chaperones GSK3β in the nucleus and cytoplasm [Yook et al., 2006].

Nuclear Snail, which represses E-cadherin expression, also causes translocation of β-catenin from the cytoplasm to the nucleus and feeds into the Wnt signalling pathway. This is a result of loss of E-cadherin-dependent intracellular epithelial junctional complexes and of a decrease in E-cadherin-mediated sequestering of β-catenin in cytoplasm [Thiery and Sleeman, 2006]. The FGF/

P13K/AKT signalling cascade is also able to downregulate GSK3β activity, and the co-activation of FGF and Wnt pathways in tumours results in more malignant phenotypes [Katoh, 2006].

Microarray analysis of Wnt5A pathways revealed that vimentin was upregulated by this pathway and suggested that Wnt5A induces EMT in a protein kinase-C-dependent manner [Dissanayake et al., 2007]. Wnt/β-catenin and the TGF-βR/Smad pathway cooperate via several mechanisms. Apart from TGF-β-induced CUTL1 that activates Wnt/β-catenin pathway mentioned earlier, TGF-β and Wnt pathway can independently or cooperatively regulate LEF/TCF target genes [Huber et al., 2005]. In c-fos oestrogen receptor oncoprotein-induced EMT, increased LEF/TCF signalling cooperates with the TGF-β-dependent pathway in maintaining mesenchymal phenotype during EMT [Eger et al., 2004]. Mesenchymal c-fos oestrogen receptor cells could re-gain an epithelial phenotype upon simultaneous inhibition of both pathways but only a partial rescue of epithelial features following inhibition of a single pathway, suggesting that targeting both pathways might be a key to efficacious inhibition of EMT and metastasis.

Sonic Hedgehog Pathway

Hedgehog-GLI (HH/GLI) signalling is required for the growth of colon carcinoma xenografts, including recurrence and metastasis, and activation of this pathway induces a robust EMT [Varnat et al., 2009]. In human esophageal squamous cell carcinoma, there was a co-expression of hedgehog and EMT signalling genes, and some mesenchymal-related genes regulated by ZEB2 (which is also a downstream gene of GLI1) [Isohata et al., 2009]. The HH/GLI signalling cascade upregulates the expression of tumorigenic gene products such as cyclin D1, c-Myc and Snail in pancreatic and prostate cancer cells [Mimeault and Batra, 2007]. Hedgehog signalling also induces autocrine PDGF receptor signalling and upregulates the Wnt pathway in skin carcinoma [Huber et al., 2005]. In human keratinocytes, the HH/GLI pathway has been shown to crosstalk with EGFR signalling, possibly at the level of, or upstream of the promoters of, direct GLI target genes [Kasper et al., 2006]. Indeed, in metastatic prostate cancer cells, the combination treatment of HH pathway antagonist cyclopamine and EGFR inhibitor gefitinib caused more apoptotic cell death and inhibited invasiveness more effectively than the single agents [Mimeault et al., 2006].

Jagged1/Notch Pathway

Like TGF-β signalling, Notch can either be tumour suppressive or tumour promoting [Huber et al., 2005]. Jagged and Delta-like ligands signal via Notch receptor towards the transcription factor CSL [Moustakas and Heldin, 2007]. Jagged1 and hairy/enhancer-of-split-related transcriptional repressor (Hey1) are induced by the TGF-βR/Smad pathway. TGF-β-induced EMT was blocked by RNA silencing of Jagged1 or Hey1 and inactivation of Notch; and in Smad3-deficient epithelial cells, the EMT phenotype as well as Jagged1 expression and Hey1 activation are not induced [Zavadil et al., 2004].

The TGF-β/Smad and Jagged/Notch pathways also cooperate to upregulate Snail or Hey1, both of which are E-box-binding transcriptional repressors [Huber et al., 2005]. Embryos lacking Notch signalling elements demonstrated reduced cardiac Snail expression and abortive endocardial EMT while overexpression of activated Notch1 induced EMT and oncogenic transformation in immortalized epithelial cells [Timmerman et al., 2004]. Slug is recruited by the Notch pathway to repress E-cadherin. Elevated levels of Slug are associated with increased expression of Jagged1 in various carcinomas and promote tumour growth and metastasis through EMT [Leong et al., 2007]. A recent study in cervical carcinoma has proposed RhoC to be an effector of Notch1 during tumour progression and demonstrated that inactivation of Notch1 and RhoC have similar phenotypic effects on EMT, including reduced motility and invasion and inhibition of actin stress fibre formation [Srivastava et al., 2010].

Integrin Signalling Pathway

Integrin complexes mediate the adhesion of epithelial and mesenchymal cells to ECM, or in the context of carcinoma, mediate the adhesion of cancer cell to surrounding ECM component in reactive stroma. ILK is a protein serine/threonine kinase that regulates several integrin-mediated cellular processes including cell adhesion, fibronectin matrix assembly and anchorage-dependent cell cycle progression [Li et al., 1999].

The signalling through β_1-integrin is required for TGF-β/MAPK signalling pathway activity. In turn, TGF-β induces the expression of disabled-2 that binds to β_1-integrin to activate integrin and form focal adhesions for cell survival during EMT [Prunier and Howe, 2005]. In pancreatic carcinoma, ECM molecules, particularly type I collagen, induce the disassembly of E-cadherin/catenin complex via the β_1-integrin/focal adhesion kinase pathway and PTEN dissociation [Imamichi and Menke, 2007]. Recently, type I collagen has been shown to promote EMT through ILK-dependent activation of nuclear factor-κB, which in turn promotes increased expression of the Snail and LEF-1 transcription factors [Medici and Nawshad, 2010]. Other components of ECM such as fibronectin and laminin have also been demonstrated to induce EMT [Giannelli et al., 2005; Sun et al., 2010].

Integrins and E-cadherin can cross-regulate each other. Integrin-mediated focal adhesion kinase phosphorylation is required for internalization of E-cadherin in colon carcinoma models [Thiery, 2003]. ILK represses E-cadherin expression through poly(ADP-ribose) polymerase-1 action which in turn modulates Snail expression [McPhee et al., 2008]. ILK also inhibits phosphorylation of GSK3β, leading to Snail accumulation and E-cadherin repression [Doble and Woodgett, 2007].

An interesting study has found that ILK could mediate sensitivity to EGFR inhibition in human hepatoma mesenchymal cells which would otherwise be less susceptible to EGFR inhibitors. These mesenchymal cells had increased AKT and STAT3 activation through elevated expression of ILK, and transforming these cells with kinase-inactive ILK resulted in increased sensitivity to EGFR inhibitors both in vitro and in an in vivo xenograft model [Fuchs et al., 2008]. While ECM integrin-mediated signalling might serve as a resistance marker to several chemotherapeutics, several data have suggested that fibronectin-induced integrin signalling could mediate sensitivity to microtubule-targeting agents [Helleman et al., 2010].

On the other hand, endocytosis of E-cadherin upon adherens junction disassembly has been shown to activate small GTPase Rap1, a member of the Ras family of GTPases to modulate integrin adhesive function. This activation of Rap1 occurs in parallel with the co-localization of Rap1 and E-cadherin at the perinuclear Rab11-positive recycling endosome compartment, the formation of Rap1/E-cadherin-catenin complexes that do not contain $p120^{ctn}$ as well as activation of Src kinase, all of which lead to the polarized redistribution of integrins and/or integrin regulators to new adhesion sites, thus inducing integrin-mediated cell-matrix adhesion [Balzac et al., 2005]. This finding suggests a potential mechanism of how cancer cells that have undergone EMT with down-regulated and internalized E-cadherin components could signal to induce integrin-mediated adhesion of the cancer cells to surrounding ECM components.

Matrix Metalloproteinases

MMPs are a family of enzymes that are able to cleave most elements of the ECM and facilitate tumour invasion and metastasis. Induced expression of MMP-3 (stromelysin-1) in mammary epithelial cells in vitro results in EMT via the induced expression of an alternatively spliced form of Rac1, which causes an increase in cellular reactive oxygen species and stimulates the expression of Snail [Radisky et al., 2005]. Snail can also increase MMP expression in EMT [Yokoyama et al., 2003]. Snail increases the promoter activity and induces the transcription of MMP-9 through MAPK and P13K pathways [Jorda et al., 2005]. In squamous cell carcinoma cells, the Ets-1 binding site in the MMP-2 promoter was shown to be critical for the activation of Snail, SIP1 and TGF-β_1 on that promoter [Taki et al., 2006]. In oral cancer, Snail-induced MMP-9 expression was found to be downstream of TGF-β/ERK 1/2 signalling [Joseph et al., 2009]. In human bladder cancer cells, small interfering RNA targeting the TGF-β type I receptor downregulated the activity of MMP-9 [Li et al., 2010]. MMPs can also activate numerous tumorigenic pathways through the release of soluble ligands. Indeed, MMP-7, or matrilysin, which is overexpressed in a variety of invasive carcinoma, may directly induce the proteolytic shedding of E-cadherin, thus inhibiting E-cadherin paracrine function and promotes migration and invasion of tumour cells [Ii et al., 2006].

Another MMP, MMP-28 (epilysin), has been found to mediate irreversible EMT in lung adenocarcinoma cells with loss of E-cadherin from the cell surface, increased levels of active TGF-β and enhanced invasive activity of the cells [Illman et al., 2006]. However, in chondrosarcoma cells (a malignant tumour of bone), the overexpression of MMP-28 led to increased organization of actin, increased adhesive and less migratory behaviour [Rodgers et al., 2009]. Further, in chondrosarcoma cells, MMP-28 could increase the expression of other MMPs, such as MMP-2 and MMP-19 [Rodgers et al., 2009], but not of MMP-9 and MT1-MMP, as seen in adenocarcinoma cells [Illman et al., 2006]. The complex and tumour type-dependent activity of this enzyme suggests that a further elucidation is needed to identify MMP-28 substrates and comprehend its role in EMT and metastasis.

Growth Factors in MET

To form a clinically significant metastasis, tumour cells must form a cohesive mass at the secondary site. The histological similarities between primary and secondary tumours suggests that cells that acquire a mesenchymal phenotype to migrate and invade away from the primary tumour must, at least partially, revert to an epithelial phenotype once they have reached the metastatic site. This has been demonstrated using the TSU-Pr1 bladder carcinoma progression series, where the increasing metastatic ability of cells following systemic seeding is associated with increases in epithelial markers [Chaffer et al., 2005]. An experiment using RNA interference to decrease FGFR2 in the most metastatic cell line reversed the MET, and this was associated with increased survival following systemic inoculation of tumour cells [Chaffer et al., 2006]. This suggests a role for FGF signalling in driving MET, reminiscent of the embryological process.

The potential roles of other growth factors in MET remain largely under-investigated relative to EMT; however, the development of other MET models such as the 'epithelialization' of prostate cancer cell lines by co-culture with hepatocytes [Yates et al., 2007] will rapidly advance the field. A study to reverse EMT determined by cellular morphology and gene expression found that treating mouse mammary gland cells with ZEB1 and ZEB2 short hairpin RNA was sufficient to upregulate the expression of epithelial proteins and re-establish epithelial features, but complete restoration of cortical F-actin requires concomitant treatment with a ROCK inhibitor [Das et al., 2009]. A study trying to re-express miR-200b in prostate cancer PC3 cells overexpressing PDGF-D led to reversal of the EMT phenotype, which was associated with the downregulation of ZEB1, ZEB2 and Slug2 expression and with the increased expression of epithelial markers [Kong et al., 2009]. The effectiveness of transcription factors and microRNAs in reversing EMT supports the concept that a programmatic process is integral to controlling MET, as well as EMT, and that targeting multiple signalling pathways is likely to be essential to modulating MET.

Summary and Perspective

Growth factors, whether derived from the tumour cells, or the surrounding parenchyma, play a key role in determining the balance of epithelial and mesenchymal traits of tumour cells. The context-dependent nature of the signalling pathways activated by individual growth factors, and the extensive crosstalk between growth factor signalling pathways provides an opportunity to selectively modulate EMT and MET, and thus, impact on the subsequent development of metastasis.

Acknowledgements

N.A.B.M. Said is supported by a scholarship from the Malaysian government's Bumiputera Academic Training Scheme. E.D. Williams is supported by a Biomedical Career Development Award from the Australian National Health and Medical Research Council (No. 519539).

References

Adam, L., M. Zhong, W. Choi, W. Qi, M. Nicoloso, A. Arora, G. Calin, H. Wang, A. Siefker-Radtke, D. McConkey, M. Bar-Eli, C. Dinney (2009) miR-200 expression regulates epithelial-to-mesenchymal transition in bladder cancer cells and reverses resistance to epidermal growth factor receptor therapy. Clin Cancer Res *15:* 5060–5072.

Allington, T.M., W.P. Schiemann (2011) The cain and Abl of epithelial-mesenchymal transition and transforming growth factor-β in mammary epithelial cells. Cells Tissues Organs *193:* 98–113.

Balzac, F., M. Avolio, S. Degani, I. Kaverina, M. Torti, L. Silengo, J.V. Small, S.F. Retta (2005) E-cadherin endocytosis regulates the activity of Rap1: a traffic light GTPase at the crossroads between cadherin and integrin function. J Cell Sci *118:* 4765–4783.

Bhowmick, N.A., M. Ghiassi, A. Bakin, M. Aakre, C.A. Lundquist, M.E. Engel, C.L. Arteaga, H.L. Moses (2000) Transforming growth factor-β_1 mediates epithelial to mesenchymal transdifferentiation through a RhoA-dependent mechanism. Mol Biol Cell *12:* 27–36.

Bierie, B., H.L. Moses (2010) Transforming growth factor beta (TGF-beta) and inflammation in cancer. Cytokine Growth Factor Rev *21:* 49–59.

Billottet, C., N. Elkhatib, J.P. Thiery, J. Jouanneau (2004) Targets of fibroblast growth factor 1 (FGF-1) and FGF-2 signaling involved in the invasive and tumorigenic behavior of carcinoma cells. Mol Biol Cell *15:* 4725–4734.

Billottet, C., M. Tuefferd, D. Gentien, A. Rapinat, J.P. Thiery, P. Broet, J. Jouanneau (2008) Modulation of several waves of gene expression during FGF-1 induced epithelial-mesenchymal transition of carcinoma cells. J Cell Biochem *104:* 826–839.

Chaffer, C.L., J.P. Brennan, J.L. Slavin, T. Blick, E.W. Thompson, E.D. Williams (2006) Mesenchymal-to-epithelial transition facilitates bladder cancer metastasis: role of fibroblast growth factor receptor-2. Cancer Res *66:* 11271–11278.

Chaffer, C.L., B. Dopheide, D.R. McCulloch, A.B. Lee, J.M. Moseley, E.W. Thompson, E.D. Williams (2005) Upregulated MT1-MMP/TIMP-2 axis in the TSU-Pr1-B1/B2 model of metastatic progression in transitional cell carcinoma of the bladder. Clin Exp Metastasis *22:* 115–125.

Chi, K.N., A. Zoubeidi, M.E. Gleave (2008) Custirsen (OGX-011): a second-generation antisense inhibitor of clusterin for the treatment of cancer. Expert Opin Investig Drugs *17:* 1955–1962.
Christiansen, J.J., A.K. Rajasekaran (2006) Reassessing epithelial to mesenchymal transition as a prerequisite for carcinoma invasion and metastasis. Cancer Res *66:* 8319–8326.
Colomiere, M., A.C. Ward, C. Riley, M.K. Trenerry, D. Cameron-Smith, J. Findlay, L. Ackland, N. Ahmed (2009) Cross talk of signals between EGFR and IL-6R through JAK2/STAT3 mediate epithelial-mesenchymal transition in ovarian carcinomas. Br J Cancer *100:* 134–144.
Cowden Dahl, K.D., R. Dahl, J.N. Kruichak, L.G. Hudson (2009) The epidermal growth factor receptor responsive miR-125a represses mesenchymal morphology in ovarian cancer cells. Neoplasia *11:* 1208–1215.
Das, S., B.N. Becker, F.M. Hoffmann, J.E. Mertz (2009) Complete reversal of epithelial to mesenchymal transition requires inhibition of both ZEB expression and the Rho pathway. BMC Cell Biol *10:* 94.
Deckers, M., M. van Dinther, J. Buijs, I. Que, C. Lowik, G. van der Pluijm, P. ten Dijke (2006) The tumor suppressor Smad4 is required for transforming growth factor beta-induced epithelial to mesenchymal transition and bone metastasis of breast cancer cells. Cancer Res *66:* 2202–2209.
Del Castillo, G., M.M. Murillo, A. Alvarez-Barrientos, E. Bertran, M. Fernandez, A. Sanchez, I. Fabregat (2006) Autocrine production of TGF-beta confers resistance to apoptosis after an epithelial-mesenchymal transition process in hepatocytes: role of EGF receptor ligands. Exp Cell Res *312:* 2860–2871.
Deng, Q.F., C.C. Zhou, C.X. Su (2009) Clinicopathological features and epidermal growth factor receptor mutations associated with epithelial-mesenchymal transition in non-small cell lung cancer. Respirology *14:* 371–376.
Dissanayake, S.K., M. Wade, C.E. Johnson, M.P. O'Connell, P.D. Leotlela, A.D. French, K.V. Shah, K.J. Hewitt, D.T. Rosenthal, F.E. Indig, Y. Jiang, B.J. Nickoloff, D.D. Taub, J.M. Trent, R.T. Moon, M. Bittner, A.T. Weeraratna (2007) The Wnt5A/protein kinase C pathway mediates motility in melanoma cells via the inhibition of metastasis suppressors and initiation of an epithelial to mesenchymal transition. J Biol Chem *282:* 17259–17271.
Doble, B.W., J.R. Woodgett (2007) Role of glycogen synthase kinase-3 in cell fate and epithelial-mesenchymal transitions. Cells Tissues Organs *185:* 73–84.
Eger, A., A. Stockinger, J. Park, E. Langkopf, M. Mikula, J. Gotzmann, W. Mikulits, H. Beug, R. Foisner (2004) Beta-catenin and TGFbeta signalling cooperate to maintain a mesenchymal phenotype after FosER-induced epithelial to mesenchymal transition. Oncogene *23:* 2672–2680.
Fischer, A.N., E. Fuchs, M. Mikula, H. Huber, H. Beug, W. Mikulits (2007) PDGF essentially links TGF-beta signaling to nuclear beta-catenin accumulation in hepatocellular carcinoma progression. Oncogene *26:* 3395–3405.
Fuchs, B.C., T. Fujii, J.D. Dorfman, J.M. Goodwin, A.X. Zhu, M. Lanuti, K.K. Tanabe (2008) Epithelial-to-mesenchymal transition and integrin-linked kinase mediate sensitivity to epidermal growth factor receptor inhibition in human hepatoma cells. Cancer Res *68:* 2391–2399.
Giannelli, G., C. Bergamini, E. Fransvea, C. Sgarra, S. Antonaci (2005) Laminin-5 with transforming growth factor-beta1 induces epithelial to mesenchymal transition in hepatocellular carcinoma. Gastroenterology *129:* 1375–1383.
Gotzmann, J., A.N. Fischer, M. Zojer, M. Mikula, V. Proell, H. Huber, M. Jechlinger, T. Waerner, A. Weith, H. Beug, W. Mikulits (2006) A crucial function of PDGF in TGF-beta-mediated cancer progression of hepatocytes. Oncogene *25:* 3170–3185.
Graham, T.R., H.E. Zhau, V.A. Odero-Marah, A.O. Osunkoya, K.S. Kimbro, M. Tighiouart, T. Liu, J.W. Simons, R.M. O'Regan (2008) Insulin-like growth factor-I-dependent up-regulation of ZEB1 drives epithelial-to-mesenchymal transition in human prostate cancer cells. Cancer Res *68:* 2479–2488.
Gregory, P.A., A.G. Bert, E.L. Paterson, S.C. Barry, A. Tsykin, G. Farshid, M.A. Vadas, Y. Khew-Goodall, G.J. Goodall (2008) The miR-200 family and miR-205 regulate epithelial to mesenchymal transition by targeting ZEB1 and SIP1. Nat Cell Biol *10:* 593–601.
Grotegut, S., D. von Schweinitz, G. Christofori, F. Lehembre (2006) Hepatocyte growth factor induces cell scattering through MAPK/Egr-1-mediated upregulation of Snail. EMBO J *25:* 3534–3545.
Hajra, K.M., E.R. Fearon (2002) Cadherin and catenin alterations in human cancer. Genes Chromosomes Cancer *34:* 255–268.
Helleman, J., M.P. Jansen, C. Burger, M.E. van der Burg, E.M. Berns (2010) Integrated genomics of chemotherapy resistant ovarian cancer: a role for extracellular matrix, TGF-beta and regulating microRNAs. Int J Biochem Cell Biol *42:* 25–30.
Huber, M.A., N. Kraut, H. Beug (2005) Molecular requirements for epithelial-mesenchymal transition during tumor progression. Curr Opin Cell Biol *17:* 548–558.
Hugo, H., M.L. Ackland, T. Blick, M.G. Lawrence, J.A. Clements, E.D. Williams, E.W. Thompson (2007) Epithelial-mesenchymal and mesenchymal-epithelial transitions in carcinoma progression. J Cell Physiol *213:* 374–383.
Ii, M., H. Yamamoto, Y. Adachi, Y. Maruyama, Y. Shinomura (2006) Role of matrix metalloproteinase-7 (matrilysin) in human cancer invasion, apoptosis, growth, and angiogenesis. Exp Biol Med (Maywood) *231:* 20–27.
Illman, S.A., K. Lehti, J. Keski-Oja, J. Lohi (2006) Epilysin (MMP-28) induces TGF-beta mediated epithelial to mesenchymal transition in lung carcinoma cells. J Cell Sci *119:* 3856–3865.
Imamichi, Y., A. Menke (2007) Signaling pathways involved in collagen-induced disruption of the E-cadherin complex during epithelial-mesenchymal transition. Cells Tissues Organs *185:* 180–190.
Isohata, N., K. Aoyagi, T. Mabuchi, H. Daiko, M. Fukaya, H. Ohta, K. Ogawa, T. Yoshida, H. Sasaki (2009) Hedgehog and epithelial-mesenchymal transition signaling in normal and malignant epithelial cells of the esophagus. Int J Cancer *125:* 1212–1221.
Jones, R.A., C.I. Campbell, G.A. Wood, J.J. Petrik, R.A. Moorehead (2009) Reversibility and recurrence of IGF-IR-induced mammary tumors. Oncogene *28:* 2152–2162.
Jorda, M., D. Olmeda, A. Vinyals, E. Valero, E. Cubillo, A. Llorens, A. Cano, A. Fabra (2005) Upregulation of MMP-9 in MDCK epithelial cell line in response to expression of the Snail transcription factor. J Cell Sci *118:* 3371–3385.
Joseph, M.J., S. Dangi-Garimella, M.A. Shields, M.E. Diamond, L. Sun, J.E. Koblinski, H.G. Munshi (2009) Slug is a downstream mediator of transforming growth factor-beta1-induced matrix metalloproteinase-9 expression and invasion of oral cancer cells. J Cell Biochem *108:* 726–736.
Kalluri, R., R.A. Weinberg (2009) The basics of epithelial-mesenchymal transition. J Clin Invest *119:* 1420–1428.
Kasper, M., H. Schnidar, G.W. Neill, M. Hanneder, S. Klingler, L. Blaas, C. Schmid, C. Hauser-Kronberger, G. Regl, M.P. Philpott, F. Aberger (2006) Selective modulation of Hedgehog/GLI target gene expression by epidermal growth factor signaling in human keratinocytes. Mol Cell Biol *26:* 6283–6298.
Katoh, M. (2005) Epithelial-mesenchymal transition in gastric cancer (review). Int J Oncol *27:* 1677–1683.
Katoh, M. (2006) Cross-talk of WNT and FGF signaling pathways at GSK3beta to regulate beta-catenin and SNAIL signaling cascades. Cancer Biol Ther *5:* 1059–1064.
Katoh, Y., M. Katoh (2009) FGFR2-related pathogenesis and FGFR2-targeted therapeutics (review). Int J Mol Med *23:* 307–311.
Kim, H.J., B.C. Litzenburger, X. Cui, D.A. Delgado, B.C. Grabiner, X. Lin, M.T. Lewis, M.M. Gottardis, T.W. Wong, R.M. Attar, J.M. Carboni, A.V. Lee (2007) Constitutively active type I insulin-like growth factor receptor causes transformation and xenograft growth of immortalized mammary epithelial cells and is accompanied by an epithelial-to-mesenchymal transition mediated by NF-kappaB and snail. Mol Cell Biol *27:* 3165–3175.

Kong, D., Y. Li, Z. Wang, S. Banerjee, A. Ahmad, H.R. Kim, F.H. Sarkar (2009) miR-200 regulates PDGF-D-mediated epithelial-mesenchymal transition, adhesion, and invasion of prostate cancer cells. Stem Cells *27:* 1712–1721.

Kong, D., Z. Wang, S.H. Sarkar, Y. Li, S. Banerjee, A. Saliganan, H.R. Kim, M.L. Cher, F.H. Sarkar (2008a) Platelet-derived growth factor-D overexpression contributes to epithelial-mesenchymal transition of PC3 prostate cancer cells. Stem Cells *26:* 1425–1435.

Kong, W., H. Yang, L. He, J.J. Zhao, D. Coppola, W.S. Dalton, J.Q. Cheng (2008b) MicroRNA-155 is regulated by the transforming growth factor beta/Smad pathway and contributes to epithelial cell plasticity by targeting RhoA. Mol Cell Biol *28:* 6773–6784.

Kowanetz, M., U. Valcourt, R. Bergstrom, C.H. Heldin, A. Moustakas (2004) Id2 and Id3 define the potency of cell proliferation and differentiation responses to transforming growth factor beta and bone morphogenetic protein. Mol Cell Biol *24:* 4241–4254.

Lenferink, A.E., C. Cantin, A. Nantel, E. Wang, Y. Durocher, M. Banville, B. Paul-Roc, A. Marcil, M.R. Wilson, M.D. O'Connor-McCourt (2010) Transcriptome profiling of a TGF-beta-induced epithelial-to-mesenchymal transition reveals extracellular clusterin as a target for therapeutic antibodies. Oncogene *29:* 831–844.

Leong, K.G., K. Niessen, I. Kulic, A. Raouf, C. Eaves, I. Pollet, A. Karsan (2007) Jagged1-mediated Notch activation induces epithelial-to-mesenchymal transition through Slug-induced repression of E-cadherin. J Exp Med *204:* 2935–2948.

Li, Y., K. Yang, Q. Mao, X. Zheng, D. Kong, L. Xie (2010) Inhibition of TGF-beta receptor I by siRNA suppresses the motility and invasiveness of T24 bladder cancer cells via modulation of integrins and matrix metalloproteinase. Int Urol Nephrol *42:* 315–323.

Li, F., Y. Zhang, C. Wu (1999) Integrin-linked kinase is localized to cell-matrix focal adhesions but not cell-cell adhesion sites and the focal adhesion localization of integrin-linked kinase is regulated by the PINCH-binding ANK repeats. J Cell Sci *112:* 4589–4599.

Lo, H.W., S.C. Hsu, W. Xia, X. Cao, J.Y. Shih, Y. Wei, J.L. Abbruzzese, G.N. Hortobagyi, M.C. Hung (2007) Epidermal growth factor receptor cooperates with signal transducer and activator of transcription 3 to induce epithelial-mesenchymal transition in cancer cells via up-regulation of TWIST gene expression. Cancer Res *67:* 9066–9076.

Lorch, J.H., J. Klessner, J.K. Park, S. Getsios, Y.L. Wu, M.S. Stack, K.J. Green (2004) Epidermal growth factor receptor inhibition promotes desmosome assembly and strengthens intercellular adhesion in squamous cell carcinoma cells. J Biol Chem *279:* 37191–37200.

Lu, Z., S. Ghosh, Z. Wang, T. Hunter (2003) Downregulation of caveolin-1 function by EGF leads to the loss of E-cadherin, increased transcriptional activity of beta-catenin, and enhanced tumor cell invasion. Cancer Cell *4:* 499–515.

McPhee, T.R., P.C. McDonald, A. Oloumi, S. Dedhar (2008) Integrin-linked kinase regulates E-cadherin expression through PARP-1. Dev Dyn *237:* 2737–2747.

Medici, D., A. Nawshad (2010) Type I collagen promotes epithelial-mesenchymal transition through ILK-dependent activation of NF-kappaB and LEF-1. Matrix Biol *26:* 161–165.

Michl, P., A.R. Ramjaun, O.E. Pardo, P.H. Warne, M. Wagner, R. Poulsom, C. D'Arrigo, K. Ryder, A. Menke, T. Gress, J. Downward (2005) CUTL1 is a target of TGF(beta) signaling that enhances cancer cell motility and invasiveness. Cancer Cell *7:* 521–532.

Mimeault, M., S.K. Batra (2007) Interplay of distinct growth factors during epithelial mesenchymal transition of cancer progenitor cells and molecular targeting as novel cancer therapies. Ann Oncol *18:* 1605–1619.

Mimeault, M., E. Moore, N. Moniaux, J.P. Henichart, P. Depreux, M.F. Lin, S.K. Batra (2006) Cytotoxic effects induced by a combination of cyclopamine and gefitinib, the selective hedgehog and epidermal growth factor receptor signaling inhibitors, in prostate cancer cells. Int J Cancer *118:* 1022–1031.

Miyake, H., I. Hara, M. Fujisawa, M.E. Gleave (2006) The potential of clusterin inhibiting antisense oligodeoxynucleotide therapy for prostate cancer. Expert Opin Investig Drugs *15:* 507–517.

Miyazono, K. (2009) Transforming growth factor-beta signaling in epithelial-mesenchymal transition and progression of cancer. Proc Jpn Acad Ser B Phys Biol Sci *85:* 314–323.

Morali, O.G., V. Delmas, R. Moore, C. Jeanney, J.P. Thiery, L. Larue (2001) IGF-II induces rapid beta-catenin relocation to the nucleus during epithelium to mesenchyme transition. Oncogene *20:* 4942–4950.

Moustakas, A., C.H. Heldin (2007) Signaling networks guiding epithelial-mesenchymal transitions during embryogenesis and cancer progression. Cancer Sci *98:* 1512–1520.

Murillo, M.M., G. del Castillo, A. Sanchez, M. Fernandez, I. Fabregat (2005) Involvement of EGF receptor and c-Src in the survival signals induced by TGF-beta1 in hepatocytes. Oncogene *24:* 4580–4587.

Nakaya, Y., G. Sheng (2008) Epithelial to mesenchymal transition during gastrulation: an embryological view. Dev Growth Differ *50:* 755–766.

Nakaya, Y., E.W. Sukowati, C. Alev, F. Nakazawa, G. Sheng (2011) Involvement of dystroglycan in epithelial-mesenchymal transition during chick gastrulation. Cells Tissues Organs *193:* 64–73.

Ozdamar, B., et al (2005) Regulation of the polarity protein Par6 by TGFβ receptors controls epithelial cell plasticity. Science *307:* 1603–1609.

Peinado, H., M. Quintanilla, A. Cano (2003) Transforming growth factor beta-1 induces snail transcription factor in epithelial cell lines: mechanisms for epithelial mesenchymal transitions. J Biol Chem *278:* 21113–21123.

Pennisi, P.A., V. Barr, N.P. Nunez, B. Stannard, D. Le Roith (2002) Reduced expression of insulin-like growth factor I receptors in MCF-7 breast cancer cells leads to a more metastatic phenotype. Cancer Res *62:* 6529–6537.

Perez-Moreno, M.A., A. Locascio, I. Rodrigo, G. Dhondt, F. Portillo, M.A. Nieto, A. Cano (2001) A new role for E12/E47 in the repression of E-cadherin expression and epithelial-mesenchymal transitions. J Biol Chem *276:* 27424–27431.

Prunier, C., P.H. Howe (2005) Disabled-2 (Dab2) is required for transforming growth factor beta-induced epithelial to mesenchymal transition (EMT). J Biol Chem *280:* 17540–17548.

Radisky, D.C., D.D. Levy, L.E. Littlepage, H. Liu, C.M. Nelson, J.E. Fata, D. Leake, E.L. Godden, D.G. Albertson, M.A. Nieto, Z. Werb, M.J. Bissell (2005) Rac1b and reactive oxygen species mediate MMP-3-induced EMT and genomic instability. Nature *436:* 123–127.

Rodgers, U.R., L. Kevorkian, A.K. Surridge, J.G. Waters, T.E. Swingler, K. Culley, S. Illman, J. Lohi, A.E. Parker, I.M. Clark (2009) Expression and function of matrix metalloproteinase (MMP)-28. Matrix Biol *28:* 263–272.

Royal, I., N. Lamarche-Vane, L. Lamorte, K. Kaibuchi, M. Park (2000) Activation of cdc42, rac, PAK, and rho-kinase in response to hepatocyte growth factor differentially regulates epithelial cell colony spreading and dissociation. Mol Biol Cell *11:* 1709–1725.

Schickel, R., S.M. Park, A.E. Murmann, M.E. Peter miR-200c regulates induction of apoptosis through CD95 by targeting FAP-1. Mol Cell *38:* 908–915.

Shintani, Y., M. Maeda, N. Chaika, K.R. Johnson, M.J. Wheelock (2008) Collagen I promotes epithelial-to-mesenchymal transition in lung cancer cells via transforming growth factor-beta signaling. Am J Respir Cell Mol Biol *38:* 95–104.

Srivastava, S., B. Ramdass, S. Nagarajan, M. Rehman, G. Mukherjee, S. Krishna (2010) Notch1 regulates the functional contribution of RhoC to cervical carcinoma progression. Br J Cancer *102:* 196–205.

Sun, X., J.D. Ritzenthaler, K. Wang, X. Zhong, E.S. White, S. Han, J. Roman (2010) The fibronectin EDA splicing variant induces epithelial-mesenchymal transition in lung cancer cells through integrin {alpha}9{beta}1-mediated activation of PI3-K and Erk. Am J Physiol Lung Cell Mol Physiol, Epub ahead of print.

Taki, M., K. Verschueren, K. Yokoyama, M. Nagayama, N. Kamata (2006) Involvement of Ets-1 transcription factor in inducing matrix metalloproteinase-2 expression by epithelial-mesenchymal transition in human squamous carcinoma cells. Int J Oncol *28:* 487–496.

Thiery, J.P. (2002) Epithelial-mesenchymal transitions in tumour progression. Nat Rev Cancer *2:* 442–454.

Thiery, J.P. (2003) Epithelial-mesenchymal transitions in development and pathologies. Curr Opin Cell Biol *15:* 740–746.

Thiery, J.P., J.P. Sleeman (2006) Complex networks orchestrate epithelial-mesenchymal transitions. Nat Rev Mol Cell Biol *7:* 131–142.

Thomson, S., F. Petti, I. Sujka-Kwok, D. Epstein, J.D. Haley (2008) Kinase switching in mesenchymal-like non-small cell lung cancer lines contributes to EGFR inhibitor resistance through pathway redundancy. Clin Exp Metastasis *25:* 843–854.

Thuault, S., U. Valcourt, M. Petersen, G. Manfioletti, C.H. Heldin, A. Moustakas (2006) Transforming growth factor-beta employs HMGA2 to elicit epithelial-mesenchymal transition. J Cell Biol *174:* 175–183.

Tian, M., W.P. Schiemann (2009) The TGF-beta paradox in human cancer: an update. Future Oncol *5:* 259–271.

Timmerman, L.A., J. Grego-Bessa, A. Raya, E. Bertran, J.M. Perez-Pomares, J. Diez, S. Aranda, S. Palomo, F. McCormick, J.C. Izpisua-Belmonte, J.L. de la Pompa (2004) Notch promotes epithelial-mesenchymal transition during cardiac development and oncogenic transformation. Genes Dev *18:* 99–115.

Tryndyak, V.P., F.A. Beland, I.P. Pogribny (2010) E-cadherin transcriptional down-regulation by epigenetic and microRNA-200 family alterations is related to mesenchymal and drug-resistant phenotypes in human breast cancer cells. Int J Cancer *126:* 2575–2583.

Tulasne, D., R. Paumelle, K.M. Weidner, B. Vandenbunder, V. Fafeur (1999) The multisubstrate docking site of the MET receptor is dispensable for MET-mediated RAS signaling and cell scattering. Mol Biol Cell *10:* 551–565.

Valles, A.M., B. Boyer, G. Tarone, J.P. Thiery (1996) Alpha 2 beta 1 integrin is required for the collagen and FGF-1 induced cell dispersion in a rat bladder carcinoma cell line. Cell Adhes Commun *4:* 187–199.

Vandewalle, C., J. Comijn, B. De Craene, P. Vermassen, E. Bruyneel, H. Andersen, E. Tulchinsky, F. Van Roy, G. Berx (2005) SIP1/ZEB2 induces EMT by repressing genes of different epithelial cell-cell junctions. Nucleic Acids Res *33:* 6566–6578.

Varnat, F., A. Duquet, M. Malerba, M. Zbinden, C. Mas, P. Gervaz, A. Ruiz i Altaba (2009) Human colon cancer epithelial cells harbour active HEDGEHOG-GLI signalling that is essential for tumour growth, recurrence, metastasis and stem cell survival and expansion. EMBO Mol Med *1:* 338–351.

Verschueren, K., J.E. Remacle, C. Collart, H. Kraft, B.S. Baker, P. Tylzanowski, L. Nelles, G. Wuytens, M.T. Su, R. Bodmer, J.C. Smith, D. Huylebroeck (1999) SIP1, a novel zinc finger/homeodomain repressor, interacts with Smad proteins and binds to 5′-CACCT sequences in candidate target genes. J Biol Chem *274:* 20489–20498.

Vincent, T., E.P. Neve, J.R. Johnson, A. Kukalev, F. Rojo, J. Albanell, K. Pietras, I. Virtanen, L. Philipson, P.L. Leopold, R.G. Crystal, A.G. de Herreros, A. Moustakas, R.F. Pettersson, J. Fuxe (2009) A SNAIL1-SMAD3/4 transcriptional repressor complex promotes TGF-beta mediated epithelial-mesenchymal transition. Nat Cell Biol *11:* 943–950.

Waerner, T., M. Alacakaptan, I. Tamir, R. Oberauer, A. Gal, T. Brabletz, M. Schreiber, M. Jechlinger, H. Beug (2006) ILEI: a cytokine essential for EMT, tumor formation, and late events in metastasis in epithelial cells. Cancer Cell *10:* 227–239.

Wang, Z., S. Sandiford, C. Wu, S.S. Li (2009) Numb regulates cell-cell adhesion and polarity in response to tyrosine kinase signalling. EMBO J *28:* 2360–2373.

Wilkins-Port, C.E., P.J. Higgins (2007) Regulation of extracellular matrix remodeling following transforming growth factor-beta1/epidermal growth factor-stimulated epithelial-mesenchymal transition in human premalignant keratinocytes. Cells Tissues Organs *185:* 116–122.

Wyatt, L., Y. Khew-Goodall (2008) PTP-Pez: a novel regulator of TGFbeta signaling. Cell Cycle *7:* 2290–2295.

Wyatt, L., C. Wadham, L.A. Crocker, M. Lardelli, Y. Khew-Goodall (2007) The protein tyrosine phosphatase Pez regulates TGFbeta, epithelial-mesenchymal transition, and organ development. J Cell Biol *178:* 1223–1235.

Yang, L., C. Lin, Z.R. Liu (2006) P68 RNA helicase mediates PDGF-induced epithelial mesenchymal transition by displacing Axin from beta-catenin. Cell *127:* 139–155.

Yates, C.C., C.R. Shepard, D.B. Stolz, A. Wells (2007) Co-culturing human prostate carcinoma cells with hepatocytes leads to increased expression of E-cadherin. Br J Cancer *96:* 1246–1252.

Yokoyama, K., N. Kamata, R. Fujimoto, S. Tsutsumi, M. Tomonari, M. Taki, H. Hosokawa, M. Nagayama (2003) Increased invasion and matrix metalloproteinase-2 expression by Snail-induced mesenchymal transition in squamous cell carcinomas. Int J Oncol *22:* 891–898.

Yook, J.I., X.Y. Li, I. Ota, C. Hu, H.S. Kim, N.H. Kim, S.Y. Cha, J.K. Ryu, Y.J. Choi, J. Kim, E.R. Fearon, S.J. Weiss (2006) A Wnt-Axin2-GSK3beta cascade regulates Snail1 activity in breast cancer cells. Nat Cell Biol *8:* 1398–1406.

Zavadil, J., L. Cermak, N. Soto-Nieves, E.P. Bottinger (2004) Integration of TGF-beta/Smad and Jagged1/Notch signalling in epithelial-to-mesenchymal transition. EMBO J *23:* 1155–1165.

Zeineldin, R., R. Martina, O. Dominic (2006) Mesenchymal transformation in epithelial ovarian tumor cells expressing epidermal growth factor receptor variant III. Mol Carcinog *45:* 851–860.

Zhang, D., T.A. LaFortune, S. Krishnamurthy, F.J. Esteva, M. Cristofanilli, P. Liu, A. Lucci, B. Singh, M.C. Hung, G.N. Hortobagyi, N.T. Ueno (2009) Epidermal growth factor receptor tyrosine kinase inhibitor reverses mesenchymal to epithelial phenotype and inhibits metastasis in inflammatory breast cancer. Clin Cancer Res *15:* 6639–6648.

Cells Tissues Organs

Cells Tissues Organs 2011;193:98–113
DOI: 10.1159/000320163

Published online: November 3, 2010

The Cain and Abl of Epithelial-Mesenchymal Transition and Transforming Growth Factor-β in Mammary Epithelial Cells

Tressa M. Allington[a] William P. Schiemann[b]

[a]Department of Pharmacology, Anschutz Medical Campus, University of Colorado Denver, Aurora, Colo., and
[b]Case Comprehensive Cancer Center, Case Western Reserve University, Cleveland, Ohio, USA

Key Words

Breast cancer · c-Abl · Epithelial-mesenchymal transition · Metastasis · Signal transduction · Transforming growth factor-β

Abstract

Transforming growth factor-β (TGF-β) normally inhibits breast cancer development by preventing mammary epithelial cell (MEC) proliferation, by inducing MEC apoptosis, and by creating cell microenvironments that maintain MEC homeostasis and prevent their uncontrolled growth and motility. Mammary tumorigenesis elicits dramatic alterations in MEC architecture and microenvironment integrity, which collectively counteract the tumor-suppressing activities of TGF-β and enable its stimulation of breast cancer invasion and metastasis. How malignant MECs overcome the cytostatic actions imposed by normal microenvironments and TGF-β, and how abnormal microenvironments conspire with TGF-β to stimulate the development and progression of mammary tumors remains largely undefined. These knowledge gaps have prevented science and medicine from implementing treatments effective in simultaneously targeting abnormal cellular microenvironments, and in antagonizing the oncogenic activities of TGF-β in developing and progressing breast cancers. c-Abl is a ubiquitously expressed nonreceptor protein tyrosine kinase that essentially oversees all aspects of cell physiology, including the regulation of cell proliferation, migration and adhesion, as well as that of cell survival. Thus, the biological functions of c-Abl are highly reminiscent of those attributed to TGF-β, including the ability to function as either a suppressor or promoter of tumorigenesis. Interestingly, while dysregulated Abl activity clearly promotes tumorigenesis in hematopoietic cells, an analogous role for c-Abl in regulating solid tumor development, including those of the breast, remains controversial. Here, we review the functions of c-Abl in regulating breast cancer development and progression, and in alleviating the oncogenic activities of TGF-β and its stimulation of epithelial-mesenchymal transition during mammary tumorigenesis.

Abbreviations used in this paper

BCR	break-point cluster region
CML	chronic myelogenous leukemia
CST-Abl	constitutively active c-Abl
EMT	epithelial-mesenchymal transition
MEC	mammary epithelial cell
PTK	protein tyrosine kinase
TGF-β	transforming growth factor-β

KARGER

Fax +41 61 306 12 34
E-Mail karger@karger.ch
www.karger.com

Accessible online at:
www.karger.com/cto

Dr. William P. Schiemann
Case Comprehensive Cancer Center, Case Western Reserve University
Wolstein Research Building, Room 2131
2103 Cornell Road, Cleveland, Ohio 44106 (USA)
Tel. +1 216 844 8797, Fax +1 216 844 7832, E-Mail William.Schiemann@case.edu

Introduction

Transforming growth factor-β (TGF-β) is a ubiquitous cytokine that fulfills fundamental roles during embryonic development, cellular differentiation, wound healing and tissue remodeling, as well as immune homeostasis [Massague, 2008; Heldin et al., 2009; Tian and Schiemann, 2009b]. In addition, TGF-β also plays an essential function in maintaining normal epithelial cell and tissue architecture, a regulatory mechanism that becomes disrupted in developing neoplasms. Indeed, as neoplastic lesions progress and become invasive, they typically circumvent the tumor-suppressing activities of TGF-β and paradoxically convert this cytokine into a potent promoter of metastatic dissemination [Benson, 2004; Buck and Knabbe, 2006; Pardali and Moustakas, 2007; Barcellos-Hoff and Akhurst, 2009; Wendt et al., 2009a]. Recent evidence has established epithelial-mesenchymal transition (EMT) as being a vital component involved in initiating oncogenic TGF-β signaling in normal and malignant cells [Heldin et al., 2009; Wendt et al., 2009a; Xu et al., 2009]. Indeed, TGF-β is a master regulator of EMT and its ability to engender polarized epithelial cells to (1) downregulate their expression of genes associated with epithelial phenotypes, including those operant in forming adherens and tight junctions; (2) remodel their actin cytoskeletons and microtubule networks; and (3) upregulate their expression of genes associated with mesenchymal phenotypes and cell motility [Heldin et al., 2009; Wendt et al., 2009a; Xu et al., 2009]. The process of EMT has recently been categorized into 3 distinct biological subtypes [Kalluri and Weinberg, 2009], namely type 1 (embryonic and developmental EMT), type 2 (tissue regeneration and fibrotic EMT) and type 3 (cancer progression and metastatic EMT). The linkage of type 3 EMT to the development of metastasis and poor clinical outcomes [Thiery, 2003] has led to intense research efforts aimed at developing novel chemotherapeutics capable of inhibiting oncogenic EMT, and as such, of improving the clinical course of patients with metastatic disease. Alternatively, identifying the molecular mechanisms that promote mesenchymal-epithelial transition (MET), which phenotypically and morphologically reverses the activities of EMT, may also offer new inroads to impede or thwart primary tumor metastasis, an idea echoed by those who attended the 3rd International TEMTIA meeting that was held in Krakow, Poland, in 2007.

c-Abl is a multifunctional nonreceptor protein tyrosine kinase (PTK) that localizes to the plasma membrane, cytoplasm and nucleus where it governs a variety of cellular functions and activities, including the (1) transduction of integrins and growth factor receptor signals; (2) induction of cell cycle arrest initiated by DNA damage; (3) regulation of actin cytoskeletal dynamics; and (4) interaction with numerous adaptor proteins and scaffold complexes [Pendergast, 1996; Plattner et al., 1999; Hamer et al., 2001; Woodring et al., 2001; Pendergast, 2002; Woodring et al., 2002; Zandy and Pendergast, 2008]. In addition, c-Abl and its relative Arg are unique among nonreceptor PTKs in that both molecules house direct actin-binding domains that enable c-Abl to sense and respond to extracellular signals coupled to altered actin cytoskeletal architectures [Woodring et al., 2001, 2002; Zandy and Pendergast, 2008]. It is interesting to note that the diverse and complex biological functions of c-Abl are surprisingly reminiscent of the pathophysiological actions of TGF-β, including its dichotomous behavior exhibited during tumorigenesis. For instance, the tumor-promoting activities of c-Abl are best exemplified by its causal initiation of chronic myelogenous leukemia (CML), wherein c-Abl is translocated and fused to the break-point cluster region (BCR) on chromosome 22, resulting in the generation of a constitutively active Abl kinase fusion protein [Druker, 2006; Wang, 2006; Hunter, 2007; Lin and Arlinghaus, 2008]. Moreover, the pharmacological development and clinical implementation of imatinib (also known as Gleevec or STI-571), which targets the ATP-binding site in the c-Abl kinase domain and inhibits its phosphotransferase activity [Druker, 2006; Wang, 2006; Hunter, 2007; Lin and Arlinghaus, 2008], has significantly improved the treatment of CML and served as a model for the rationale design of protein kinase inhibitors [Druker, 2006; Soverini et al., 2008]. Although dysregulated c-Abl activity clearly promotes tumorigenesis in hematopoietic cells, the role of c-Abl in regulating tumorigenesis in solid tumors remains controversial. In fact, recent clinical trials designed to assess the efficacy of c-Abl antagonism in preventing breast cancer progression failed to observe any clinical benefit in imatinib-treated breast cancer patients. Moreover, these same studies found imatinib to cause significant toxicity and elicit disease progression in breast cancer patients [Modi et al., 2005; Chew et al., 2008; Cristofanilli et al., 2008]. Along these lines, our recently published study showed that imatinib administration failed to provide any therapeutic benefit to mice bearing aggressive mammary tumors, and instead, this same pharmacological treatment tended to produce larger breast tumors as compared with those observed in their vehicle-treated counterparts (fig. 1) [Allington et al., 2009]. Remarkably, this same study demonstrated that engineering late-stage metastatic breast cancer cells to stably express a constitutively active c-Abl mutant resulted in their morphologic and phenotypic reversion both in vitro and in vivo, as well as circumvented the oncogenic activities of TGF-β and its ability to induce EMT [Allington et al., 2009]. Clearly, a deeper and more thorough understanding of pathophysiological functions of c-Abl in regulating solid tumor development and progression is needed for science and medicine to successfully advance the use of targeted chemotherapies against c-Abl and against various effectors activated by oncogenic TGF-β signaling.

Here, we review recent findings that directly impact our understanding of the dichotomous roles played by c-Abl during mammary tumorigenesis and discuss emerging evidence suggesting that chemotherapeutic targeting of c-Abl activation, not inhibition, may offer new inroads to suppress breast cancer progression and the oncogenic activities of TGF-β, particularly its induction of EMT and metastasis in developing neoplasms of the breast.

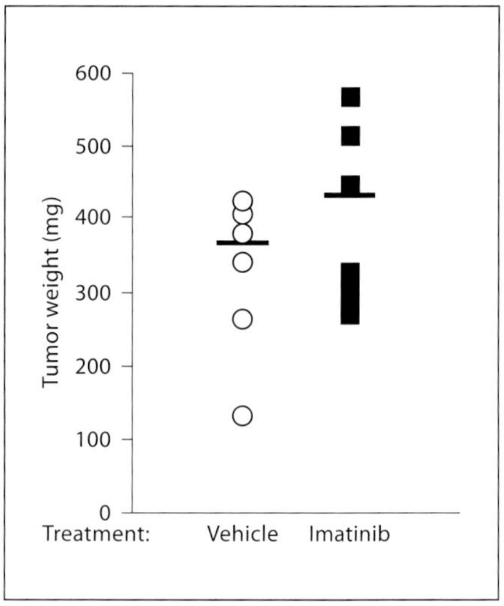

Fig. 1. c-Abl antagonism fails to inhibit mammary tumor growth in mice. Female Balb/c mice were injected orthotopically with syngeneic 4T1 cells and treated daily beginning on day 8 after engraftment with either vehicle or imatinib (50 mg/kg/day) as indicated. Primary tumors were removed surgically and weighed at days 24 and 27 after engraftment. Bars indicate the mean tumor weight per group (6 mice/group). Reprinted with kind permission from Allington et al. [2009].

Abl Signaling and Cancer Progression

c-Abl was originally identified as the cellular counterpart to the Abelson murine leukemia virus, v-Abl [Wang et al., 1984]. Subsequent studies established that c-Abl exists in 2 isoforms in mammals (1a or 1b in humans and I or IV in mice), and that this large (approximately 140 kDa) nonreceptor PTK contains a variety of modular domains that enable c-Abl to bind numerous signaling and scaffolding proteins. Figure 2 depicts the structural features of human and murine c-Abl isoforms, both of which house (1) Src homology 2 (SH2) and SH3 domains; (2) a proline-rich adaptor-binding motif; (3) a PTK domain; (4) 3 nuclear localization signals and 1 nuclear export signal; (5) 3 high-mobility group-like boxes that function cooperatively in binding DNA; and (6) globular and filamentous actin-binding domains [Woodring et al., 2002; Hunter, 2007]. The presence of functional nuclear localization signals and nuclear export signal motifs localizes c-Abl to both the cytoplasmic and nuclear compartments in quiescent cells, as well as enables c-Abl to translocate to the nucleus in response to a variety of extracellular stimuli [Lewis et al., 1996; Wen et al., 1996; Taagepera et al., 1998; Plattner et al., 1999; Woodring et al., 2002]. In nontransformed cells, the activation status of c-Abl is tightly controlled and its PTK activity is retained in an inactive conformation through intramolecular c-Abl interactions [Woodring et al., 2002; Hunter, 2007]. Indeed, displacing either the N-terminal autoinhibitory Cap region or the SH2/SH3 domains of c-Abl by the binding of its substrates or effector molecules rapidly and transiently stimulates this PTK, whose activity is downregulated following its ubiquitination and proteosomal degradation [Echarri and Pendergast, 2001; Woodring et al., 2002; Zhu and Wang, 2004]. Cytoplasmic c-Abl is activated by a variety of growth factors and cytokines, by reactive oxygen species, and by cell attachment and mechanotransduction that directs c-Abl to adherens complexes and regions of actin cytoskeletal remodeling [Woodring et al., 2002; Zhu and Wang, 2004]. Nuclear c-Abl is also activated by reactive oxygen species and by DNA damage that couples c-Abl to the regulation of cell survival and apoptosis [Agami et al., 1999; Vigneri and Wang, 2001; Truong et al., 2003; Chau et al., 2004]. Interestingly, both of the oncogenic forms of c-Abl, namely BCR-Abl and v-Abl, are unable to enter the nucleus, and their enforced nuclear expression induces apoptosis, not cellular transformation [Woodring et al., 2002; Zhu and Wang, 2004; Suzuki and Shishido, 2007]. Thus, the pathophysiological output of c-Abl activation ultimately reflects a conglomeration of the initiating signal, the cellular context and the cellular locale wherein c-Abl is stimulated.

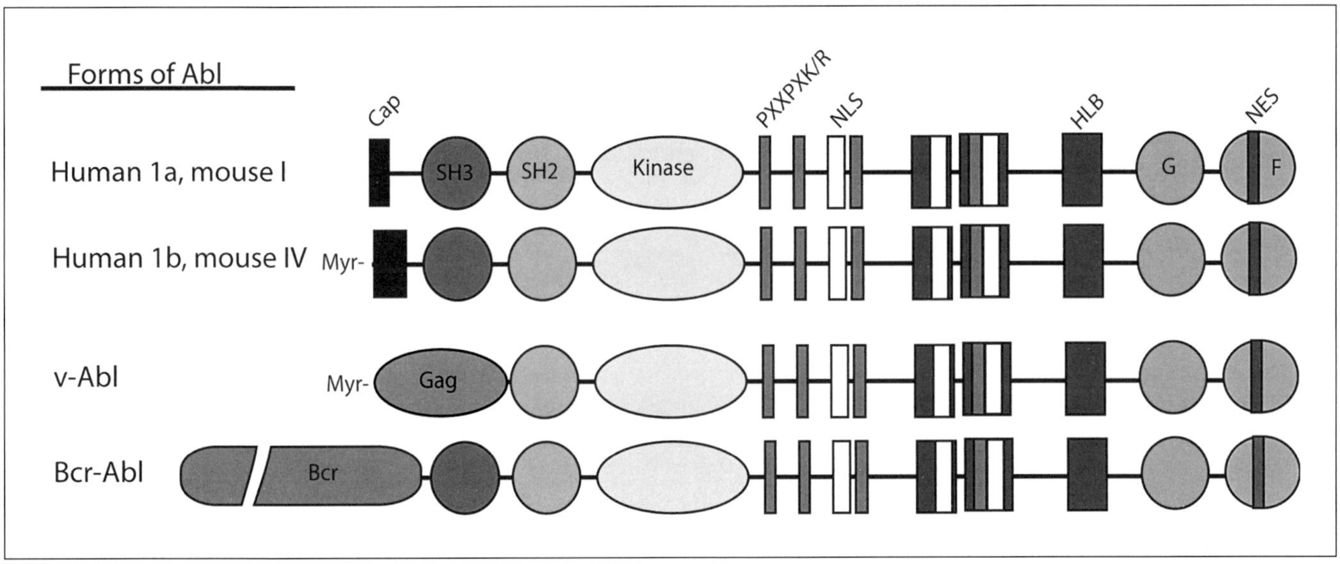

Color version available online

Fig. 2. Schematic depiction of the functional domains of human (1a and 1b) and murine (I and IV) Abl isoforms. The N terminus of c-Abl contains either an autoinhibitory Cap region or a consensus motif for myristoylation (black), which is followed by SH3 (blue; colors refer to the online version only) and SH2 (pink) domains, which is followed by the catalytic PTK domain (kinase, yellow). The central region of c-Abl possesses 4 PXXPXK/R sequences (purple), 3 nuclear localization sequences (NLS, white), and 3 high-mobility group-like boxes (HLB, green). Finally, the C terminus of c-Abl houses domains for binding globular (G, orange) and filamentous (F, gray) actin, as well as a nuclear export sequence (NES, brown). The oncogenic forms of Abl (v-Abl and BCR-Abl) contain modified N-terminal regions that disrupt the autoinhibitory functions normally mediated by the Cap region, which elicits constitutive PTK activity. The aberrant N terminus in v-Abl comprises a viral Gag sequence (light blue), while that in BCR-Abl comprises a portion of the N terminus of the BCR (red).

As mentioned above, the oncogenic potential of c-Abl was elucidated by the discovery that c-Abl can be fused to the BCR region on chromosome 22, an untoward translocation event that gives rise to BCR-Abl and its ability to induce CML development and progression [Druker, 2006; Hunter, 2007]. The synthesis and implementation of imatinib (Gleevec) to antagonize the phosphotransferase activity of Abl revolutionized the treatment of CML by eliciting response rates of about 98% in patients with the chronic phase of CML at the time of diagnosis [Mauro and Druker, 2001; Mauro et al., 2002; Druker, 2006]. In stark contrast to its causal role in initiating hematopoietic cancers, a definitive function for c-Abl in promoting the formation and progression of solid tumors, including those of the breast, remains an active and controversial area of research. For instance, early cell biology studies found that the phosphorylation of Crk by c-Abl inhibits fibroblast and carcinoma cell motility by preventing the formation of Crk:p130Cas complexes [Kain and Klemke, 2001; Kain et al., 2003]. In addition, hepatocyte growth factor signaling and its stimulation of thyroid cancer cell migration was potentiated significantly in imatinib-treated cells as compared with their vehicle-treated counterparts [Frasca et al., 2001], suggesting that c-Abl activity suppresses carcinoma motility. With respect to cancers of the breast, c-Abl activation has been associated with enhanced breast cancer cell proliferation, invasion, survival and anchorage-independent growth [Plattner et al., 1999; Srinivasan and Plattner, 2006; Lin and Arlinghaus, 2008; Srinivasan et al., 2008], and with their transformation by Src [Sirvent et al., 2007]. In stark contrast, c-Abl was observed to be essential in suppressing mammary tumorigenesis mediated by ephrin B2/ephrin B [Noren et al., 2006]. Moreover, we recently discovered that constitutive c-Abl activity abrogates the oncogenic behaviors of TGF-β in late-stage breast cancer cells, resulting in their phenotypic and morphologic reversion both in vitro and in vivo (see below) [Allington et al., 2009]. These latter findings suggest that imatinib administration may be contraindicated in breast cancer patients. Accordingly, recent clinical trials designed to assess the efficacy of c-Abl antagonism in preventing breast cancer progression have met with disappointing results, including the presence of severe drug

Table 1. Role of c-Abl in solid tumor progression

Study type	Disease/cells	Major finding	Reference
Abl as a tumor promoter			
Preclinical	lung cancer	increased c-Crk expression is associated with aggressive phenotypes	Miller et al., 2003
Preclinical	lung cancer	imatinib and Fus1 inhibit c-Abl and anchorage-independent growth of H1299 cells	Lin et al., 2007b
Preclinical	breast cancer	constitutive c-Abl activation is elicited by dysregulated EGFR, HER2 and Src, leading to increased cell invasion	Srinivasan and Plattner 2006
Preclinical	breast cancer	c-Abl mediates Src-transformation and survival of breast cancer cells	Sirvent et al., 2007
Preclinical	breast cancer	c-Abl mediates IGF-1 receptor-stimulated breast cancer progression	Srinivasan et al., 2008
Abl as a tumor suppressor			
Preclinical	colon cancer	c-Abl activates p73α/GADD45α, leading to apoptosis in response to DNA mismatch repair	Li et al., 2008
Preclinical	colon cancer	c-Abl activates p73α/GADD45α, leading to G2 arrest after induction of DNA mismatch repair	Wagner et al., 2008
Preclinical	breast cancer	ephrin B2/ephrin B4 suppress breast cancer tumorigenicity via activation of a c-Abl/Crk/MMP-2-signaling axis	Noren et al., 2006
Preclinical	thyroid cancer	imatinib enhances thyroid cancer cell motility in response to HGF	Frasca et al., 2001
Preclinical	breast cancer	activated c-Abl suppresses oncogenic TGF-β signaling, inhibits EMT and reverts breast cancer tumorigenicity in vitro and in vivo	Allington et al., 2009
Clinical phase I	breast cancer	imatinib offered no clinical benefit in PDGF receptor-positive metastatic breast cancer	Cristofanilli et al., 2008
Clinical phase II	breast cancer	imatinib provided no therapeutic benefit against invasive breast cancer patients	Modi et al., 2005
Clinical phase II	breast cancer	imatinib and capecitabine treatment failed to improve the clinical course of metastatic breast cancer patients	Chew et al., 2008
Clinical phase I/II	prostate cancer	imatinib administration either alone or in combination promoted disease progression and severe toxicity	Lin et al., 2006, 2007a
Clinical phase II	pancreatic cancer	imatinib administration fails to offer any therapeutic protection against pancreatic cancer	Chen et al., 2006; Gharibo et al., 2008

EGFR = Epidermal growth factor receptor; HER2 = human epidermal growth factor receptor 2; IGF-1 = insulin growth factor 1; MMP-2 = matrix metalloproteinase 2; HGF = hepatocyte growth factor; PDGF = platelet-derived growth factor.

toxicities and the initiation of disease progression [Modi et al., 2005; Chew et al., 2008; Cristofanilli et al., 2008]. Similar detrimental clinical outcomes were observed in pancreatic [Chen et al., 2006; Gharibo et al., 2008] and prostate [Lin et al., 2006, 2007a] cancer patients subjected to imatinib administration.

Table 1 summarizes the dichotomous roles of c-Abl in regulating solid tumor development and progression, and in doing so, highlights the need to identify novel biomarkers capable of staging and stratifying cancer patients on the basis of their c-Abl expression and signaling profiles.

TGF-β Signaling and EMT

TGF-β is a pluripotent cytokine that plays essential roles in regulating mammalian development and differentiation, and in maintaining tissue homeostasis [Benson, 2004; Buck and Knabbe, 2006; Barcellos-Hoff and Akhurst, 2009; Tian and Schiemann, 2009b]. The versatile nature of TGF-β is emphasized by the fact that virtually all cells in the metazoan body are capable of both producing and responding to this cytokine. TGF-β is now recognized as a potent tumor suppressor that prevents the dysregulated growth and survival of cells, particularly those of epithelial, endothelial and hematopoietic origins [Massague, 2008; Heldin et al., 2009; Tian and Schiemann, 2009b]. The process of tumorigenesis and its associated genetic, epigenetic and microenvironmental alterations enable early-stage cancer cells to inactivate the cytostatic activities of TGF-β through mechanisms that remain incompletely understood. As these neoplastic cells continue to evolve towards advanced malignancy, they ultimately acquire the ability to convert the cytostatic functions of TGF-β into those capable of driving neoplastic progression, including the induction of tumor growth, invasion and metastatic dissemination [Benson, 2004; Buck and Knabbe, 2006; Barcellos-Hoff and Akhurst, 2009; Tian and Schiemann, 2009b]. The functional conversion of TGF-β behavior during tumorigenesis is known as the 'TGF-β paradox', whose eventual interpretation and translation holds the key to developing novel chemotherapies capable of preferentially targeting the oncogenic activities of TGF-β [Schiemann, 2007].

An important consequence of TGF-β signaling is its potential to induce EMT, a process whereby immotile, polarized epithelial cells transdifferentiate into highly motile, apolar fibroblastoid-like cells [Heldin et al., 2009; Wendt et al., 2009a; Xu et al., 2009]. Essential features exhibited by epithelial cells undergoing EMT include (1) diminished cell polarity owing to the downregulated expression of epithelial cell markers (e.g., E-cadherin, zona occludens 1 and β_4-integrin); (2) remodeled actin cytoskeletal architectures; (3) upregulated expression of fibroblast markers and genes operant in cell motility and invasion (e.g., vimentin, N-cadherin, α-smooth muscle actin, Twist); and (4) acquired expansion of cells that possess stem cell-like properties and phenotypes [Heldin et al., 2009; Wendt et al., 2009a; Xu et al., 2009]. Importantly, recent studies by our group have shown that the initiation of oncogenic TGF-β signaling coincides with its stimulation of EMT in normal and malignant MECs [Galliher and Schiemann, 2006, 2007; Lee et al., 2008; Neil et al., 2008; Neil and Schiemann, 2008; Neil et al., 2009; Tian and Schiemann, 2009a; Wendt and Schiemann, 2009; Wendt et al., 2009b], suggesting that the eventual development and implementation of pharmacological agents capable of uncoupling TGF-β from EMT may one day improve the clinical course of breast cancer patients.

The ability of TGF-β to induce EMT commences upon its binding to the TGF-β type II receptor, which then recruits, transphosphorylates and activates TGF-β type I receptor, which then phosphorylates and stimulates the latent TGF-β transcription factors, Smad2 and Smad3. Following their activation, Smad2/3 interact physically with the co-Smad, Smad4, which enables the resulting heterocomplexes to translocate to the nucleus where they associate with a variety of transcriptional activators and repressors to govern the expression of TGF-β-responsive genes in a cell- and context-specific manner [Heldin et al., 2009; Wendt et al., 2009a]. The coupling of TGF-β to Smad2/3 stimulation, which is commonly referred to as either 'Smad2/3-dependent' or 'canonical' TGF-β signaling, plays an essential role in governing all aspects of the pathophysiological activities of TGF-β, including its induction of EMT [Oft et al., 1996; Valcourt et al., 2005; see also Masszi and Kapus, 2011, this issue]. In addition to its stimulation of canonical Smad2/3 signaling, we and others have identified a variety of noncanonical effectors whose activation by TGF-β also mediate fundamental functions of this cytokine [for review, see Lamouille and Derynck, 2011, this issue]. With respect to its induction of EMT, TGF-β must also activate (1) MAP kinase family members, particularly ERK1/2 [Xie et al., 2004] and p38 MAPK [Bhowmick et al., 2001; Galliher and Schiemann, 2007; Galliher-Beckley and Schiemann, 2008]; (2) focal adhesion complex proteins, including β_1- and β_3-integrins [Bhowmick et al., 2001; Galliher and Schiemann, 2006], Src [Galliher and Schiemann, 2006, 2007], focal adhesion kinase [Wendt and Schiemann, 2009] and p130Cas [Wendt et al., 2009b]; (3) nuclear factor-κB [Huber et al., 2004; Neil and Schiemann, 2008] and its downstream effector, cyclooxygenase 2 [Neil et al., 2008], which promotes EMT by initiating an autocrine prostaglandin E_2:EP_2 receptor signaling loop [Tian and Schiemann, 2009a]; (4) phosphoinositide 3-kinase and its downstream effectors, AKT and mTOR [Bakin et al., 2000; Lamouille and Derynck, 2007; Lamouille and Derynck, 2011]; (5) small guanosine triphosphate-binding proteins, including cdc42, Rac1 and RhoA [Wendt et al., 2009a]; and (6) PAR6 and its recruitment of the E3 ligase, Smurf1 [Ozdamar et al., 2005]. Although the precise contribution of canonical and noncanonical TGF-β signaling in mediating the various subtypes of EMT has yet to be clarified, it is known that the activation of both pathways is necessary for the faithful initiation and completion of EMT by TGF-β and its ability to confer stem cell-like properties to epithelial cells, whose newfound plasticity enables metastatic cancer cells to thrive in otherwise hostile secondary sites [Polyak and Weinberg, 2009]. Readers desiring more in-depth discussions of the molecular mechanisms that underlie the ability of TGF-β to induce EMT are directed to several recent and comprehensive reviews [Heldin et al., 2009; Wendt et al., 2009a; Xu et al., 2009; Lamouille and Derynck, 2011].

c-Abl Activation Suppresses EMT and Breast Cancer Progression

An essential component of EMT centers on the dissolution of adherens junctions and the remodeling of the actin cytoskeleton, both of which enable transitioning cells to acquire motile and invasive phenotypes [Heldin et al., 2009; Wendt et al., 2009a; Xu et al., 2009]. Interestingly, c-Abl activity has been associated with both the assembly and dissolution of adherens junctions and with altered actin dynamics and architectures through its ability to bind globular and filamentous actin [Woodring et al., 2001, 2002, 2004; Zandy et al., 2007; Zandy and Pendergast, 2008]. Thus, the process of EMT presents a unique situation in which the paradoxical functions of c-Abl and TGF-β may intersect during mammary tumorigenesis. For instance, c-Abl essentially governs all biological decisions made by cells, including whether they proliferate, migrate or invade, or even whether they live or die [Zhu and Wang, 2004; Lin and Arlinghaus, 2008]. In fact, the physiological functions performed by c-Abl in many ways parallel those played by TGF-β, including their capacity to serve as tumor suppressors or promoters in a cell- and context-specific manner [Massague, 2008; Tian and Schiemann, 2009b]. Given the obvious pathophysiological similarities that exist between TGF-β and c-Abl in epithelial cells, we hypothesized c-Abl as an essential player in determining the morphologies and phenotypes of MECs, including their ability to undergo EMT in response to TGF-β. We tested this hypothesis by manipulating the expression or activity of c-Abl via several complementary approaches: (1) loss of c-Abl function by pharmacological inhibition (i.e. imatinib), by retroviral transduction of a kinase-dead c-Abl mutant or by lentiviral transduction of a shRNA against c-Abl; or (2) gain of c-Abl function by retroviral transduction of a constitutively active c-Abl mutant (CST-Abl). These c-Abl manipulations were applied to 2 murine MEC cell lines to interrogate the potential linkage between c-Abl and TGF-β: (1) normal murine NMuMG mammary gland cells, which are nontransformed and exhibit normal cuboidal epithelial architectures that readily undergo a robust EMT in response to TGF-β [Sokol et al., 2005; Galliher and Schiemann, 2006, 2007; Galliher-Beckley and Schiemann, 2008; Lee et al., 2008; Neil et al., 2008; Neil and Schiemann, 2008; Neil et al., 2009; Wendt and Schiemann, 2009; Wendt et al., 2009b]; and (2) malignant, metastatic 4T1 cells, which are a late-stage model of TGF-β-responsive breast cancer [Galliher-Beckley and Schiemann, 2008; Lee et al., 2008; Neil and Schiemann, 2008; Yang et al., 2008; Tian and Schiemann, 2009a; Wendt and Schiemann, 2009; Wendt et al., 2009b]. Figure 3a shows that c-Abl expression and activity were essential for maintaining normal MEC morphology, such that measures resulting in a loss of c-Abl function elicited an EMT response, while those measures resulting in a gain of c-Abl function produced a 'hyper-epithelial' response that was resistant to EMT and invasion stimulated by TGF-β [Allington et al., 2009]. The morphological alterations induced by inactivating c-Abl also transpired in normal human MECs [Allington et al., 2009], and more importantly, gene expression analyses confirmed the ability of c-Abl deficiency to increase mesenchymal gene expression (table 2). Thus, c-Abl inactivation results in morphological, transcriptional and migrational changes suggestive of those observed during EMT stimulated by TGF-β.

Table 2. c-Abl deficiency elicits an EMT transcriptional signature in NMuMG cells

NMuMG cells		Average relative mRNA, %	
		(–) TGF-β	(+) TGF-β
E-cadherin	scram	100.0	58.1 ± 8.7
	shAbl	104.6 ± 8.7	47.6 ± 7.8
N-cadherin	scram	100.0	856.0 ± 14.6
	shAbl	345.9 ± 21.1	1,050.9 ± 47.4
Vimentin	scram	100.0	475.6 ± 40.9
	shAbl	1,135.1 ± 26.9	858.0 ± 28.9
Twist	scram	100.0	295.3 ± 33.2
	shAbl	569.5 ± 20.3	683.9 ± 49.8

Quiescent parental (scrambled shRNA, scram) or c-Abl-deficient (shAbl) normal murine mammary gland cells (NMuMG) were incubated in the absence or presence of TGF-β_1 (5 ng/ml) for 48 h, at which point total RNA was isolated and subjected to semiquantitative real-time PCR analysis. Data are the mean (±SE; n = 3) percent change in EMT marker gene expression relative to that observed in untreated parental normal murine mammary gland cells.

Extending these analyses to metastatic 4T1 cells demonstrated that CST-Abl expression was sufficient in reducing cell scattering and promoting stronger cell-cell junctions in traditional 2D culture systems (fig. 3b). The morphological differences induced by c-Abl activation were greatly exaggerated when these same cells were propagated in compliant 3D organotypic cultures. Indeed, in stark contrast to the large and irregularly shaped organoids formed by parental and loss of c-Abl function 4T1 cells, those expressing CST-Abl formed dramatically smaller and perfectly spherical organoids that appeared to undergo a partial hollowing (fig. 3c, d). In addition, CST-Abl expression reinstated the cytostatic activities of TGF-β in 4T1 cells in part by (1) acting as a broad-spectrum suppressor of matrix metalloproteinase expression [Allington et al., 2009], and (2) overriding the tumor-promoting signals engendered by rigid microenvironments [Allington et al., 2009]. Thus, enforced activation of c-Abl in metastatic MECs may provide a novel means to alleviate the oncogenic activities of TGF-β and, consequently,

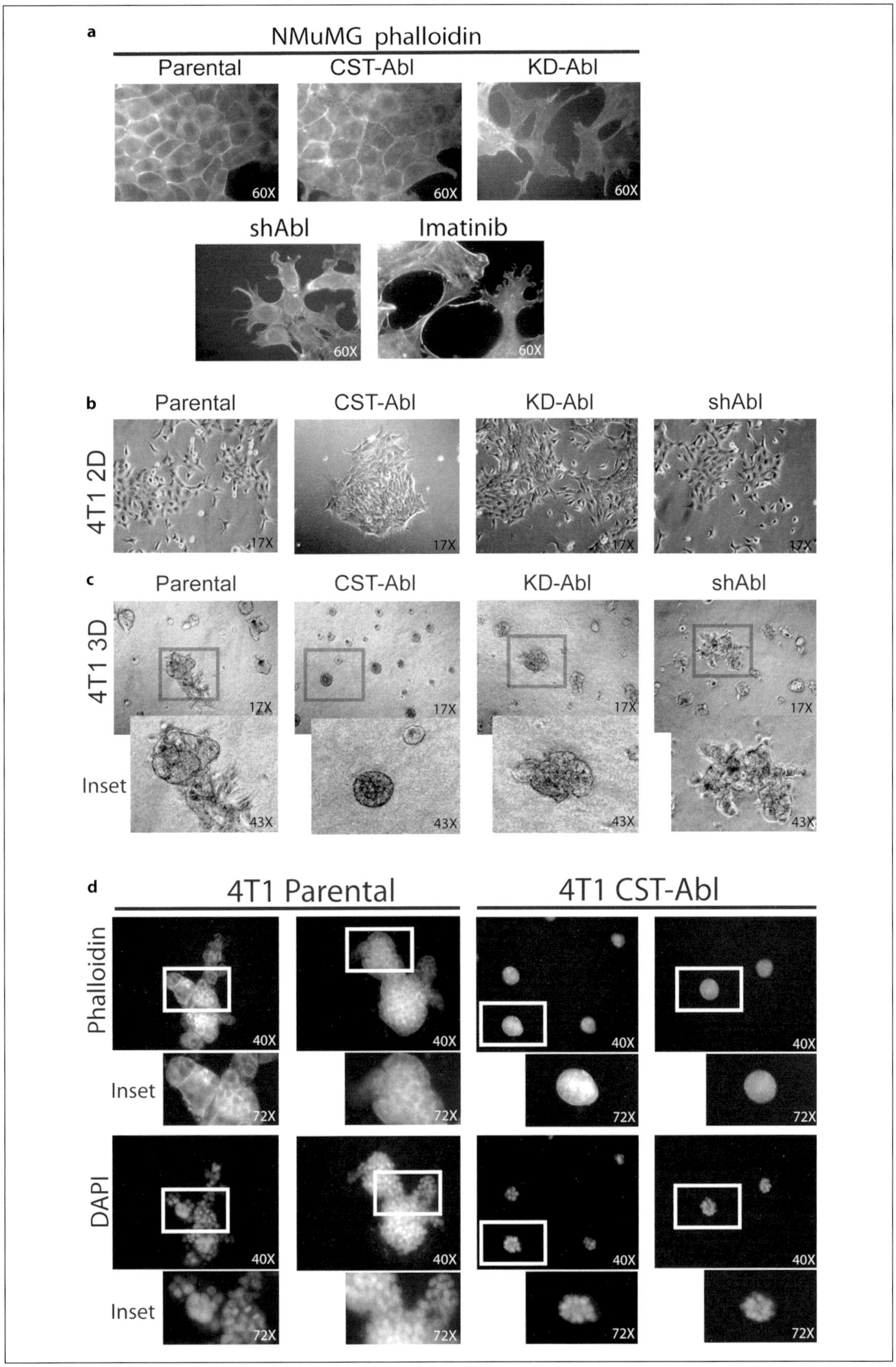

(For legend see next page.)

to phenotypically and morphologically normalize the malignant behaviors of breast cancer cells.

We tested the validity of the above supposition by orthotopically engrafting parental and CST-Abl-expressing 4T1 cells in syngeneic Balb/c mice. As expected [Galliher-Beckley and Schiemann, 2008; Neil and Schiemann, 2008; Wendt and Schiemann, 2009; Wendt et al., 2009b], parental 4T1 cells rapidly formed palpable tumors that necessitated host euthanization by day 28 due to excessive tumor burden (fig. 4a). Remarkably, every animal injected with CST-Abl-expressing 4T1 cells failed to develop palpable tumors during the course of the study (fig. 4a) and to exhibit overt signs of disease during necropsy [Allington et al., 2009]. Surprisingly, clonogenic assays facilitated the reisolation CST-Abl-expressing 4T1 cells from the mammary fat pads of mice that were euthanized on day 51 (fig. 4b). Collectively, these findings suggest that measures capable of enforcing c-Abl activation may represent a novel means to abrogate the oncogenic activities of TGF-β in cancers of the breast, and as such, to one day to improve the prognosis and treatment of patients with metastatic breast cancer. c-Abl may also influence the latency and dormancy of disseminated breast cancer in the form of micrometastases.

Chemotherapeutic Targeting of c-Abl in Breast Cancer: Friend or Foe?

Since the inception of the National Cancer Act of 1971, science and medicine have waged an all-out battle aimed at conquering cancer. Although considerable progress has been achieved in terms of our understanding of the molecular mechanisms that underlie neoplastic development and progression, cancer itself remains a significant health concern and burden in the United States. In fact, 1 in 4 deaths in the United States results from cancer, which is also the leading cause of death in individuals younger than 85 years of age [Jemal et al., 2009]. Despite these grim statistics, overall cancer incidence and mortality rates have begun to decline over the last decade, including those for breast cancer which annually contributes to more than 40,000 deaths and 192,000 new invasive cases of this deadly disease [Jemal et al., 2009]. Continuing along this positive trend will require the development of new diagnostic and chemotherapeutic regimens, as well as the elucidation of new knowledge of how cancer cells acquire the 6 essential phenotypes, or hallmarks, necessary to become malignant. Included in this phenotypic list is the ability of cancer cells to (1) disregard cytostatic signals; (2) grow autonomously; (3) stimulate angiogenesis; (4) ignore apoptotic signals; (5) become immortal; and (6) invade and metastasize [Hanahan and Weinberg, 2000]. The inability of developing neoplasms to acquire each of these phenotypes prevents their conversion to aggressive states, suggesting that these cancer hallmarks represent various rate-limiting steps during malignant development. Although EMT is not a recognized hallmark of tumorigenesis, type 3 EMT is essential for the acquisition of invasive and metastatic phenotypes by cancer cells and their development of chemoresistance. Thus, pharmacological targeting of individual cancer hallmarks and EMT, both singly and in combination, may offer new inroads to effectively treat the development and dissemination of human malignancies, particularly those of the breast.

Our findings showing that the c-Abl activation circumvents and overrides the oncogenic activities of TGF-β in normal and malignant MECs are intriguing in terms of their scientific and biological significance. For instance, alterations within tumor microenvironments can either restrain or free breast cancer progression in a manner that mirrors the conversion of TGF-β function from a suppressor to a promoter of tumor invasion and metastasis [Bierie and Moses, 2006]. Moreover, mounting evidence indicates that TGF-β promotes breast cancer progression in part via its reprogramming of MEC microenvironments and their cellular architectures. In attempting to circumvent the oncogenic activities of TGF-β in mammary tumors, science and medicine have employed a 'TGF-β centric' approach that is likely to fail

Fig. 3. Constitutive c-Abl activity suppresses EMT and induces MET in metastatic MECs. KD-Abl = Kinase-dead c-Abl mutant; shAbl = c-Abl deficient. **a** Direct FITC-conjugated phalloidin immunofluorescence was performed to monitor the actin cytoskeletal architecture in c-Abl-manipulated normal murine mammary gland (NMuMG) cells, which readily acquired mesenchymal morphologies in loss of c-Abl function MECs. **b** Bright-field images of c-Abl-manipulated 4T1 cells grown in traditional 2D tissue culture systems. Gain of c-Abl function elicited an apparent MET in 4T1 cells. **c**, **d** c-Abl-manipulated 4T1 cells were propagated for 7 days in compliant 3D organotypic cultures prior to analyzing their growth and morphology by capturing bright-field images (**c**), or by staining with FITC-conjugated phalloidin and DAPI (**d**). Gain of c-Abl function suppressed acinar growth and promoted normal acinar development, including partial hollowing of the resulting organoids. All are representative of 2–3 independent experiments and were reprinted with kind permission from Allington et al. [2009].

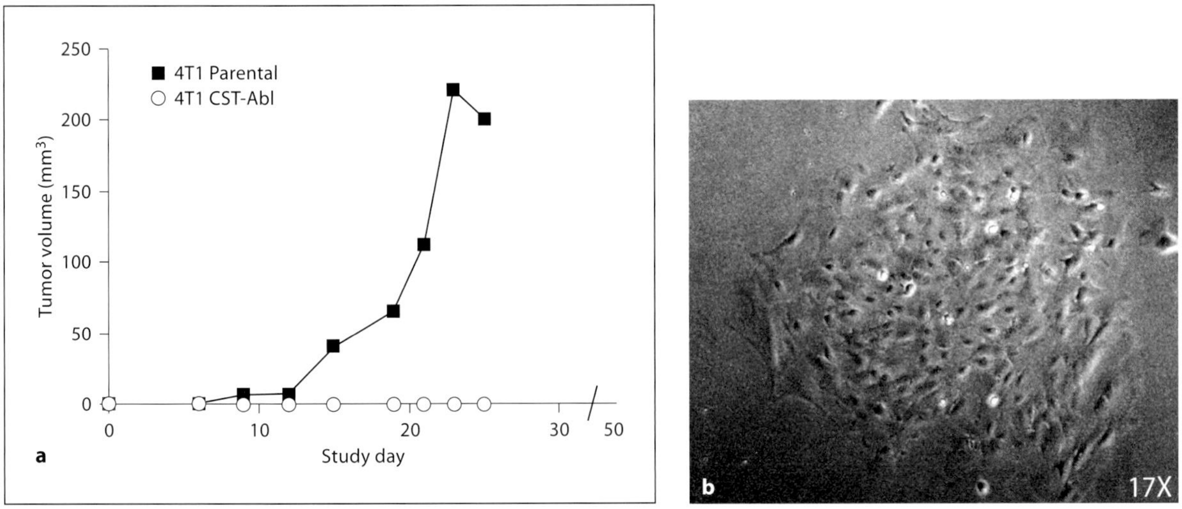

Fig. 4. Enforced c-Abl activation abrogates the growth of metastatic MECs in mice. **a** Female Balb/c mice were injected orthotopically with syngeneic parental (i.e. empty vector) or CST-Abl-expressing 4T1 cells (10,000 cells/animal; 12 animals/group), whose ability to grow as tumors was measured using digital calipers over a period of 30 days. Reprinted with kind permission from Allington et al. [2009]. **b** The mammary glands of mice injected with CST-Abl-expressing 4T1 cells were excised at day 51 after engraftment, and were subsequently dissociated enzymatically to produce a heterogeneous, single-cell suspension that was subjected to a clonogenic assay to reisolate reverted CST-Abl-expressing 4T1 cells.

clinically because targeted TGF-β therapies (i.e. both large and small molecule inhibitors) uniformly function as pan-TGF-β antagonists whose activities are subject to the phenomena underlying the 'TGF-β paradox' – i.e. the ability of mammary tumorigenesis to convert TGF-β from a tumor suppressor to a tumor promoter [Schiemann, 2007]. Pan-TGF-β antagonists are also inadequate in accounting for the pleiotropic functions of TGF-β in (1) governing MEC architectures and microenvironments, and (2) regulating tumor-associated stromal components. Thus, these findings underscore the necessity to design and implement rapid diagnostic tests capable of discriminating cancer patients most likely to benefit from targeted TGF-β therapies from those individuals most likely to be harmed by TGF-β antagonism.

A potential alternative to antagonizing all cellular responses to TGF-β may involve the implementation of a targeted approach that selectively inactivates specific noncanonical TGF-β effectors that preferentially promote its oncogenic activities. We have provided preclinical evidence that supports the therapeutic potential of this alternative approach (e.g., inactivation of αvβ3 integrin, Src, focal adhesion kinase, nuclear factor-κB, cyclooxygenase 2, or EP_2 receptor) [Galliher-Beckley and Schiemann, 2008; Neil and Schiemann, 2008; Tian and Schiemann, 2009a; Wendt and Schiemann, 2009; Wendt et al., 2009b]; however, complete disease resolution has yet to be achieved using these applications due to their inability to phenotypically normalize and revert malignant MEC behaviors, architectures and microenvironments. Our findings demonstrate that the enforced activation of c-Abl can fulfill this latter requirement, and in doing so, can promote the phenotypic normalization and reversion of highly malignant, late-stage breast cancers in mice (fig. 4) [Allington et al., 2009]. To our knowledge, c-Abl activation represents the first bona fide tool competent to ablate the oncogenic activities of TGF-β, thereby restoring its cytostatic function in normalized and reverted MECs. Indeed, a bold extension of our findings leads us to propose that the development and implementation of allosteric c-Abl activators may one day provide a paradigm shifting the strategy to treat metastatic breast cancers. Clearly, the notion of chemically stimulating c-Abl is disconcerting to many scientists and clinicians, particularly since c-Abl has been linked to the oncogenic activities of the receptors for epidermal growth factor, platelet-derived growth factor and insulin-like growth factor 1, to the transforming activities of Src and signal transducer and activator of transcription 3, and to the prosurvival activities of ERK5 [Plattner et al., 1999; Srinivasan and Plattner, 2006; Sirvent et al., 2007; Lin and Arlinghaus, 2008; Srinivasan et al., 2008]. However, in all cases, it remains difficult to gauge the extent to which off-target effects of imatinib and other c-Abl inhibitors contribute to their apparent effectiveness against breast cancer cells in vitro. Moreover, data obtained in human clinical [Modi et al., 2005; Chen et al., 2006; Lin et al., 2006, 2007a; Chew et al., 2008; Cristofanilli et al., 2008; Gharibo et al., 2008] and murine preclinical trials (fig. 1) [Allington et al., 2009] clearly demonstrate the inability of imatinib to provide any chemotherapeutic benefit towards cancers of the breast. Along these lines, overexpression of c-Abl or the enforced nuclear expression of oncogenic Abl mutants (e.g., BCR-Abl or v-Abl) all fail to elicit cellular transformation [Zhu and Wang, 2004; Suzuki and Shishido, 2007], which points to the possibility that targeted c-Abl activation may in fact be well tolerated by normal MECs. Indeed, we find that MECs are exquisitely sensitive to subtle changes in c-Abl activity [Allington et al., 2009], and as such, we anticipate that even submaximal activation of c-Abl will prove sufficient to induce MET and suppress mammary tumorigenesis stimulated by TGF-β, thereby improving the clinical course of patients with metastatic breast cancer.

Unanswered Questions and Future Directions

Although our ability to accept or reject the aforementioned hypothesis clearly awaits additional experimentation in a variety of genetically distinct human breast cancer subtypes and tissues (e.g., luminal A vs. luminal B vs. ErbB2 vs. basal-like vs. normal-like) [Perou et al., 2000; Sorlie et al., 2001; Sorlie et al., 2003], our findings are nonetheless provocative and potentially paradigm changing with respect to redefining the role of c-Abl in regulating mammary gland development and neoplasia, and to establishing c-Abl as a novel suppressor of oncogenic TGF-β signaling in breast and other epithelial-derived cancers in part by inducing their phenotypic and morphologic normalization [Allington et al., 2009]. Figure 5 depicts our current understanding of the role of c-Abl in regulating normal and malignant MEC behavior and in suppressing the oncogenic activities of TGF-β. Interestingly, we find that inactivating noncanonical TGF-β effectors is sufficient in abrogating the ability of TGF-β to promote breast cancer progression in a manner somewhat reminiscent of that mediated by enforced c-Abl activation. These parallels raise a number of interesting questions, including (1) does c-Abl suppress mammary tumorigenesis by inhibiting EMT, or by stimulating MET; (2) does enforced c-Abl activation alter the selection or expansion of breast cancer stem cells; (3) does cytoplasmic or nuclear c-Abl activation mediate its antitumor activities; (4) does the initiation of oncogenic TGF-β signaling uncouple c-Abl from activation by TGF-β; and (5) do the tumor-suppressing activities of c-Abl require signaling inputs by TGF-β? These questions and their potential for directing the future development and implementation of c-Abl chemotherapies during mammary tumorigenesis are discussed below.

Although c-Abl activation clearly promotes the acquisition of epithelial phenotypes in normal and malignant MECs (fig. 3) [Allington et al., 2009], it remains to be determined whether this event reflects the ability of c-Abl to inhibit EMT, or conversely, to stimulate MET. This question also bears important clinical relevance because inhibiting EMT or stimulating MET are both likely to be most effective in preventing the exit of metastatic cells from the primary tumor; however, the induction of MET may be contraindicated should this process be found to play an essential role in promoting the outgrowth of micrometastatic lesions. Our findings show that c-Abl deficiency or inactivation both elicit EMT, while c-Abl activation induces a 'hyperepithelial' morphology that normalizes and reverts the phenotypes of metastatic breast cancer cells (fig. 3, 4) [Allington et al., 2009]. Along these lines, epithelial cells naturally tend to drift and acquire mesenchymal characteristics in response to extended 2D culture durations, suggesting perhaps that the process of becoming 'mesenchymal' may reflect a more energetically favorable and stable state than that needed to become 'epithelial'. Alternatively, the nearly infinite stiffness of 2D culture systems may serve as an aberrant signal that drives epithelial cells to acquire mesenchymal-like properties as a means to compensate and survive in extremely rigid microenvironments [Butcher et al., 2009; Erler and Weaver, 2009]. In fact, we observed microenvironmental tension to be sufficient in overriding the cytostatic activities of TGF-β, an event that was circumvented by CST-Abl expression [Allington et al., 2009]. Thus, our findings are consistent with the notion that enforced c-Abl activation stimulates MET, as opposed to simply inhibiting EMT. Future studies need to thoroughly address this issue, as well as to explore the potential linkage between c-Abl and known inducers of MET, including Pax-2, Cdx2 and frizzled-7 [Hugo et al., 2007].

Recently, human and mouse MECs were observed to acquire stem cell-like properties when stimulated to un-

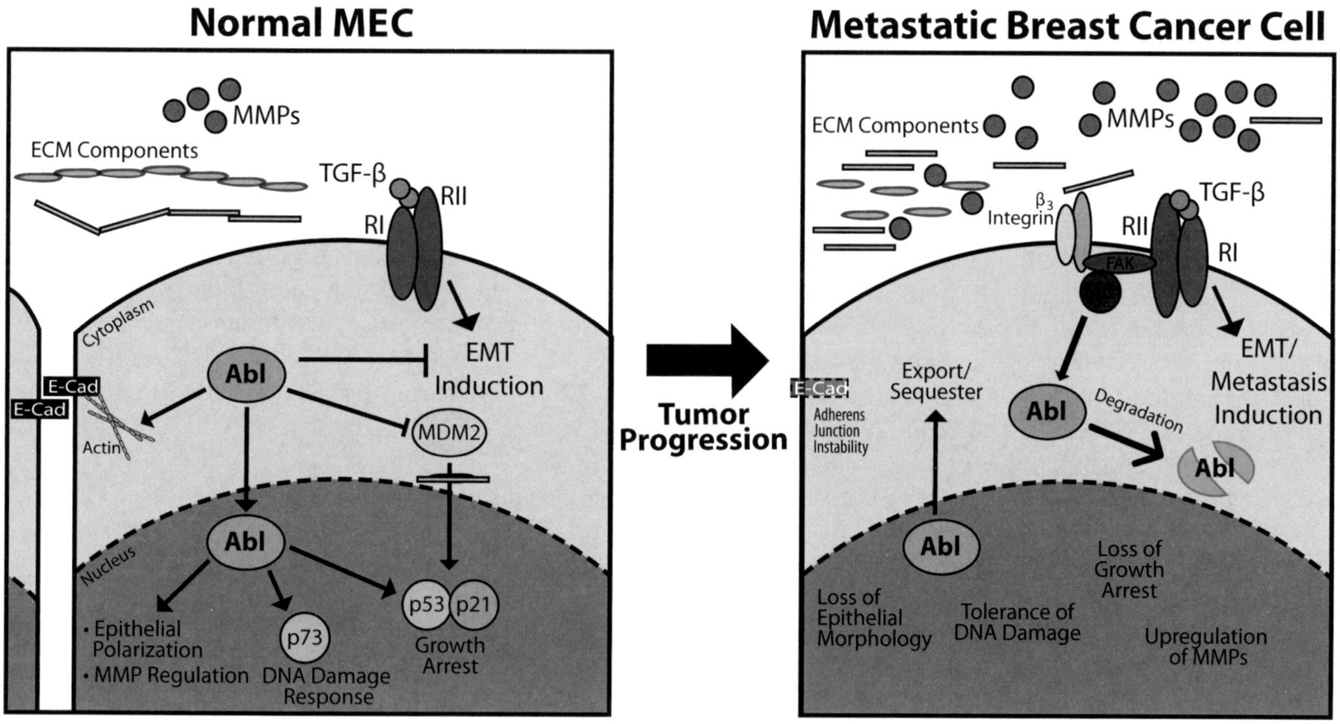

Color version available online

Fig. 5. Schematic depiction of the role of c-Abl in suppressing EMT and oncogenic TGF-β signaling in normal and malignant MECs. In normal MECs, c-Abl activation (1) maintains adherens junction stability and cortical actin architecture; (2) mediates growth arrest in response to TGF-β and DNA damage; and (3) represses MMP expression and secretion. As developing mammary neoplasms become more and more malignant, oncogenic TGF-β signaling in conjunction with focal adhesion complex activation (e.g., β_3-integrin/focal adhesion kinase/Src) may promote the degradation of c-Abl and its uncoupling from the tumor-suppressing activities of TGF-β. The loss of c-Abl function ushers in the initiation of EMT and its dissolution of adherens junctions, its production and activation of matrix metalloproteinases, and its circumvention of cytostasis induced by TGF-β and DNA damage, which collectively enhance breast cancer progression and metastatic dissemination to distant locales. RI/RII = TGF-β type I receptor/TGF-β type II receptor; E-cad = E-cadherin; MDM2 = murine double minute 2.

dergo EMT by TGF-β [Mani et al., 2008]. Mechanistically, upregulated Id1 expression may function in dictating whether TGF-β expands or contracts the pool of cancer stem cells [Tang et al., 2007], and consequently, whether TGF-β suppresses or promotes mammary tumorigenesis. Indeed, inhibiting TGF-β signaling pharmacologically in cancer stem cells elicited MET and their acquisition of less aggressive, more epithelial-like morphologies [Shipitsin et al., 2007]. Our demonstration that activated c-Abl phenotypically and morphologically reverts the malignant behaviors of late-stage breast cancer cells (fig. 3, 4) [Allington et al., 2009] raises 2 interesting questions – does enforced c-Abl activation suppress the selection and expansion of cancer stem cells, and conversely, does imatinib administration promote solid tumor progression by enlarging the population of stem cell-like progenitors in post-EMT carcinoma cells? Thus, future studies clearly need to investigate these important issues as well.

As mentioned above, the strong epithelial morphologies and phenotypes induced by c-Abl activation suggest that this PTK stimulates MET, presumably by functioning in the cytoplasm to affect adherens junctions and cytoskeletal architectures. However, in response to diverse extracellular stimuli (integrins), c-Abl is translocated to the nucleus where it functions in regulating DNA damage and mismatch repair responses [Lewis et al., 1996; Baskaran et al., 1997; Taagepera et al., 1998]. Moreover, c-Abl activation during DNA damage-induced apoptosis requires its coupling to the p53 relative, p73 [Yuan et al., 1999; Shaul, 2000]. Thus, the relative contributions of cytoplasmic and nuclear c-Abl in suppressing mammary tumorigenesis remains an important and unanswered question. With this idea in mind, we observed the expression of CST-Abl to greatly enhance the induction of p21 expression by TGF-β [Allington et al., 2009] and to induce 4T1 organoids to express robust quantities of p73, suggesting that the morphological reversion of 4T1 acinar structures is partially dependent upon nuclear c-Abl signaling inputs [Allington and Schiemann, unpubl. observation]. Accordingly, we have found that CST-Abl expression is sufficient in resensitizing 4T1 cells to death induced by the DNA-damaging agent, 6-thioguanine (Allington and Schiemann, data not shown). Thus, while 6-thioguanine has previously failed as a single-agent chemotherapeutic for breast cancer, our findings suggest that combining enforced c-Abl activation with 6-thioguanine or other DNA damage-inducing agents may offer new inroads to alleviating breast cancer progression.

Finally, we found that TGF-β administration leads to a very transient activation of c-Abl in MECs [Allington et al., 2009], which is rapidly followed by their degradation of c-Abl in a manner that coincides with initiation of EMT [Allington and Schiemann, unpubl. observation]. Based on these findings, we speculate that the end result of c-Abl activation by TGF-β results in the Src-dependent degradation of c-Abl [Allington and Schiemann, unpubl. observation; Echarri and Pendergast, 2001; Woodring et al., 2002; Zhu and Wang, 2004], and consequently, in the acquisition of EMT phenotypes stimulated by TGF-β. This model clearly contrasts with the ability of TGF-β to couple to c-Abl activation via a phosphoinositide 3-kinase- and p21-activated kinase-2-dependent pathway in fibroblasts [Daniels et al., 2004; Wang et al., 2005; Wilkes and Leof, 2006]. Despite these disparate activities for c-Abl in MECs and fibroblasts, it remains plausible that the ability of TGF-β to induce EMT requires the inactivation and degradation of c-Abl in epithelial cells (fig. 5). Along these lines, we have recently observed TGF-β stimulation of EMT to drastically reduce the expression and activity of c-Abl in both the cytoplasm and nucleus of normal MECs. Moreover, the kinetics of c-Abl degradation mirrored that for the acquisition of focal adhesion complex signaling by TGF-β, and more importantly, chemotherapeutic targeting of focal adhesion complexes was sufficient in protecting c-Abl from degradation induced by TGF-β [Allington and Schiemann, unpubl. observation]. Interestingly, augmented [Galliher and Schiemann, 2006, 2007; Galliher-Beckley and Schiemann, 2008; Neil et al., 2008; Neil and Schiemann, 2008; Neil et al., 2009; Tian and Schiemann, 2009a; Wendt and Schiemann, 2009; Wendt et al., 2009b] and attenuated [Bhowmick et al., 2004a, 2004b; Cheng et al., 2005; Yang et al., 2008] TGF-β signaling in mammary carcinoma cells has been associated with disease progression, which raises a second interesting question – can c-Abl activation morphologically and phenotypically revert the malignant behaviors of breast cancer cells that can no longer respond to TGF-β? Future studies need to address this important issue, as well as determine how EMT dictates the expression, activation and localization of c-Abl in normal and malignant MECs. Indeed, answering these important questions may provide novel information capable of one day (1) staging and stratifying the treatment of mammary carcinomas based on their c-Abl and TGF-β signatures; and (2) enhancing our understanding of the 'TGF-β paradox' in promoting metastatic disease in breast cancer patients.

Acknowledgements

We thank members of the Schiemann Laboratory for the critical comments and reading of the manuscript. W.P.S. was supported by grants from the National Institutes of Health (CA114039 and CA129359), the Komen Foundation (BCTR0706967) and the Department of Defense (BC084651), while T.M.A was supported by the Department of Defense (BC083323).

References

Agami, R., G. Blandino, M. Oren, Y. Shaul (1999) Interaction of c-Abl and p73alpha and their collaboration to induce apoptosis. Nature *399:* 809–813.

Allington, T.M., A.J. Galliher-Beckley, W.P. Schiemann (2009) Activated Abl kinase inhibits oncogenic TGF-β signaling and tumorigenesis in mammary tumors. FASEB J *23:* 4231–4243.

Bakin, A.V., A.K. Tomlinson, N.A. Bhowmick, H.L. Moses, C.L. Arteaga (2000) Phosphatidylinositol 3-kinase function is required for TGF-β-mediated epithelial to mesenchymal transition and cell migration. J Biol Chem *275:* 36803–36810.

Barcellos-Hoff, M.H., R.J. Akhurst (2009) TGF-β in breast cancer: too much, too late. Breast Cancer Res *11:* 202.

Baskaran, R., L.D. Wood, L.L. Whitaker, C.E. Canman, S.E. Morgan, Y. Xu, C. Barlow, D. Baltimore, A. Wynshaw-Boris, M.B. Kastan, J.Y. Wang (1997) Ataxia telangiectasia mutant protein activates c-Abl tyrosine kinase in response to ionizing radiation. Nature *387:* 516–519.

Benson, J.R. (2004) Role of TGF-β in breast carcinogenesis. Lancet Oncol *5:* 229–239.
Bhowmick, N.A., A. Chytil, D. Plieth, A.E. Gorska, N. Dumont, S. Shappell, M.K. Washington, E.G. Neilson, H.L. Moses (2004a) TGF-β signaling in fibroblasts modulates the oncogenic potential of adjacent epithelia. Science *303:* 848–851.
Bhowmick, N.A., E.G. Neilson, H.L. Moses (2004b) Stromal fibroblasts in cancer initiation and progression. Nature *432:* 332–337.
Bhowmick, N.A., R. Zent, M. Ghiassi, M. McDonnell, H.L. Moses (2001) Integrin β_1 signaling is necessary for TGF-β activation of p38MAPK and epithelial plasticity. J Biol Chem *276:* 46707–46713.
Bierie, B., H.L. Moses (2006) Tumour microenvironment: TGF-β: the molecular Jekyll and Hyde of cancer. Nat Rev Cancer *6:* 506–520.
Buck, M.B., C. Knabbe (2006) TGF-β signaling in breast cancer. Ann NY Acad Sci *1089:* 119–126.
Butcher, D.T., T. Alliston, V.M. Weaver (2009) A tense situation: forcing tumour progression. Nat Rev Cancer *9:* 108–122.
Chau, B.N., T.T. Chen, Y.Y. Wan, J. DeGregori, J.Y. Wang (2004) Tumor necrosis factor-α-induced apoptosis requires p73 and c-ABL activation downstream of RB degradation. Mol Cell Biol *24:* 4438–4447.
Chen, J., C. Rocken, B. Nitsche, C. Hosius, H. Gschaidmeier, S. Kahl, P. Malfertheiner, M.P. Ebert (2006) The tyrosine kinase inhibitor imatinib fails to inhibit pancreatic cancer progression. Cancer Lett *233:* 328–337.
Cheng, N., N.A. Bhowmick, A. Chytil, A.E. Gorksa, K.A. Brown, R. Muraoka, C.L. Arteaga, E.G. Neilson, S.W. Hayward, H.L. Moses (2005) Loss of TGF-β type II receptor in fibroblasts promotes mammary carcinoma growth and invasion through upregulation of TGF-α-, MSP- and HGF-mediated signaling networks. Oncogene *24:* 5053–5068.
Chew, H.K., W.E. Barlow, K. Albain, D. Lew, A. Gown, D.F. Hayes, J. Gralow, G.N. Hortobagyi, R. Livingston (2008) A phase II study of imatinib mesylate and capecitabine in metastatic breast cancer: Southwest Oncology Group Study 0338. Clin Breast Cancer *8:* 511–515.
Cristofanilli, M., P. Morandi, S. Krishnamurthy, J.M. Reuben, B.N. Lee, D. Francis, D.J. Booser, M.C. Green, B.K. Arun, L. Pusztai, A. Lopez, R. Islam, V. Valero, G.N. Hortobagyi (2008) Imatinib mesylate (Gleevec) in advanced breast cancer-expressing c-Kit or PDGFR-β: clinical activity and biological correlations. Ann Oncol *19:* 1713–1719.
Daniels, C.E., M.C. Wilkes, M. Edens, T.J. Kottom, S.J. Murphy, A.H. Limper, E.B. Leof (2004) Imatinib mesylate inhibits the profibrogenic activity of TGF-β and prevents bleomycin-mediated lung fibrosis. J Clin Invest *114:* 1308–1316.
Druker, B.J. (2006) Circumventing resistance to kinase-inhibitor therapy. N Engl J Med *354:* 2594–2596.
Echarri, A., A.M. Pendergast (2001) Activated c-Abl is degraded by the ubiquitin-dependent proteasome pathway. Curr Biol *11:* 1759–1765.
Erler, J.T., V.M. Weaver (2009) Three-dimensional context regulation of metastasis. Clin Exp Metastasis *26:* 35–49.
Frasca, F., P. Vigneri, V. Vella, R. Vigneri, J.Y. Wang (2001) Tyrosine kinase inhibitor STI571 enhances thyroid cancer cell motile response to hepatocyte growth factor. Oncogene *20:* 3845–3856.
Galliher, A.J., W.P. Schiemann (2006) β_3 integrin and Src facilitate TGF-β mediated induction of epithelial-mesenchymal transition in mammary epithelial cells. Breast Cancer Res *8:* R42.
Galliher, A.J., W.P. Schiemann (2007) Src phosphorylates Tyr284 in TGF-β type II receptor and regulates TGF-β stimulation of p38 MAPK during breast cancer cell proliferation and invasion. Cancer Res *67:* 3752–3758.
Galliher-Beckley, A.J., W.P. Schiemann (2008) Grb2 binding to Tyr284 in TβR-II is essential for mammary tumor growth and metastasis stimulated by TGF-β. Carcinogenesis *29:* 244–251.
Gharibo, M., L. Patrick-Miller, L. Zheng, L. Guensch, P. Juvidian, E. Poplin (2008) A phase II trial of imatinib mesylate in patients with metastatic pancreatic cancer. Pancreas *36:* 341–345.
Hamer, G., I.S. Gademan, H.B. Kal, D.G. de Rooij (2001) Role for c-Abl and p73 in the radiation response of male germ cells. Oncogene *20:* 4298–4304.
Hanahan, D., R.A. Weinberg (2000) The hallmarks of cancer. Cell *100:* 57–70.
Heldin, C.H., M. Landstrom, A. Moustakas (2009) Mechanism of TGF-β signaling to growth arrest, apoptosis, and epithelial-mesenchymal transition. Curr Opin Cell Biol *21:* 166–176.
Huber, M.A., N. Azoitei, B. Baumann, S. Grunert, A. Sommer, H. Pehamberger, N. Kraut, H. Beug, T. Wirth (2004) NF-κB is essential for epithelial-mesenchymal transition and metastasis in a model of breast cancer progression. J Clin Invest *114:* 569–581.
Hugo, H., M.L. Ackland, T. Blick, M.G. Lawrence, J.A. Clements, E.D. Williams, E.W. Thompson (2007) Epithelial-mesenchymal and mesenchymal-epithelial transitions in carcinoma progression. J Cell Physiol *213:* 374–383.
Hunter, T. (2007) Treatment for chronic myelogenous leukemia: the long road to imatinib. J Clin Invest *117:* 2036–2043.
Jemal, A., R. Siegel, E. Ward, Y. Hao, J. Xu, M.J. Thun (2009) Cancer statistics, 2009. CA Cancer J Clin *59:* 225–249.
Kain, K.H., S. Gooch, R.L. Klemke (2003) Cytoplasmic c-Abl provides a molecular 'Rheostat' controlling carcinoma cell survival and invasion. Oncogene *22:* 6071–6080.
Kain, K.H., R.L. Klemke (2001) Inhibition of cell migration by Abl family tyrosine kinases through uncoupling of Crk-CAS complexes. J Biol Chem *276:* 16185–16192.
Kalluri, R., R.A. Weinberg (2009) The basics of epithelial-mesenchymal transition. J Clin Invest *119:* 1420–1428.
Lamouille, S., R. Derynck (2007) Cell size and invasion in TGF-β-induced epithelial to mesenchymal transition is regulated by activation of the mTOR pathway. J Cell Biol *178:* 437–451.
Lamouille, S., R. Derynck (2011) Emergence of the phosphoinositide 3-kinase-akt-mammalian target of rapamycin axis in transforming growth factor-β-induced epithelial-mesenchymal transition. Cells Tissues Organs *193:* 8–22.
Lee, Y.H., A.R. Albig, M. Regner, B.J. Schiemann, W.P. Schiemann (2008) Fibulin-5 initiates epithelial-mesenchymal transition (EMT) and enhances EMT induced by TGF-β in mammary epithelial cells via a MMP-dependent mechanism. Carcinogenesis *29:* 2243–2251.
Lewis, J.M., R. Baskaran, S. Taagepera, M.A. Schwartz, J.Y. Wang (1996) Integrin regulation of c-Abl tyrosine kinase activity and cytoplasmic-nuclear transport. Proc Natl Acad Sci USA *93:* 15174–15179.
Li, L.S., J.C. Morales, A. Hwang, M.W. Wagner, D.A. Boothman (2008) DNA mismatch repair-dependent activation of c-Abl/p73α/GADD45alpha-mediated apoptosis. J Biol Chem *283:* 21394–21403.
Lin, A.M., B.I. Rini, M.K. Derynck, V. Weinberg, M. Park, C.J. Ryan, J.E. Rosenberg, G. Bubley, E.J. Small (2007a) A phase I trial of docetaxel/estramustine/imatinib in patients with hormone-refractory prostate cancer. Clin Genitourin Cancer *5:* 323–328.
Lin, A.M., B.I. Rini, V. Weinberg, K. Fong, C.J. Ryan, J.E. Rosenberg, L. Fong, E.J. Small (2006) A phase II trial of imatinib mesylate in patients with biochemical relapse of prostate cancer after definitive local therapy. BJU Int *98:* 763–769.
Lin, J., R. Arlinghaus (2008) Activated c-Abl tyrosine kinase in malignant solid tumors. Oncogene *27:* 4385–4391.
Lin, J., T. Sun, L. Ji, W. Deng, J. Roth, J. Minna, R. Arlinghaus (2007b) Oncogenic activation of c-Abl in non-small cell lung cancer cells lacking FUS1 expression: inhibition of c-Abl by the tumor suppressor gene product Fus1. Oncogene *26:* 6989–6996.
Mani, S.A., W. Guo, M.J. Liao, E.N. Eaton, A. Ayyanan, A.Y. Zhou, M. Brooks, F. Reinhard, C.C. Zhang, M. Shipitsin, L.L. Campbell, K. Polyak, C. Brisken, J. Yang, R.A. Weinberg (2008) The epithelial-mesenchymal transition generates cells with properties of stem cells. Cell *133:* 704–715.

Massague, J. (2008) TGF-β in Cancer. Cell *134:* 215–230.
Masszi, A., A. Kapus (2011) Smaddening complexity: The role of Smad3 in epithelial-myofibroblast transition. Cells Tissues Organs *193:* 41–52.
Mauro, M.J., B.J. Druker (2001) STI571: targeting BCR-ABL as therapy for CML. Oncologist *6:* 233–238.
Mauro, M.J., M. O'Dwyer, M.C. Heinrich, B.J. Druker (2002) STI571: a paradigm of new agents for cancer therapeutics. J Clin Oncol *20:* 325–334.
Miller, C.T., G. Chen, T.G. Gharib, H. Wang, D.G. Thomas, D.E. Misek, T.J. Giordano, J. Yee, M.B. Orringer, S.M. Hanash, D.G. Beer (2003) Increased C-CRK proto-oncogene expression is associated with an aggressive phenotype in lung adenocarcinomas. Oncogene *22:* 7950–7957.
Modi, S., A.D. Seidman, M. Dickler, M. Moasser, G. D'Andrea, M.E. Moynahan, J. Menell, K.S. Panageas, L.K. Tan, L. Norton, C.A. Hudis (2005) A phase II trial of imatinib mesylate monotherapy in patients with metastatic breast cancer. Breast Cancer Res Treat *90:* 157–163.
Neil, J.R., K.M. Johnson, R.A. Nemenoff, W.P. Schiemann (2008) Cox-2 inactivates Smad signaling and enhances EMT stimulated by TGF-β through a PGE2-dependent mechanisms. Carcinogenesis *29:* 2227–2235.
Neil, J.R., W.P. Schiemann (2008) Altered TAB1:IκB kinase interaction promotes TGF-β-mediated NF-κB activation during breast cancer progression. Cancer Res *68:* 1462–1470.
Neil, J.R., M. Tian, W.P. Schiemann (2009) X-linked inhibitor of apoptosis protein and its E3 ligase activity promote TGF-β-mediated NF-κB activation during breast cancer progression. J Biol Chem *284:* 21209–21217.
Noren, N.K., G. Foos, C.A. Hauser, E.B. Pasquale (2006) The EphB4 receptor suppresses breast cancer cell tumorigenicity through an Abl-Crk pathway. Nat Cell Biol *8:* 815–825.
Oft, M., J. Peli, C. Rudaz, H. Schwarz, H. Beug, E. Reichmann (1996) TGF-β_1 and Ha-Ras collaborate in modulating the phenotypic plasticity and invasiveness of epithelial tumor cells. Genes Dev *10:* 2462–2477.
Ozdamar, B., R. Bose, M. Barrios-Rodiles, H.R. Wang, Y. Zhang, J.L. Wrana (2005) Regulation of the polarity protein Par6 by TGF-β receptors controls epithelial cell plasticity. Science *307:* 1603–1609.
Pardali, K., A. Moustakas (2007) Actions of TGF-β as tumor suppressor and pro-metastatic factor in human cancer. Biochim Biophys Acta *1775:* 21–62.
Pendergast, A.M. (1996) Nuclear tyrosine kinases: from Abl to WEE1. Curr Opin Cell Biol *8:* 174–181.
Pendergast, A.M. (2002) The Abl family kinases: mechanisms of regulation and signaling. Adv Cancer Res *85:* 51–100.
Perou, C.M., T. Sorlie, M.B. Eisen, M. van de Rijn, S.S. Jeffrey, C.A. Rees, J.R. Pollack, D.T. Ross, H. Johnsen, L.A. Akslen, O. Fluge, A. Pergamenschikov, C. Williams, S.X. Zhu, P.E. Lonning, A.L. Borresen-Dale, P.O. Brown, D. Botstein (2000) Molecular portraits of human breast tumours. Nature *406:* 747–752.
Plattner, R., L. Kadlec, K.A. DeMali, A. Kazlauskas, A.M. Pendergast (1999) c-Abl is activated by growth factors and Src family kinases and has a role in the cellular response to PDGF. Genes Dev *13:* 2400–2411.
Polyak, K., R.A. Weinberg (2009) Transitions between epithelial and mesenchymal states: acquisition of malignant and stem cell traits. Nat Rev Cancer *9:* 265–273.
Schiemann, W.P. (2007) Targeted TGF-β chemotherapies: friend or foe in treating human malignancies? Expert Rev Anticancer Ther *7:* 609–611.
Shaul, Y. (2000) c-Abl: activation and nuclear targets. Cell Death Differ *7:* 10–16.
Shipitsin, M., L.L. Campbell, P. Argani, S. Weremowicz, N. Bloushtain-Qimron, J. Yao, T. Nikolskaya, T. Serebryiskaya, R. Beroukhim, M. Hu, M.K. Halushka, S. Sukumar, L.M. Parker, K.S. Anderson, L.N. Harris, J.E. Garber, A.L. Richardson, S.J. Schnitt, Y. Nikolsky, R.S. Gelman, K. Polyak (2007) Molecular definition of breast tumor heterogeneity. Cancer Cell *11:* 259–273.
Sirvent, A., A. Boureux, V. Simon, C. Leroy, S. Roche (2007) The tyrosine kinase Abl is required for Src-transforming activity in mouse fibroblasts and human breast cancer cells. Oncogene *26:* 7313–7323.
Sokol, J.P., J.R. Neil, B.J. Schiemann, W.P. Schiemann (2005) The use of cystatin C to inhibit epithelial-mesenchymal transition and morphological transformation stimulated by TGF-β. Breast Cancer Res *7:* R844–R853.
Sorlie, T., C.M. Perou, R. Tibshirani, T. Aas, S. Geisler, H. Johnsen, T. Hastie, M.B. Eisen, M. van de Rijn, S.S. Jeffrey, T. Thorsen, H. Quist, J.C. Matese, P.O. Brown, D. Botstein, P. Eystein Lonning, A.L. Borresen-Dale (2001) Gene expression patterns of breast carcinomas distinguish tumor subclasses with clinical implications. Proc Natl Acad Sci USA *98:* 10869–10874.
Sorlie, T., R. Tibshirani, J. Parker, T. Hastie, J.S. Marron, A. Nobel, S. Deng, H. Johnsen, R. Pesich, S. Geisler, J. Demeter, C.M. Perou, P.E. Lonning, P.O. Brown, A.L. Borresen-Dale, D. Botstein (2003) Repeated observation of breast tumor subtypes in independent gene expression data sets. Proc Natl Acad Sci USA *100:* 8418–8423.
Soverini, S., G. Martinelli, I. Iacobucci, M. Baccarani (2008) Imatinib mesylate for the treatment of chronic myeloid leukemia. Expert Rev Anticancer Ther *8:* 853–864.
Srinivasan, D., R. Plattner (2006) Activation of Abl tyrosine kinases promotes invasion of aggressive breast cancer cells. Cancer Res *66:* 5648–5655.
Srinivasan, D., J.T. Sims, R. Plattner (2008) Aggressive breast cancer cells are dependent on activated Abl kinases for proliferation, anchorage-independent growth and survival. Oncogene *27:* 1095–1105.
Suzuki, J., T. Shishido (2007) Regulation of cellular transformation by oncogenic and normal Abl kinases. J Biochem *141:* 453–458.
Taagepera, S., D. McDonald, J.E. Loeb, L.L. Whitaker, A.K. McElroy, J.Y. Wang, T.J. Hope (1998) Nuclear-cytoplasmic shuttling of C-ABL tyrosine kinase. Proc Natl Acad Sci USA *95:* 7457–7462.
Tang, B., N. Yoo, M. Vu, M. Mamura, J.S. Nam, A. Ooshima, Z. Du, P.Y. Desprez, M.R. Anver, A.M. Michalowska, J. Shih, W.T. Parks, L.M. Wakefield (2007) TGF-β can suppress tumorigenesis through effects on the putative cancer stem or early progenitor cell and committed progeny in a breast cancer xenograft model. Cancer Res *67:* 8643–8652.
Thiery, J.P. (2003) Epithelial-mesenchymal transitions in development and pathologies. Curr Opin Cell Biol *15:* 740–746.
Tian, M., W.P. Schiemann (2009a) PGE2 receptor EP2 mediates the antagonistic effect of COX-2 on TGF-β signaling during mammary tumorigenesis. FASEB J *24:* 1105–1116.
Tian, M., W.P. Schiemann (2009b) The TGF-β paradox in human cancer: an update. Future Oncol *5:* 259–271.
Truong, T., G. Sun, M. Doorly, J.Y. Wang, M.A. Schwartz (2003) Modulation of DNA damage-induced apoptosis by cell adhesion is independently mediated by p53 and c-Abl. Proc Natl Acad Sci USA *100:* 10281–10286.
Valcourt, U., M. Kowanetz, H. Niimi, C.H. Heldin, A. Moustakas (2005) TGF-β and the Smad signaling pathway support transcriptomic reprogramming during epithelial-mesenchymal cell transition. Mol Biol Cell *16:* 1987–2002.
Vigneri, P., J.Y. Wang (2001) Induction of apoptosis in chronic myelogenous leukemia cells through nuclear entrapment of BCR-ABL tyrosine kinase. Nat Med *7:* 228–234.
Wagner, M.W., L.S. Li, J.C. Morales, C.L. Galindo, H.R. Garner, W.G. Bornmann, D.A. Boothman (2008) Role of c-Abl kinase in DNA mismatch repair-dependent G2 cell cycle checkpoint arrest responses. J Biol Chem *283:* 21382–21393.
Wang, J.Y. (2006) Eph tumour suppression: the dark side of Gleevec. Nat Cell Biol *8:* 785–786.
Wang, J.Y., F. Ledley, S. Goff, R. Lee, Y. Groner, D. Baltimore (1984) The mouse c-Abl locus: molecular cloning and characterization. Cell *36:* 349–356.
Wang, S., M.C. Wilkes, E.B. Leof, R. Hirschberg (2005) Imatinib mesylate blocks a non-Smad TGF-beta pathway and reduces renal fibrogenesis in vivo. FASEB J *19:* 1–11.

Wen, S.T., P.K. Jackson, R.A. Van Etten (1996) The cytostatic function of c-Abl is controlled by multiple nuclear localization signals and requires the p53 and Rb tumor suppressor gene products. EMBO J *15:* 1583–1595.

Wendt, M.K., T.M. Allington, W.P. Schiemann (2009a) Mechanisms of the epithelial-mesenchymal transition by TGF-β. Future Oncol *5:* 1145–1168.

Wendt, M.K., W.P. Schiemann (2009) Therapeutic targeting of the focal adhesion complex prevents oncogenic TGF-β signaling and metastasis. Breast Cancer Res *11:* R68.

Wendt, M.K., J.A. Smith, W.P. Schiemann (2009b) p130Cas is required for mammary tumor growth and TGF-β-mediated metastasis through regulation of Smad2/3 activity. J Biol Chem *284:* 34145–34156.

Wilkes, M.C., E.B. Leof (2006) TGF-β activation of c-Abl is independent of receptor internalization and regulated by phosphatidylinositol 3-kinase and PAK2 in mesenchymal cultures. J Biol Chem *281:* 27846–27854.

Woodring, P.J., T. Hunter, J.Y. Wang (2001) Inhibition of c-Abl tyrosine kinase activity by filamentous actin. J Biol Chem *276:* 27104–27110.

Woodring, P.J., E.D. Litwack, D.D. O'Leary, G.R. Lucero, J.Y. Wang, T. Hunter (2002) Modulation of the F-actin cytoskeleton by c-Abl tyrosine kinase in cell spreading and neurite extension. J Cell Biol *156:* 879–892.

Woodring, P.J., J. Meisenhelder, S.A. Johnson, G.L. Zhou, J. Field, K. Shah, F. Bladt, T. Pawson, M. Niki, P.P. Pandolfi, J.Y. Wang, T. Hunter (2004) c-Abl phosphorylates Dok1 to promote filopodia during cell spreading. J Cell Biol *165:* 493–503.

Xie, L., B.K. Law, A.M. Chytil, K.A. Brown, M.E. Aakre, H.L. Moses (2004) Activation of the Erk pathway is required for TGF-β1-induced EMT in vitro. Neoplasia *6:* 603–610.

Xu, J., S. Lamouille, R. Derynck (2009) TGF-β-induced epithelial to mesenchymal transition. Cell Res *19:* 156–172.

Yang, L., J. Huang, X. Ren, A.E. Gorska, A. Chytil, M. Aakre, D.P. Carbone, L.M. Matrisian, A. Richmond, P.C. Lin, H.L. Moses (2008) Abrogation of TGF-β signaling in mammary carcinomas recruits Gr-1+CD11b+ myeloid cells that promote metastasis. Cancer Cell *13:* 23–35.

Yuan, Z.M., H. Shioya, T. Ishiko, X. Sun, J. Gu, Y.Y. Huang, H. Lu, S. Kharbanda, R. Weichselbaum, D. Kufe (1999) p73 is regulated by tyrosine kinase c-Abl in the apoptotic response to DNA damage. Nature *399:* 814–817.

Zandy, N.L., A.M. Pendergast (2008) Abl tyrosine kinases modulate cadherin-dependent adhesion upstream and downstream of Rho family GTPases. Cell Cycle *7:* 444–448.

Zandy, N.L., M. Playford, A.M. Pendergast (2007) Abl tyrosine kinases regulate cell-cell adhesion through Rho GTPases. Proc Natl Acad Sci USA *104:* 17686–17691.

Zhu, J., J.Y. Wang (2004) Death by Abl: a matter of location. Curr Top Dev Biol *59:* 165–192.

Cells
Tissues
Organs

Cells Tissues Organs 2011;193:114–132
DOI: 10.1159/000320179

Published online: November 2, 2010

Cooperative Signaling between Oncostatin M, Hepatocyte Growth Factor and Transforming Growth Factor-β Enhances Epithelial to Mesenchymal Transition in Lung and Pancreatic Tumor Models

Gretchen M. Argast Peter Mercado Iain J. Mulford Matthew O'Connor David M. Keane Salam Shaaban David M. Epstein Jonathan A. Pachter Julie L.C. Kan

Department of Cancer Biology, OSI Pharmaceuticals, Inc., Farmingdale, N.Y., USA

Key Words
Epithelial-mesenchymal transition · Growth factors · Cytokines · Cancer · Cell biology

Abstract
Epithelial to mesenchymal transition (EMT) plays a dual role in tumor progression. It enhances metastasis of tumor cells by increasing invasive capacity and promoting survival, and it decreases tumor cell sensitivity to epithelial cell-targeting agents such as epithelial growth factor receptor kinase inhibitors. In order to study EMT in tumor cells, we have characterized 3 new models of ligand-driven EMT: the CFPAC1 pancreatic tumor model and the H358 and H1650 lung tumor models. We identified a diverse set of ligands that drives EMT in these models. Hepatocyte growth factor and oncostatin M induced EMT in all models, while transforming growth factor-β induced EMT in both lung models. We observed morphologic, marker and phenotypic changes in response to chronic ligand treatment. Interestingly, stimulation with 2 ligands resulted in more pronounced EMT compared with single-ligand treatment, demonstrating a spectrum of EMT states induced by parallel signaling, such as the JAK and PI3K pathways. The EMT changes observed in response to the ligand were reversed upon ligand withdrawal, demonstrating the 'metastable' nature of these models. To study the impact of EMT on cell morphology and invasion in a 3D setting, we cultured cells in a semisolid basement membrane extract. Upon stimulation with EMT ligands, the colonies exhibited changes to EMT markers and showed phenotypes ranging from modest differences in colony architecture (CFPAC1) to complex branching structures (H358, H1650). Collectively, these 3 models offer robust cell systems with which to study the roles that EMT plays in cancer progression.

Abbreviations used in this paper

ECM	extracellular matrix
EGF	epidermal growth factor
EMT	epithelial to mesenchymal transition
GAPDH	glyceraldehyde-3-phosphate dehydrogenase
HGF	hepatocyte growth factor
IL	interleukin
MET	mesenchymal to epithelial transition
NSCLC	non-small cell lung carcinoma
OSM	oncostatin M
TGF-β	transforming growth factor-β
TNF	tumor necrosis factor

KARGER
Fax +41 61 306 12 34
E-Mail karger@karger.ch
www.karger.com

1422–6405/11/1932–0114$38.00/0

Accessible online at:
www.karger.com/cto

Dr. Gretchen M. Argast
OSI Pharmaceuticals, Inc.
1 Bioscience Park Drive
Farmingdale, NY 11735 (USA)
Tel. +1 631 962 0794, Fax +1 631 845 5671, E-Mail gargast@osip.com

Introduction

Originally described as a developmental program, epithelial to mesenchymal transition (EMT) is now considered a possible mechanism whereby epithelial tumor cells acquire mesenchymal characteristics that improve metastatic efficiency [Lee et al., 2006; Gavert and Ben-Ze'ev, 2008; Turley et al., 2008]. In the current model of cancer progression, epithelial tumor cells undergo EMT to become more invasive, less proliferative and more resistant to anoikis. After acquiring mesenchymal characteristics, the cells are more adept at infiltrating surrounding tissues and surviving in ectopic sites. Once localized to a metastatic site, the cells undergo mesenchymal to epithelial transition (MET) to restore the more proliferative phenotype and establish a stable secondary tumor.

The importance of EMT in cancer progression is indicated clinically by the identification of E-cadherin expression in primary tumors as a prognostic marker in prostate cancer [Gravdal et al., 2007] and as a predictive marker of response to the epidermal growth factor (EGF) receptor inhibitor erlotinib in lung cancer [Thomson et al., 2005; Yauch et al., 2005], pancreatic and colorectal cancer [Buck et al., 2007] as well as in hepatocellular cancer [Fuchs et al., 2008]. Studies comparing signaling pathways in epithelial and mesenchymal cell lines from tumors have shown hyperactivation of AKT in erlotinib-insensitive cell lines compared with erlotinib-sensitive lines, suggesting a basis for the differential sensitivity [Buck et al., 2006b; Fuchs et al., 2008]. This has led to a rational design in combination drug therapy involving erlotinib and AKT pathway inhibitors to reduce the growth and survival of primary tumor cells [Buck et al., 2006a].

To elucidate mechanisms of EMT and identify critical targets for therapy, in vitro models must be able to capture the shift from an epithelial to a mesenchymal phenotype in tumor cells. Ideally, the models would exhibit a spectrum of changes consistent with the varying states of EMT observed in vivo. Current in vitro models are limited in diversity, often with incomplete EMT as the endpoint. For example, A549 is the most commonly used model to study EMT in non-small cell lung carcinoma (NSCLC) [Illman et al., 2006; Shintani et al., 2008], yet it consists of a mixed population of epithelial and mesenchymal cells under normal culture conditions, suggesting the line undergoes EMT with minimal stimulation. Of the ligand-driven A549 models, transforming growth factor-β (TGF-β) is the most common driver of EMT, either directly or indirectly as a secondary stimulus. While this has led to a detailed understanding of TGF-β-induced EMT in A549 cells, identification of models in different lines with unique ligands will reveal new mechanisms of EMT and key signaling pathways.

TGF-β is well characterized as a stimulus of EMT in development during neural crest formation and gastrulation [Sanders et al., 1993; Duband et al., 1995; Kitase et al., 2011]. In vitro, TGF-β induces EMT in both normal [Valcourt et al., 2005] and transformed cell lines [Kasai et al., 2005] and has become the predominant ligand used in in vitro EMT models of NSCLC and other cancers [Medici et al., 2006; Gal et al., 2008]. In cancer progression it has 2 well-documented roles: in primary tumors, TGF-β inhibits growth, while more advanced cancer cells are often refractory to its growth-inhibitory effects and are able to use TGF-β signaling to promote metastases [Tang et al., 2003]. Novel signaling pathways involved in TGF-β regulation of EMT are detailed in the current issue [Lamouille and Derynck, 2011; Allington and Schiemann, 2011]. The role of EMT in the stage-specific responses to TGF-β is currently not well understood, but is gaining attention [Kohn et al., 2010].

The hepatocyte growth factor (HGF)/c-Met signaling pathway is also an established inducer of EMT in normal and transformed cells. In development, HGF/c-Met signaling is required for induction of EMT in myogenic precursor cells, resulting in delamination from the epithelial dermomyotome and migration of the cells to specific sites such as the limb bud [Bladt et al., 1995]. In transgenic animals, overexpression of HGF or c-Met wild-type or mutationally activated c-Met induces a wide variety of tumors of both epithelial and mesenchymal origin [Takayama et al., 1997; Graveel et al., 2005; Ponzo et al., 2009]. In patients, overexpression of HGF and c-Met are strongly associated with invasive and metastatic tumors [Birchmeier et al., 2003; Ponzo et al., 2009], and mutational activation of c-Met is associated with hereditary papillary renal carcinoma [Schmidt et al., 1997].

Whereas TGF-β and HGF are well-known drivers of EMT, oncostatin M (OSM) has only recently been identified as an EMT factor. OSM is a member of the interleukin (IL)-6 family of cytokines which includes leukemia inhibitory factor, ciliary neurotrophic factor, cardiotrophin-1, IL-31 and IL-11. It is a pleiotropic cytokine secreted by neutrophils, macrophages and activated T cells. The receptors for IL-6 cytokines are heterodimers or -trimers between ligand-specific α-subunit receptors and the gp130 protein [Kishimoto et al., 1995]. In contrast to other IL-6 family cytokines, OSM binds to gp130 instead of its 2 α-subunit receptors, leukemia inhibitory factor receptor and OSM β receptor [Mosley et al., 1996]. The gp130 receptor couples agonist binding to activation of several signal transduction pathways in the cell including JAK/STAT, Ras/Raf/MAPK and PI3K/AKT. OSM has also been shown to activate the stress MAP kinases JNK and p38 [Boing et al., 2006].

OSM plays a significant role in the inflammatory process by restoring homeostasis through regulation of proteins known to control tissue remodeling and wound repair [Bamber et al., 1998]. It also induces invasion in breast cancer lines through secretion of vascular endothelial growth factor as part of a signaling loop stimulated by granulocyte macrophage colony-stimulating factor [Queen et al., 2005]. OSM plays dual roles in its regulation of proliferation and differentiation as both stimulator and inhibitor, depending on the model. For example, OSM suppresses cell growth in a number of tumor cell lines but can stimulate proliferation in fibroblasts, smooth muscle cells and Kaposi sarcoma cells [for a review, see Gomez-Lechon, 1999]. It has not been described as an EMT factor in development, but it was shown to induce nontransformed proximal tubular epithelial cells to undergo a transition to the myofibroblast morphology [Pollack et al., 2007]. The diversity of functions induced by OSM appears to play a role in cancer progression as expression of the OSM receptor in cervical squamous cell carcinoma correlates with poor patient survival [Ng et al., 2007].

Here, we present 3 reversible ligand-induced models of EMT in which OSM, HGF and TGF-β play key roles in inducing morphological and phenotypic changes consistent with EMT. Analysis of signaling pathways identified JAK and PI3K as necessary for EMT in these models.

Materials and Methods

Cell Culture and Treatment

NCI-H358 and NCI-H1650 cells were cultured in RPMI-1640 medium (Gibco, No. 21870) with 10% fetal bovine serum (Sigma), 1 mM sodium pyruvate (Gibco, No. 11360), 2 mM L-glutamine (Gibco, No. 25030) and 10 mM HEPES (Gibco, No. 15630). CFPAC1 cells were cultured in DMEM medium (Gibco, No. 11960) with 10% fetal bovine serum and 2 mM L-glutamine. For chronic ligand treatment, cells were seeded in normal growth medium and stimulated the following day (day 0) with 100 ng/ml HGF (Peprotech, No. 100-39), 100 ng/ml OSM (R&D Systems, 295-OM), 10 ng/ml TGF-β_1 (EMD Biosciences, No. 616450), 25 ng/ml tumor necrosis factor (TNF)-α (R&D Systems, No. 210-TA), or 100 ng/ml EGF (R&D Systems, No. 236-EG). Cells were pretreated with inhibitor [JAK inhibitor 1, 0.25 μM (EMD Biosciences, No. 420099); PI3K inhibitor LY294002, 10 μM (EMD Biosciences, No. 440202); MEK inhibitor 1, 1 μM (EMD Biosciences, No. 444937)] for 30 min. Medium, ligand and inhibitors were refreshed on day 4. For reversion experiments, cells were passaged on day 7 and reseeded without ligand. For all experiments, cells were harvested on day 7 for protein or fixed for immunofluorescence. For short-term ligand stimulation (online suppl. fig. 1A, www.karger.com/doi/10.1159/320179), cells were plated on day 1, and on the following day, pretreated with inhibitor for 2 h, followed by stimulation with the ligand for 15 min.

Western Blots

Cells were washed with PBS, scraped into RIPA buffer (Sigma, No. R0278) containing 200 μM sodium vanadate and protease and phosphatase inhibitor cocktails (Sigma, P2850, P8340, P5726), and centrifuged. Standard Western blotting protocols were followed. Primary antibody sources are as follows: E-cadherin (Santa Cruz, No. sc21791), vimentin (BD Pharmingen, No. 550513), Zeb1 (Santa Cruz, No. sc25388), Snail (Cell Signaling, No. 4719), glyceraldehyde-3-phosphate dehydrogenase (GAPDH; Santa Cruz, No. sc25778), actin (Sigma No. A1978), p-STAT3 (Y705; Cell Signaling, No. 9145), total STAT3 (Cell Signaling, No. 9139), p-Akt (S473; Cell Signaling, No. 9271), total Akt (Cell Signaling, No. 9272), pERK (T202/Y204; Cell Signaling, No. 4377), total ERK (Cell Signaling, No. 9102). Western blots were developed with Pierce Supersignal Femto substrate using the Kodak Image Station 4000MM or Alpha Innotech Fluorchem™ SP. Densitometry was performed using the Alpha Innotech Fluorchem software. Bands were first normalized to either GAPDH or actin levels and then converted to fold change relative to untreated/DMSO controls.

Immunofluorescence/Confocal Microscopy

Cells were plated on glass coverslips and treated as described. Standard immunofluorescence staining protocols were followed. Primary antibody sources are E-cadherin (Santa Cruz, No. sc21791) and vimentin (Chemicon, No. AB5733). Stained cells were captured on a Leica DMRXE microscope/SP2 scanner using Leica Confocal Software.

Migration/Invasion

Cells were stimulated with ligand in the presence of serum for 6 days. On day 6, medium was changed to serum-free medium with ligand. On day 7, cells were plated in modified Boyden chambers (Trevigen Cultrex, No. 3458-096-K) in serum-free medium in the upper chamber and 3× ligand/10% fetal bovine serum in the lower chamber. For invasion assays, membranes were coated with type IV collagen (included in the assay kit). After 24 (migration) or 48 h (invasion), cells attached to the underside of the membrane were quantified using calcein-AM stain read on a fluorescent plate reader (Wallac). Significance was determined by unpaired t test with a cutoff value of $p < 0.01$.

Doubling Time

Cells were treated with ligand for 7 days and then replated at equal numbers in 6-cm plates. At days 3, 5, 7, 10 and 12, cells were counted in duplicate plates and the average cell numbers were used to calculate doubling time according to the multiple time point method at www.doubling-time.com.

Quantitative PCR

Cells were plated and stimulated as described above (Cell Culture and Treatment). CFPAC1 cells were harvested after 1 and 7 days of treatment. H358 and H1650 cells were harvested after 7 days of treatment. RNA was isolated using RNAqueous-4 PCR Kit (Ambion, AM1914). Samples were DNase treated using the Turbo DNA-Free kit (Ambion, AM1907) and reverse-transcribed using Superscript III (Invitrogen, 18080-044) for quantitative PCR analysis. Taqman primers and locked-nucleic acid probes were designed using ProbeFinder software (Universal Probe Library, Roche). For mRNA analysis, real-time PCR was performed using the ABI 7900HT series PCR machine. Thermocycling conditions were as follows: 50°C for 2 min, 95°C for 10 min, 95°C for 15 s, 50°C for 10 s, and 60°C for 1 min. Data were collected over 45 cycles and then normalized to GAPDH, and further normalized to the untreated control sample.

3D Matrigel Culture

Eighty microliters of cold growth factor-reduced Matrigel (BD Biosciences, No. 354230) was plated per well into 8-well chamber slides (Labtek II, Nunc No. 154534) and solidified at 37°C. Cells were diluted in complete medium containing 2% Matrigel, to give 5,000 cells per 300 μl. Three hundred microliters was aliquoted into each well and incubated at 37°C, 5% CO_2 overnight. Medium was aspirated and replaced with 120 μl per well of medium containing 2% Matrigel and ligand treatments. Cells were grown for 14 days, feeding every 3–4 days. Cells were imaged by phase contrast.

3D Immunofluorescence and Confocal Imaging

Cells were fixed in 2% paraformaldehyde (Electron Microscopy Sciences, No. 15710)/PBS (Gibco, No.14190) for 10–20 min at room temperature, washed with PBS and permeabilized with 0.1% Triton X-100 (Sigma, No. P1379) in PBS for 20 min. Cells were blocked with 3% bovine serum albumin/PBS for 1 h then incubated with primary antibody in blocking buffer overnight at room temperature. Dilutions are as follows: anti-E-cadherin (Santa Cruz, No. sc21791) 1:75; anti-vimentin (Millipore, No. AB5733) 1:2,000. Cells were washed in PBS and incubated with secondary antibodies overnight at room temperature in the dark: anti-mouse Alexa Fluor 488 nm (Invitrogen, No. A11029) 1:600; anti-chicken Alexa Fluor 568 nm (Invitrogen, No. A11041) 1:600. Cells were washed 3 × 20 min in PBS, the third wash containing 5 μM TO-PRO3 (Invitrogen, No. T3605), and mounted with ProLong Gold antifade reagent (Invitrogen, No. P36934). Cells were imaged on a Leica DMRXE microscope/SP2 scanner using Leica Confocal Software.

Results

Ligand-Induced Morphological Changes in New Models of EMT

To identify new in vitro models of EMT, we performed a screen of approximately 60 ligands against a diverse set of 30 tumor cell lines over a 7-day incubation period. The selected cell lines represented breast, colon, lung, pancreatic and prostate cancer. In the panel of ligands, we included growth factors, cytokines and extracellular matrix (ECM) components (see online suppl. table 1 for ligands and concentrations used). Many of the ligands were chosen because of their reported association with EMT (either in development or in disease) or with metastasis. We also included inflammatory factors because of the association between inflammation and cancer. The ligands were used at or above concentrations reported in the literature and were kept in the growth medium for the 7-day incubation period, which included 1 change of medium and ligand. Overall, there were only a few robust responses to single ligands in this screen. For some cell lines, we expanded the screen to include stimulation with combinations of ligands. We observed EMT-like changes with ligands that are known inducers of EMT such as TGF-β and HGF, but we also found that the inflammatory cytokine OSM, alone or in combination with other ligands, induced morphological and marker changes characteristic of EMT. We identified 3 models for further characterization: NCI-H358 and NCI-H1650 NSCLC cells and CFPAC1 pancreatic cancer cells.

When treated with a single ligand or with dual-ligand combinations, cells transitioned from the characteristic epithelial cobblestone morphology with well-defined cell-cell contacts to the scattered, spindle-shaped morphology characteristic of mesenchymal cells (fig. 1). Single ligands were variable in their ability to induce pronounced EMT changes. In H358 cells, HGF induced the strongest morphological change as a single ligand, followed by TGF-β and OSM. In H1650 cells, HGF also induced the most significant morphological changes as a single ligand, with OSM and TGF-β inducing negligible changes. In addition to HGF, TGF-β and OSM, H1650 cells also responded to EGF and TNF-α with responses comparable with HGF and TGF-β, respectively. Of the 3 models, CFPAC1 cells underwent the most pronounced changes with single-ligand stimulation (HGF or OSM). CFPAC1 cells did not respond to TGF-β, but did respond to another gp130 receptor ligand, IL-6, when used in combination with soluble IL-6 receptor (data not shown). Within any model, we noted that dual-ligand combinations generally induced more advanced EMT than single ligands. Depending on the model and ligands used, there was a spectrum of EMT changes induced by the various combinations, providing a means to study the different steps involved for EMT in cancer cells.

EMT Marker Changes in Lung and Pancreatic Cancer Models

To examine molecular changes in response to ligand stimulation in the 3 models, we analyzed expression of

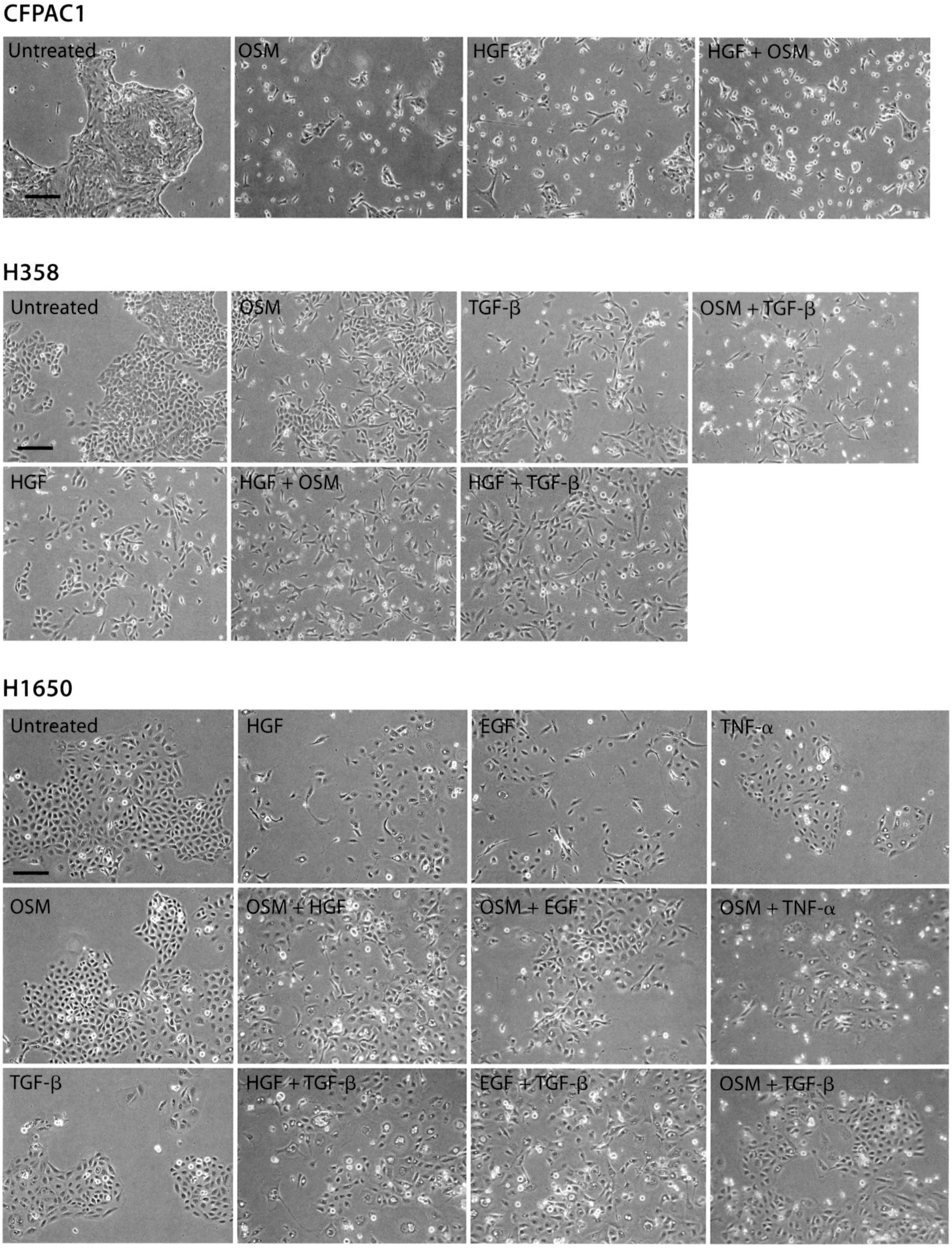

Fig. 1. EMT morphological changes are induced by single- and dual-ligand treatment. CFPAC1, H358 and H1650 cells were stimulated with the indicated ligands for 7 days and photographed for representative morphological changes. Cells were photographed with a 10× objective. Scale bars = 0.2 mm.

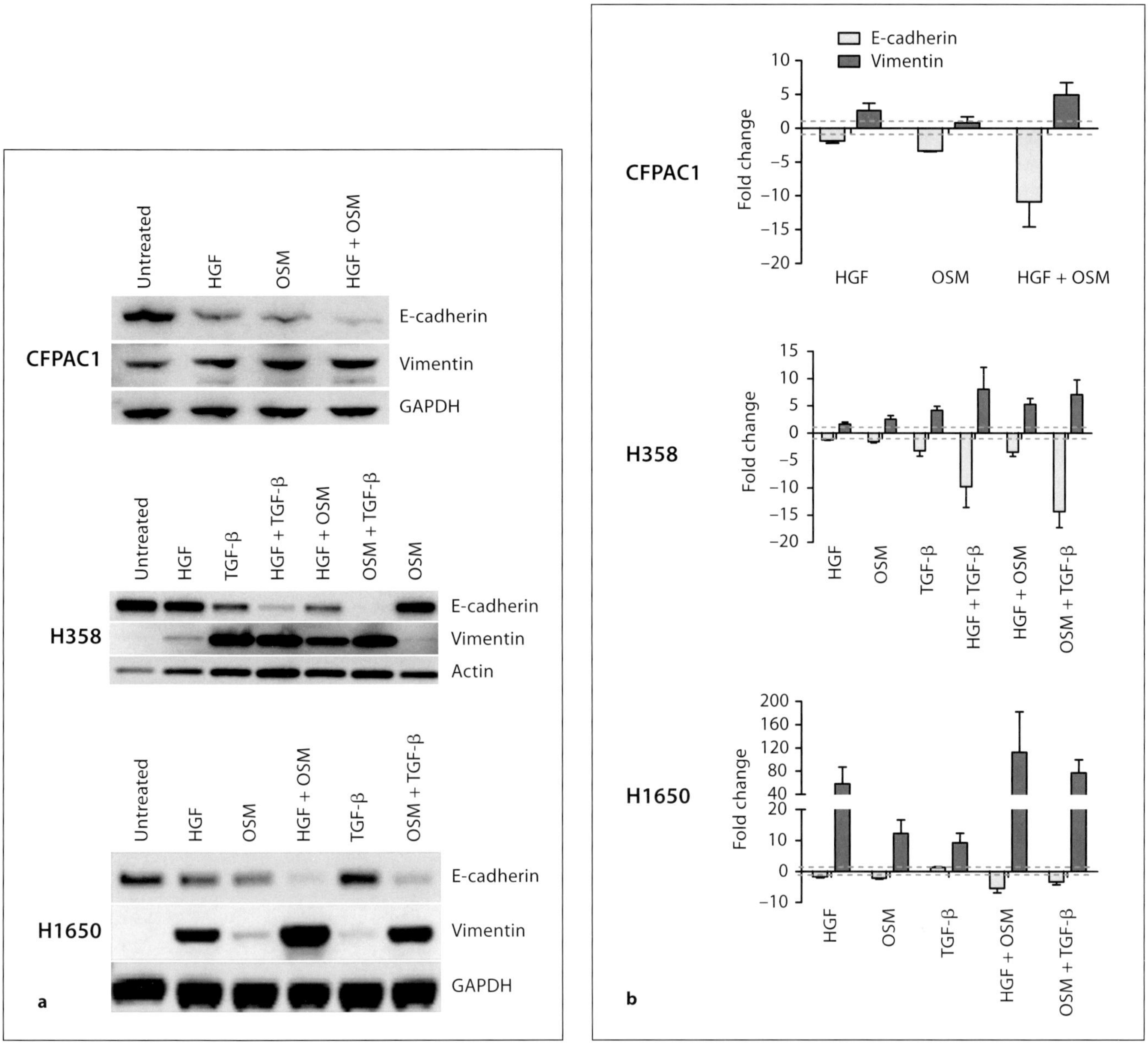

Fig. 2. EMT marker changes are induced by single- and dual-ligand treatment. **a** Cells treated for 7 days were harvested and analyzed for epithelial (E-cadherin) and mesenchymal (vimentin) markers by Western blot. Results are representative of at least 3 independent experiments. **b** Western blots were quantified by densitometry, normalized to loading control, and converted to fold change relative to untreated cells. Results represent the average and SEM from 3 experiments.

epithelial and mesenchymal cell markers. Overall, the morphological changes illustrated in figure 1 were accompanied by changes in epithelial and mesenchymal markers (fig. 2). We will confine the presented data to those involving OSM, HGF and TGF-β, as they are the most common ligands between the 3 models. In each model, we noted a continuum of EMT states induced by single and dual ligands as indicated by changes in the epithelial marker E-cadherin and the mesenchymal marker vimentin (quantified as average fold change between repeat experiments in fig. 2b). In the CFPAC1 model, the ligands induced differential degrees of EMT, as follows: OSM = HGF < HGF + OSM. For the H358 model, the relationship was OSM = HGF < TGF-β

< HGF + OSM < HGF + TGF-β < OSM + TGF-β, and for the H1650 model, the relationship was OSM = TGF-β < HGF < OSM + TGF-β < OSM + HGF. In the CFPAC1 model, there was an expression of vimentin in the basal state, suggesting some of the cells may undergo spontaneous EMT. In the H358 model, changes in both E-cadherin and vimentin were consistent and robust. In the H1650 model, we observed strong changes to vimentin, but more modest changes to E-cadherin. In sum, the changes in morphology and marker expression exhibited a spectrum of EMT from partial EMT with single ligands to advanced EMT with dual-ligand treatments.

Localization of E-cadherin on the cell membrane in adherens junctions is required for its function in cell-cell adhesion, and translocation of E-cadherin from the membrane to the cytosol is an indication of loss of E-cadherin function. With single-ligand treatments in the H358 and H1650 models, we observed modest changes in E-cadherin expression by Western blot, but more significant morphological changes indicative of partial EMT. To examine whether the morphological changes correlated better with E-cadherin localization than with total E-cadherin expression, we determined whether the E-cadherin that remained in the cells was functional. We monitored subcellular localization of E-cadherin and vimentin after ligand treatment by immunofluorescence and confocal microscopy. Whereas single-ligand treatment with HGF or OSM did not strongly downregulate E-cadherin expression, it did cause translocation of the protein from the membrane to the cytoplasm (fig. 3). Single-ligand treatment with HGF or OSM resulted in modest upregulation of vimentin in cells on the periphery of cell clusters, as well as in internal cells. These results indicate that the partial EMT induced by HGF or OSM can be characterized by loss of functional E-cadherin with a modest upregulation of vimentin.

Ligand Treatments Induce EMT-Like Transcriptional Reprogramming

The transcription factors comprising the Snail, Twist and Zeb families are frequently called the 'master regulators' of EMT, stressing the importance of cellular transcriptional reprogramming during EMT [Nieto, 2002; Peinado et al., 2007]. In order to understand the extent of transcriptional reprogramming in each of these models, we analyzed changes in mRNA of the transcription factors as well as in a panel of epithelial and mesenchymal genes in response to single- and dual-ligand treatment in the 3 models (tables 1–3). In the CFPAC1 model, changes in mRNA levels after 1 and 7 days of stimulation were quantified by quantitative PCR, while the H358 and H1650 models were stimulated for 7 days only. A 3-fold cutoff was imposed to determine which genes changed over the course of the experiment. Epithelial genes are listed first (CDH1 through TJP3) and mesenchymal genes including transcription factors are listed second (ACTN1 through ZEB2). In the CFPAC1 model (table 1), TWIST1, ZEB1 and ZEB2 were the only EMT transcription factors upregulated. When looking at patterns of gene changes to the epithelial and the mesenchymal genes as 2 classes of genes, there were more changes to mesenchymal markers compared with epithelial markers. In the H358 model (table 2), EMT progression correlated with SNAI1, SNAI2, ZEB1 and ZEB2 upregulation. Overall, there were more changes observed in this model compared with the CFPAC1 model, with approximately equal changes to epithelial and mesenchymal genes. The gene changes in the H358 model also illustrate cooperative signaling, as either HGF or OSM alone induced few changes, but together, they affected 11 of the 19 EMT genes surveyed. In the H1650 model (table 3), the transcription factors affected were SNAI2, ZEB1 and ZEB2. Here, we observed more changes to mesenchymal genes compared with epithelial genes. Some genes were driven by all treatments (VCAN, VIM), some were OSM driven (ITGB3, ZEB1, ZEB2), and some were dependent on cooperative signaling between 2 ligands (CLDN3, TJP3).

Ligand-Induced EMT Requires JAK and PI3K Signaling

To identify the signaling pathways required for EMT in these models, we examined the effects of blocking the MEK, JAK and PI3K pathways on ligand-induced EMT, since these pathways are downstream targets of HGF, OSM and TGF-β. Preliminary studies were performed to determine concentrations of the inhibitors sufficient to block downstream signaling (online suppl. fig. 1A). Experiments were run for 7 days with ligand in the presence of the inhibitors for the duration of the experiment.

In all 3 models, inhibition of the JAK pathway completely blocked morphological and marker changes induced by OSM, and partially blocked changes induced by OSM + HGF and OSM + TGF-β. As shown in figure 4 and in online supplementary tables 2–4, downregulation of E-cadherin and upregulation of vimentin are both blocked by the JAK inhibitor in OSM-stimulated CFPAC1, H358 and H1650 cells. Online supplementary figure 1B shows the corresponding morphological changes. In the HGF + OSM and TGF-β + OSM dual-ligand

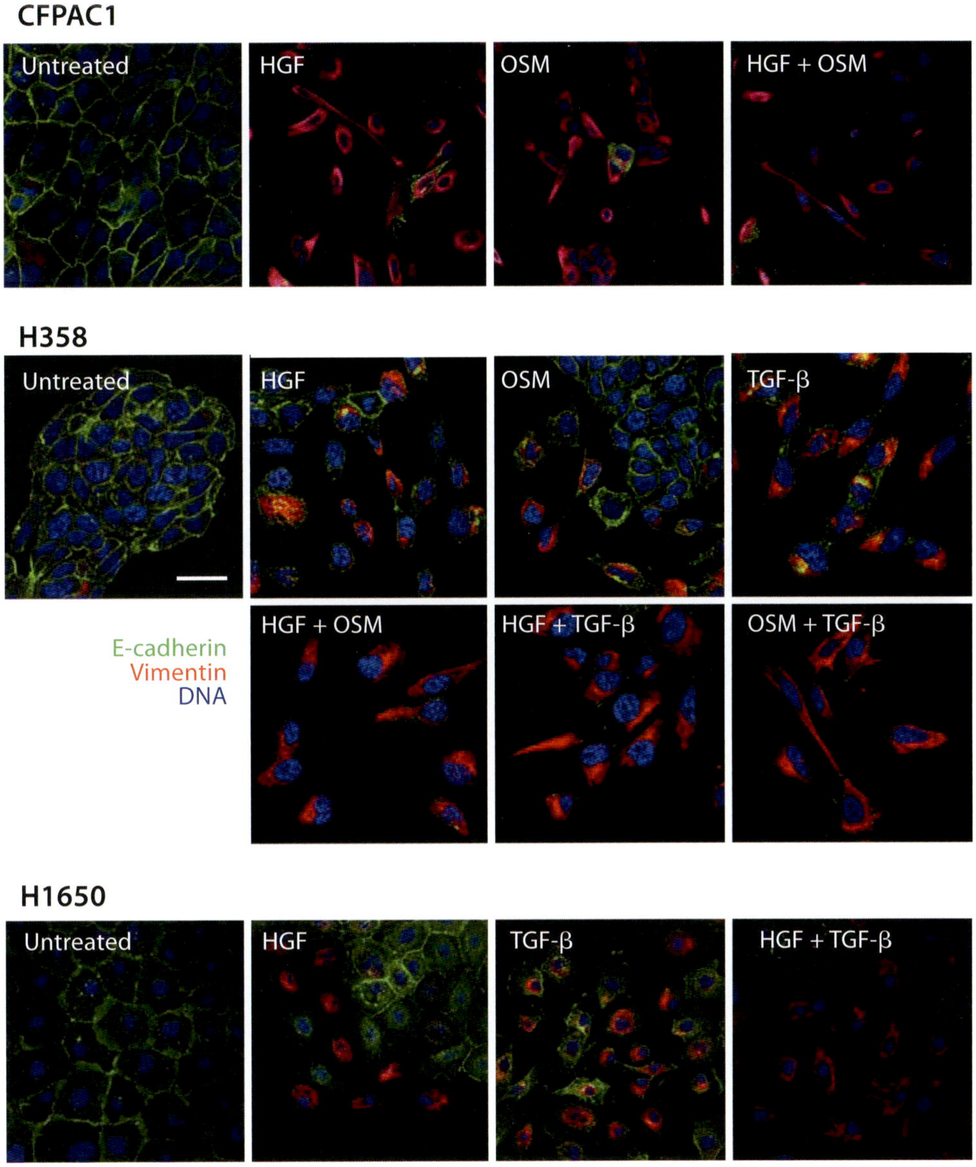

Fig. 3. E-cadherin expression and localization changes are induced by single- and dual-ligand treatment. Cells were fixed after 7 days of ligand treatment and stained for E-cadherin (green), vimentin (red) and DNA (blue), and imaged by confocal microscopy with a 63× objective. Scale bar = 0.05 mm. Results are representative of at least 3 experiments.

models, inhibition of JAK only partially blocked morphological and marker changes as judged by concurrent inhibition of both downregulation of E-cadherin and upregulation of vimentin. For example, in the CFPAC1 HGF + OSM model, inhibition of JAK restores some E-cadherin, but does not block upregulation of vimentin. In the H358 HGF + OSM model, inhibition of JAK restores E-cadherin to untreated levels, but does not completely block upregulation of vimentin. In the H1650 HGF + OSM model, inhibition of JAK completely restores E-cadherin and strongly, but not completely, inhibits upregulation of vimentin and Zeb1. These results indicate that the dual-ligand models depend on multiple parallel pathways from both ligands to drive EMT.

In studies designed to understand the role of the MEK and PI3K pathways in EMT, we noted that there is cooperativity of these 2 pathways relating to marker and morphology changes, respectively. Analysis of EMT changes dependent on MEK activity revealed that it plays a role in the EMT marker changes and not in morphology. Inhibition of the MEK pathway had no effect on EMT morphology induced by any of the ligands in any of the models. However, the MEK inhibitor did partially block the induction of vimentin in OSM-stimulated CFPAC1 cells

Table 1. EMT transcriptional reprogramming in CFPAC1 cells: fold change in mRNA compared with untreated cells

CFPAC1	HGF		OSM		HGF + OSM	
	day 1	day 7	day 1	day 7	day 1	day 7
CDH1	NC	NC	NC	–3.06	NC	–4.31
CLDN3	–	NC	–	NC	–	–
ERBB3	–	NC	–	NC	–	–
MMP7	NC	NC	NC	NC	NC	NC
MTA3	NC	NC	NC	NC	NC	NC
OCLN	–	NC	–	NC	–	–
TJP3	–	NC	–	NC	–	–
ACTN1	NC	NC	NC	NC	NC	NC
CDH2	NC	NC	NC	NC	NC	NC
ITGB3	NC	3.57	31.39	106.2	23.08	86.19
PLAUR	NC	NC	NC	NC	NC	NC
SNAI1	NC	NC	NC	NC	NC	3.05
SNAI2	NC	NC	NC	NC	NC	NC
SPARC	NC	–5.41	NC	–33	NC	NC
TWIST1	NC	612	NC	3.3	–3.28	675
VCAN	–	NC	–	NC	–	–
VIM	NC	NC	NC	NC	NC	5.23
ZEB1	NC	NC	NC	3.00	NC	3.80
ZEB2	NC	NC	3.52	13.7	3.45	22.41

NC = No change; – = not done.

Table 2. EMT transcriptional reprogramming in H358 cells: fold change in mRNA compared with untreated cells

H358	HGF	OSM	TGF-β	OSM+ TGF-β	HGF+ OSM
CDH1	NC	NC	NC	–21.30	–5.8
CLDN3	NC	NC	–6.89	–38.52	–8.97
ERBB3	NC	NC	–4.47	–16.77	NC
MMP7	NC	NC	NC	–9.52	–8.45
MTA3	NC	NC	NC	NC	NC
OCLN	NC	NC	NC	–27.95	NC
TJP3	NC	NC	–25.51	–85.67	–13.52
ACTN1	NC	NC	4.87	4.32	NC
CDH2	NC	NC	5.44	3.46	NC
ITGB3	NC	4.17	16.52	17.82	7.05
PLAUR	NC	NC	3.1	4.61	NC
SNAI1	NC	NC	8.29	13.97	2.67
SNAI2	NC	NC	4.19	3.82	NC
SPARC	NC	NC	68.39	21.82	3.42
TWIST1	NC	NC	NC	NC	NC
VCAN	NC	NC	13.82	9.68	3.39
VIM	NC	NC	16.52	16.77	8.69
ZEB1	NC	3.02	16.21	36.20	18.08
ZEB2	3.26	6.96	28.22	114.55	23.41

NC = No change; – = not done.

and HGF + OSM and TGF-β + OSM stimulated H1650 cells, without affecting E-cadherin levels.

We also observed differential effects on EMT morphology and markers when blocking the PI3K pathway. Inhibition of PI3K affected EMT morphological changes induced by all ligand treatments in H358 cells to varying degrees. The PI3K inhibitor completely blocked morphological changes induced by OSM, whereas EMT induced by HGF, TGF-β, HGF + OSM or TGF-β + OSM was affected to a lesser extent. We did not observe any robust changes in markers that correlated with the morphological changes. In H1650 cells, the PI3K inhibitor partially blocked changes to E-cadherin and vimentin induced by OSM and HGF + OSM, but not by TGF-β + OSM. It also blocked morphological changes induced by all 3 treatments. CFPAC1 cells are dependent on PI3K activity for proliferation and survival. The concentration of the PI3K inhibitor necessary to block PI3K activity substantially decreased the number of cells over the 7-day incubation (online suppl. fig. 1B), but it did not affect expression of E-cadherin or vimentin in the remaining cells.

Since we have shown that cooperative signaling plays an important role in EMT, we examined the effects of

Table 3. EMT transcriptional reprogramming in H1650 cells: fold change in mRNA compared with untreated cells

H1650	HGF	OSM	TGF-β	HGF+ OSM	OSM+ TGF-β
CDH1	NC	NC	NC	NC	NC
CLDN3	NC	NC	NC	NC	–4.41
ERBB3	NC	NC	NC	NC	NC
MMP7	NC	3.66	3.15	NC	3.58
MTA3	NC	NC	NC	NC	NC
OCLN	NC	NC	NC	NC	NC
TJP3	NC	NC	NC	–4.07	–8.17
ACTN1	NC	NC	NC	NC	NC
CDH2	NC	NC	NC	NC	NC
ITGB3	NC	13.25	NC	16.3	20.35
PLAUR	NC	NC	NC	NC	NC
SNAI1	NC	NC	NC	NC	NC
SNAI2	6.43	3.44	4.9	6.76	10.47
SPARC	NC	NC	NC	NC	NC
TWIST1	NC	NC	NC	NC	NC
VCAN	6.71	3.88	5.04	12.4	13.95
VIM	4.92	4.18	3.99	11.6	12.72
ZEB1	NC	3.15	NC	12.84	8.17
ZEB2	NC	4.43	NC	21.51	7.66

NC = No change; – = not done.

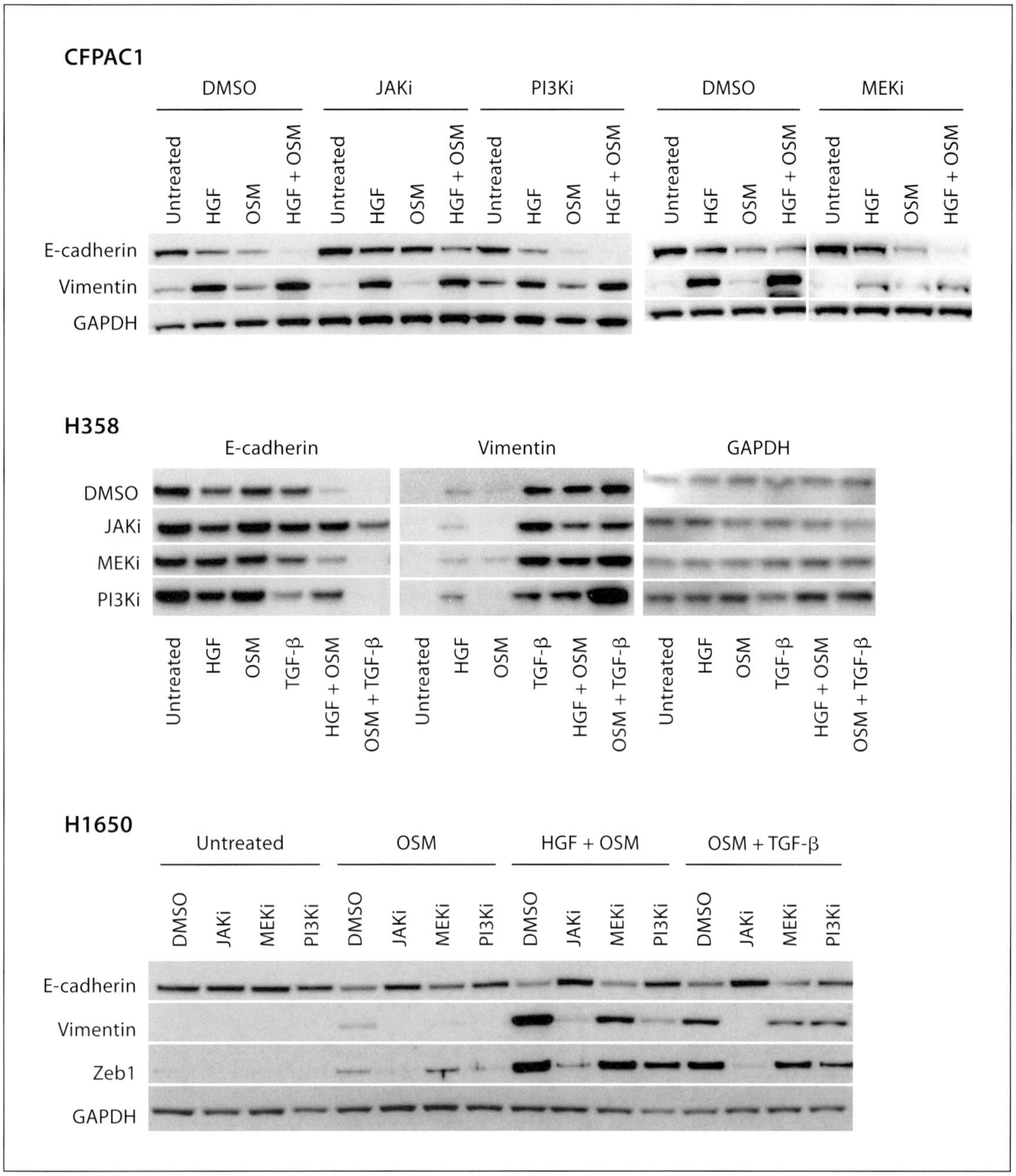

Fig. 4. Analysis of signaling pathways required for single- and dual-ligand-induced EMT. Cells were treated with ligands for 7 days in the presence or absence of JAK (JAKi), MEK (MEKi) and PI3K inhibitors (PI3Ki). Cells were harvested for protein for immunoblot analysis of EMT markers. DMSO treatment lysates were run on each blot and shown to illustrate relative changes in markers within each blot. Results are representative of at least 2 experiments. Quantification of these blots is shown in online supplementary tables 2–4.

combining inhibitors to block multiple pathways and looked for synergistic effects. In H358 cells, we found that no combination of inhibitors showed effects greater than either inhibitor used alone (data not shown).

Morphological and Marker Changes Correlate with a Mesenchymal Phenotype

In addition to morphology and marker status, epithelial and mesenchymal cells differ in phenotypic characteristics. Mesenchymal cells tend to be more invasive and

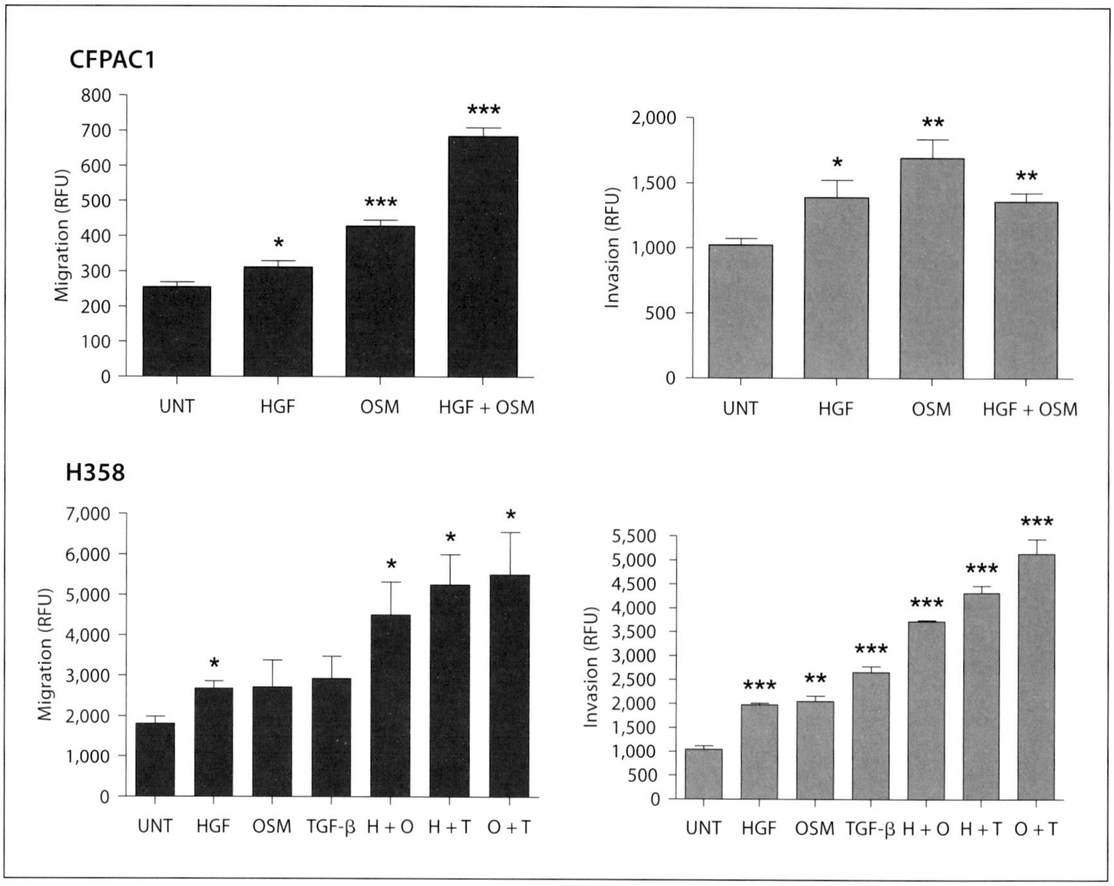

Fig. 5. Seven-day ligand treatment results in a more invasive phenotype. Cells were treated with the ligand for 7 days then assayed for migration after 24 h and invasion after 48 h by modified Boyden chamber assay in the presence of the ligand. * $p < 0.01$; ** $p < 0.001$; *** $p < 0.0001$. RFU = Relative fluorescence units; UNT = untreated cells; H + O = HGF + OSM; H + T = HGF + TGF-β; O + T = OSM + TGF-β.

less proliferative than their epithelial counterparts. To determine if protein changes induced by ligand treatment correlate with phenotypic changes characteristic of mesenchymal cells, we looked for increased migration rates and decreased proliferation rates after 7 days of EMT ligand treatment. We measured migration in a modified Boyden chamber assay after 24 h, and invasion in collagen-IV-coated modified Boyden chambers after 48 h. In the H358 and CFPAC1 models, unstimulated cells showed little migration or invasion (fig. 5). In H358 cells, single-ligand treatments resulted in increased migration and invasion, and dual-ligand treatment resulted in stronger responses compared with single ligands. We observed similar results in CFPAC1 migration; however, invasion was not as robust, even in response to dual-ligand stimulation. In H1650 cells, we consistently observed marker changes and morphological changes with ligand stimulation, but effects on migration and invasion were modest and quite variable, suggesting EMT does not have a strong impact on H1650 cell motility (data not shown).

As another indicator of the mesenchymal phenotype, we determined the doubling time of unstimulated and stimulated cells in each of the models, looking for longer doubling times after 7-day stimulation with EMT ligands. Table 4 shows that in CFPAC1 and H358 cells, single-ligand treatments resulted in longer doubling times compared with unstimulated cells. Furthermore, dual-ligand treatments increased doubling times over any single ligand, with the longest doubling time of >5 days (H358; OSM + TGF-β). In response to single-ligand stimulation, doubling time in H1650 cells either did not change (TGF-β) or decreased modestly (HGF, OSM), and dual-ligand stimulation resulted in either a modest increase (HGF + OSM) or no change (HGF + TGF-β, OSM + TGF-β) in doubling time. Here, again, there was little impact of EMT on the phenotype of H1650 cells, but in H358 and CFPAC1 cells, EMT caused a decrease in proliferation, which is a phenotype characteristic of mesenchymal cells.

EMT Induced by Ligand Treatment Is Reversible

The phenotype of mesenchymal cells allows for invasion of the basement membrane and dissemination of tumor cells into the circulatory system. However, in order to establish a cohesive tumor, cells must be able to form contacts and proliferate, a phenotype more consistent with epithelial cells. Therefore, the model of metastasis which states that cells undergo EMT to metastasize, also states that disseminated mesenchymal tumor cells undergo MET in order to grow at an ectopic site. To determine whether EMT in these models is reversible, we examined the reversion of ligand-induced EMT changes over 15 days in response to ligand withdrawal. We present the results for the H358 HGF + OSM model in online supplementary figures 2A, B and figure 6. CFPAC1 and H1650 cells behaved similarly and are shown in online supplementary figures 2C, D. After 6 days of culture without ligand, HGF- and OSM-treated H358 cells had lost most of their mesenchymal characteristics. The cells regained epithelial cell-cell contacts and grew in clusters, similar to untreated cells. Cells treated with HGF + OSM required more time (12–15 days) to revert compared with cells treated with HGF or OSM alone. EMT-associated changes in cell markers also reverted after 6 days (single ligand) and 9 days (dual ligands) as shown by upregulation of E-cadherin and downregulation of vimentin and Snail (fig. 6a). By immunofluorescence, E-cadherin was membrane localized as early as day 3 of reversion (online suppl. fig. 2B). By day 6, all conditions had clusters of cells growing with membrane-localized E-cadherin and no vimentin. The remaining vimentin expression was seen mostly in isolated cells. By day 9, the staining in the reverted cells looked indistinguishable from untreated cells. However, Zeb1 was still expressed at higher levels in HGF + OSM cells as compared with control cells even at 15 days (fig. 6a), suggesting the reversion is not complete for dual-ligand treatment.

We also determined whether the phenotypic changes were reversed upon ligand withdrawal by examining cells that had undergone EMT for 7 days, followed by a 14-day reversion. For these experiments, we focused on H358 cells as they showed the strongest response to the ligand after 7 days. Figure 6b shows that all HGF and OSM-treated cell populations reverted to the untreated phenotype after 14 days. However, in the invasion assays, the single-ligand-treated cells reverted back to a phenotype comparable with untreated cells, but the dual-ligand-treated cells showed reduced but significant differences in invasion compared with untreated cells. These results show that the cells had maintained some of the mesenchymal phenotype even though morphology and markers were epithelial.

Table 4. Change in doubling time (h) induced by EMT ligands

	CFPAC1	H358	H1650
Untreated	36.0 ± 3.46	34.0 ± 2.83	53.4 ± 0
HGF	41.2 ± 5.94	49.1 ± 5.80	46.7 ± 2.33
OSM	54.7 ± 10.25	37.0 ± 7.00	46.7 ± 1.13
TGF-β	–	50.7 ± 6.08	54.8 ± 4.03
HGF + OSM	57.7 ± 3.11	94.7 ± 40.5	60.0 ± 3.96
HGF + TGF-β	–	51.8 ± 11.0	50.0 ± 0.78
OSM + TGF-β	–	157.5 ± 7.78	53.7 ± 3.68

Data are means ± SD.

Induction of EMT in 3D Culture of H358 Cells

Traditional 2D culture has been instrumental in identifying morphological and molecular changes in cells undergoing EMT in a simplified environment. We next examined EMT changes induced in a 3D setting where cell-cell contacts and cell-ECM contacts more closely resemble conditions in vivo. For each of the models, we stimulated cells in 3D Matrigel matrix over 14 days, and they were stained for E-cadherin and vimentin (fig. 7). Untreated CFPAC1 cells grew as multiple round nodules attached together, with many developing hollow acinus-like structures. E-cadherin was expressed on the membrane in all colonies, and vimentin was observed at low levels in most colonies. Cells grown in HGF and OSM showed lower E-cadherin and higher vimentin expression compared with unstimulated cells. Most of the marker changes were observed in the cells on the periphery of the colony, much like what is observed in human tumors with cells undergoing EMT only on the tumor surface. HGF + OSM also changed the growth pattern of the colonies from a more organized architecture with multiple nodules and acinar-like structures to a more simplified morphology consisting of spheres filled with cells.

Untreated H358 cells grew as round colonies with little vimentin and strong E-cadherin membrane staining. Similar to 2D culture, HGF or OSM alone triggered modest changes in markers and morphology, with some induction of vimentin, but little change to E-cadherin ex-

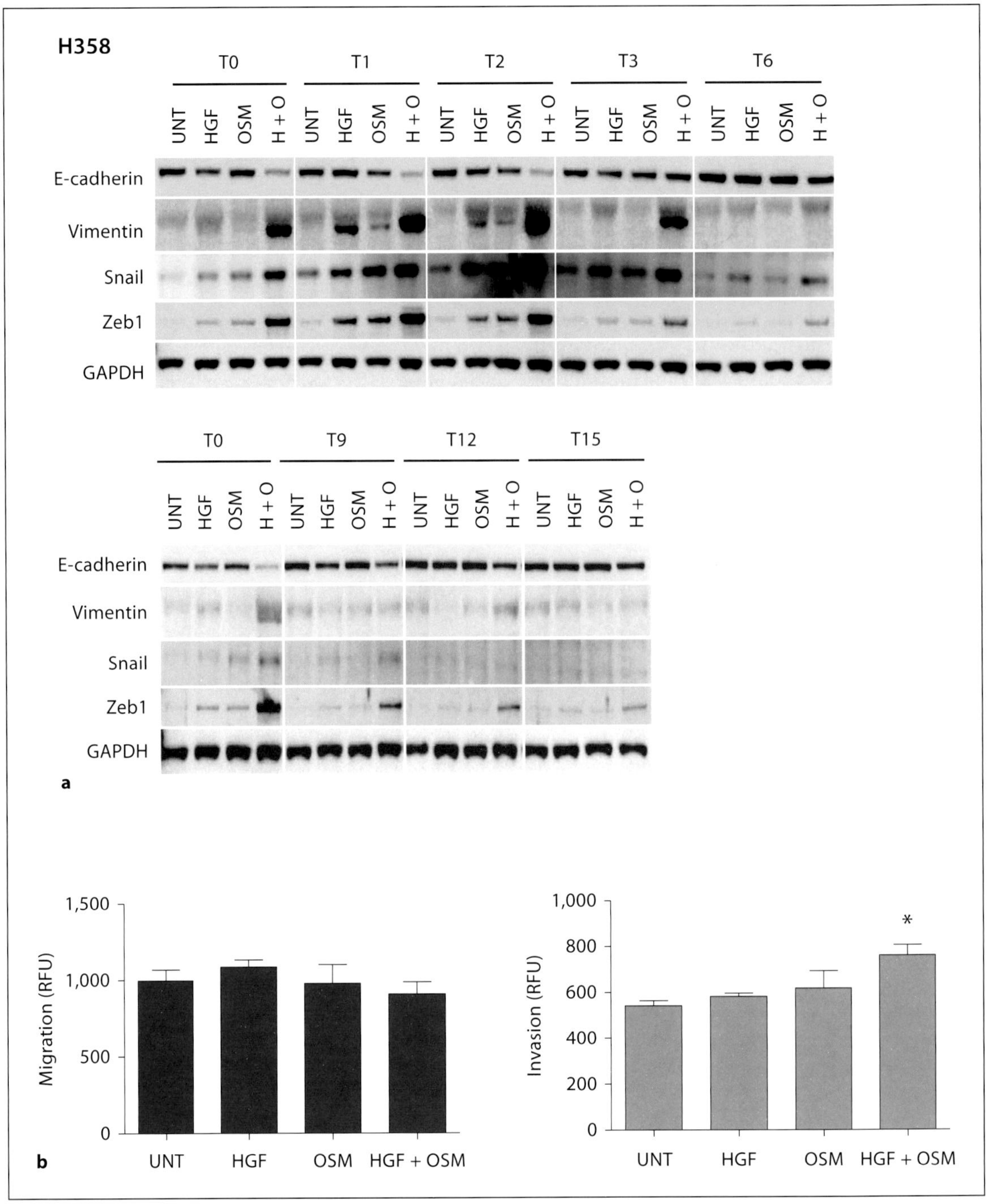

Fig. 6. EMT induced by single- and dual-ligand treatment for 7 days is reversible. H358 cells were treated with single or dual ligands for 7 days. On day 7 (T0), cells were replated in normal growth medium without the ligand and harvested on the indicated day after ligand withdrawal (T1–T15). **a** Lysates were prepared for Western blot analysis of marker changes. T0 lysates were run on each blot and shown to illustrate relative changes in markers within each blot. **b** After 14 days of ligand withdrawal, cells were assayed for migration and invasion by modified Boyden chamber assay. * $p < 0.01$. UNT = Untreated cells; H + O = HGF + OSM; RFU = relative fluorescence units.

pression or localization (data not shown). In contrast, TGF-β stimulation induced a striking change in both morphology and markers. Almost all cells expressed vimentin, and few expressed E-cadherin. When present, E-cadherin staining was weak and only observed in cells in the center of the colony. The morphology of the colonies showed cells clearly invading into the matrix, the hallmark phenotype of a mesenchymal cell. While all dual-ligand treatments induced comparable changes in 2D culture, there were marked differences between treatments in a 3D setting. HGF + OSM showed only modest differences from either ligand alone in both morphology and markers. In contrast, TGF-β + OSM and TGF-β + HGF (data not shown) treatments induced colony growth as a loose association of cells expressing high levels of vimentin and low levels of E-cadherin. In summary, TGF-β alone and in combination induced more advanced EMT in 3D culture than HGF or OSM.

While H1650 cells showed modest changes with EMT in the 2D setting, they showed the most dramatic phenotypic change in the 3D culture. In the untreated cells, colonies grew as either filled or hollow spheres expressing E-cadherin and very little vimentin. Here, again, single-ligand stimulation caused only minor architectural changes in the colonies compared with untreated cultures. Vimentin was upregulated in all single-ligand cultures. Dual-ligand stimulation caused formation of complex 3D branching structures that formed a meshwork of cord-like structures. In comparing the architecture between stimuli, there were differences between HGF + OSM and HGF + TGF-β cultures. In the HGF + OSM colonies, E-cadherin was found in the main body of the colony, but not in the invading structures. Vimentin was not expressed in the main body but was found in the invading structures. In contrast, in HGF + TGF-β treated cells, vimentin was expressed more ubiquitously.

Discussion

In development, EMT is an exquisitely controlled program of cellular conversion to the mesenchymal phenotype, followed either by reversion back to an epithelial phenotype, or by further differentiation at a distant site. Data from cell culture models and patient tumors show that EMT in cancer is considerably less regulated and frequently incomplete. For example, LaGamba et al. [2005] identified 1,109 genes regulated at least 2-fold in the developing mouse palate undergoing EMT, a TGF-β-dependent transition (see also Kitase et al. [2011] in the current issue). In contrast, mouse mammary EpH4 cells transformed with HA-Ras and stimulated with TGF-β showed 2-fold regulation of only 34 genes [Jechlinger et al., 2003] with an overlap of 13 genes between the 2 lists [Turley et al., 2008]. The interpretation of these data has led to the controversial hypothesis that cancer cells selectively hijack those elements of the developmental EMT program that are necessary to invade surrounding tissues and provide a survival advantage for disseminating cells. Currently, the hypothesis is being refined to include recent data that suggest EMT may impart this survival advantage through acquisition of a stem cell phenotype [Mani et al., 2008; Wellner et al., 2009].

In vitro and in vivo analyses of invading tumor cells show multiple cell morphologies associated with invading fronts, questioning the requirement for a complete loss of the epithelial phenotype or the acquisition of a true mesenchymal phenotype in order to increase metastatic efficiency. In our 2D single-ligand EMT models, HGF, TGF-β and OSM were able to induce partial EMT, with TGF-β inducing the most significant marker changes. However, the changes in morphology induced by each ligand after 7 days were notably different. For example, in the H358 model, HGF induced more scattering relative to the other 2, OSM induced more elongated, fibroblast-like cells, and TGF-β induced morphology with aspects of both. These differences in EMT endpoints are also observed in our 3D models. HGF and OSM stimulate partial EMT with some marker changes to cells on the colony surface and subtle morphological changes, while TGF-β induced striking changes to markers and architecture within the colony. Thus, with these 3 ligands, we demonstrate a spectrum in EMT induced by varying stimuli which will enable investigation into the significance of partial EMT in cancer progression.

Elucidation of the signaling pathways required for EMT in the 3 models has identified potential therapeutic targets to block EMT and cancer progression in vivo. Both the JAK and PI3K inhibitors were able to partially block EMT even in the dual-ligand models, demonstrating that they are both necessary but not sufficient for EMT in this model. Previous reports show that the PI3K/AKT pathway is required for the resistance of mesenchymal cells to EGF receptor inhibitor-induced death [Buck et al., 2006b; Fuchs et al., 2008]. Our work suggests that a possible mechanism of AKT-regulated mesenchymal cell survival is through induction or maintenance of the mesenchymal phenotype. The role of JAK/STAT signaling in survival is not well characterized, and it will be interesting to determine whether it contributes to the decreased

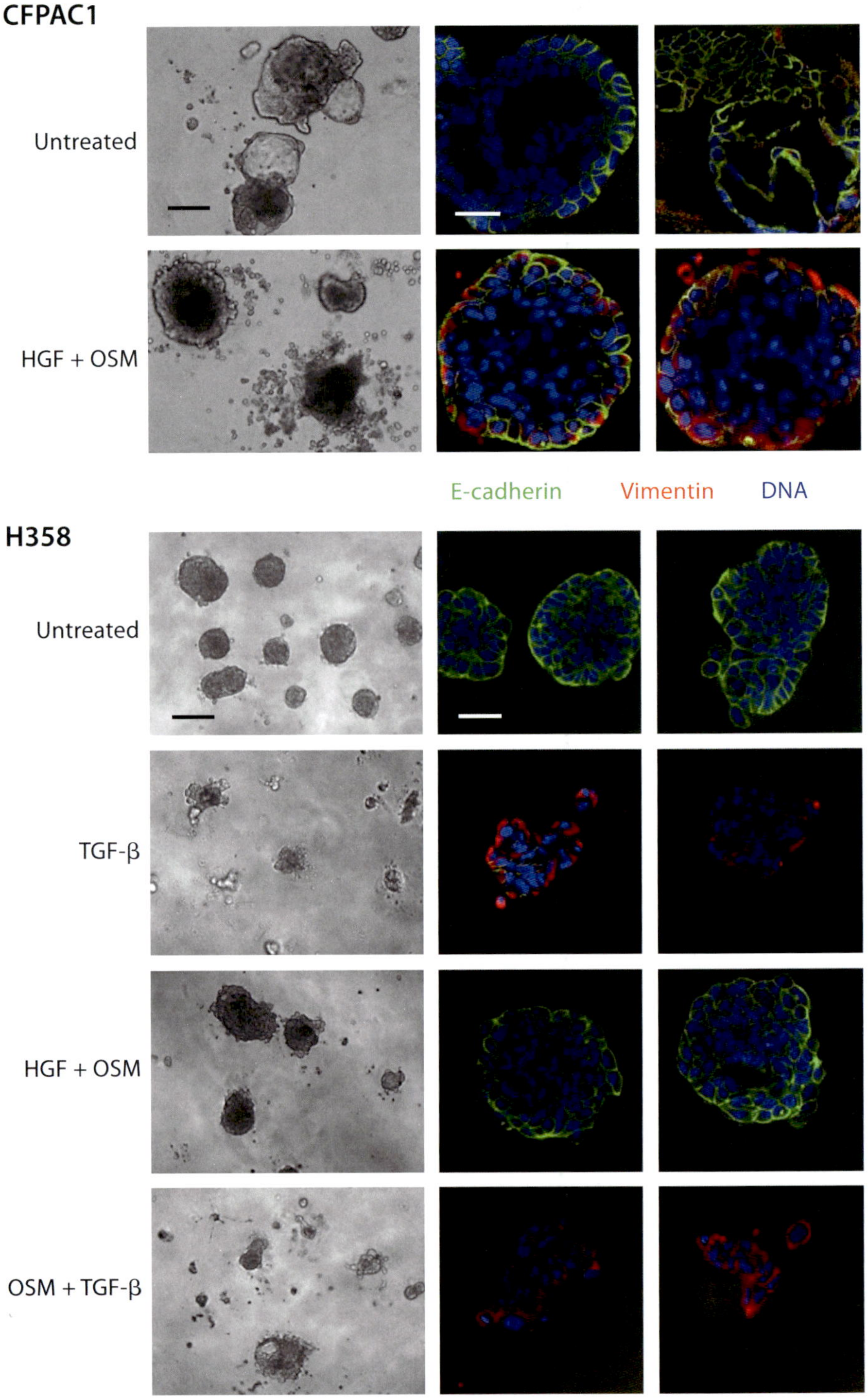

Fig. 7. EMT induced in 3D Matrigel culture. Cells were seeded in solid Matrigel matrix and cultured for 14 days in the presence of the ligand. Cells were imaged under phase contrast at the time of fixation with a 10× objective. Scale bars = 0.2 mm. Cultures were then stained for E-cadherin and vimentin and imaged by confocal microscopy with a 63× objective. Scale bars = 0.05 mm.

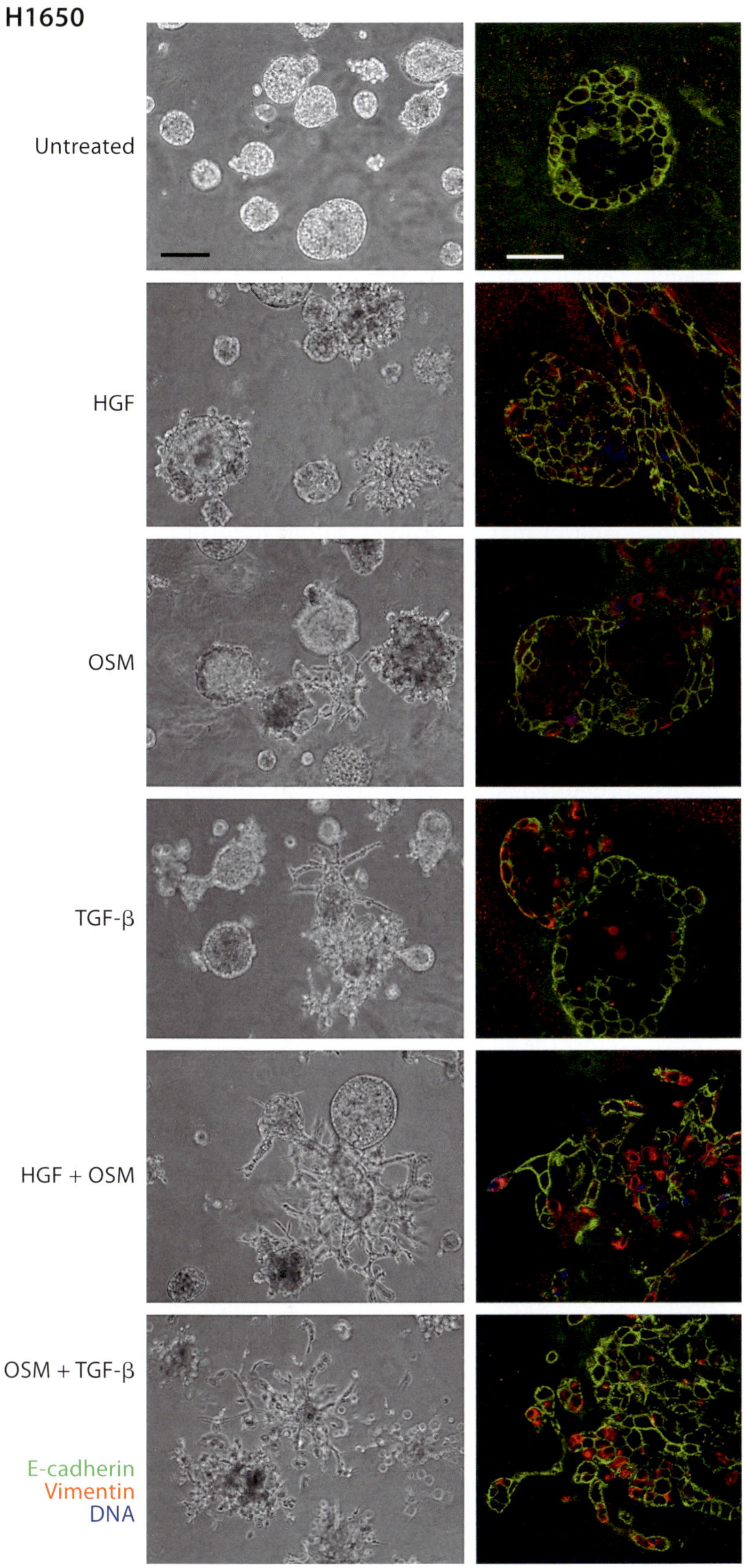
H1650
Untreated
HGF
OSM
TGF-β
HGF + OSM
OSM + TGF-β
E-cadherin
Vimentin
DNA

sensitivity of mesenchymal cells to apoptosis. In contrast, the MEK inhibitor did not block HGF- or TGF-β-induced EMT, consistent with findings in A549 human lung carcinoma cells [Kasai et al., 2005]. This is contrary to studies in normal murine mammary gland [Xie et al., 2004], Madin-Darby canine kidney [Schramek et al., 2003; Medici et al., 2006] and HepG2 cells [Grotegut et al., 2006] that show TGF-β- and HGF-induced EMT is MEK dependent. Two of these cell lines are nontransformed, suggesting that transformed cells may upregulate pathways to compensate for loss of MEK/ERK signaling in EMT, but nontransformed cells are more tightly controlled. Taken together, these data identify multiple signaling pathways able to drive EMT, and the variable nature of the endpoint in different ligand models.

The complexity of EMT signaling is illustrated in the diversity of ligands able to induce EMT in development and cancer. TGF-β and HGF are well-documented inducers of EMT in both nontransformed and transformed cell lines. Growth factors fibroblast growth factor, insulin-like growth factors 1/2, EGF and platelet-derived growth factor also induce EMT in vitro and in vivo [Huber et al., 2005]. The downstream signaling required for EMT induced by these factors includes the signaling pathways we examined, as well as the nuclear factor-kB pathway. In our screen for EMT models, we identified OSM as a ligand able to induce EMT by itself and enhance EMT in cooperation with other ligands in the 3 models described here as well as in others (data not shown). The role of inflammatory cytokines in EMT is largely supported by TNF-driven models in which nuclear factor-kB is the main signaling driver. However, OSM has also been shown to induce an epithelial to myofibroblast transition in proximal tubular epithelial cells leading to renal fibrosis [Nightingale et al., 2004; Pollack et al., 2007]. This model of OSM-induced EMT was dependent on JAK/STAT signaling, as was our model. Our work suggests that OSM also has a role in inducing EMT in tumor cells leading to increased invasiveness, with possible effects on metastasis.

In addition to the ligands investigated here, the developmental pathways Wnt/β-catenin, Notch and Hedgehog are well characterized for their roles in neural crest formation and gastrulation and are increasingly identified as inducers of EMT in transformed cells. The array of ligands and pathways able to induce EMT offers tumor cells multiple options in progressing to a more metastatic phenotype. It will be interesting to note whether cells from one cancer type preferentially activate specific pathways, but regardless, the diversity of EMT signaling pathways will likely require the availability of multiple combinations of targeted therapy agents to effectively block EMT in cancer.

In both development and cancer, the microenvironment plays an important role in inducing or maintaining EMT. The ligands in our EMT models also suggest interaction between the tumor cells, ECM and stromal cells. HGF is expressed by nonparenchymal cells and is stored in the ECM. OSM is secreted by platelets and macrophages during inflammation. TGF-β is expressed ubiquitously and is secreted into the ECM and blood. Each of these ligands was able to induce a partial EMT, but by combining any 2 of the 3 ligands, we observed enhanced changes in morphology, markers and phenotypes. While each of the single-ligand treatments resulted in qualitatively different EMT endpoints, most of the dual-ligand treatments looked similar to each other morphologically and in marker profiles. Other in vitro models of EMT have also shown cooperation between TGF-β and growth factors [Shimao et al., 1999; Grande et al., 2002] and TGF-β and cytokines [Bates and Mercurio, 2003]. Thus, cooperativity between ligands originating from cells both in the tumor and in the supporting tissues may be a common mechanism to achieve more advanced EMT.

A key concept in the model of EMT in metastasis is the requirement for cells to revert to an epithelial state after localization to a distant site. While the mesenchymal state offers the advantages of cell motility and survival under anchorage-independent conditions, it is not conducive to growth of a cohesive secondary tumor. When mesenchymal cells undergo MET, they regain cell-cell junctions and proliferative capacity. In most of the models presented here, ligand withdrawal is sufficient to restore the epithelial markers, morphology and phenotype, indicating the cells are in a 'metastable' state under ligand stimulation. We noted that cells treated with a single ligand took less time to revert than dual-ligand-treated cells, demonstrating that the more advanced the EMT, the longer the cells take to undergo MET.

In conclusion, the models of EMT presented here capture many aspects of EMT observed in vivo and offer defined systems to elucidate the complex signaling and changes involved in the mechanism of cancer progression and metastasis.

References

Allington, T.M., W.P. Schiemann (2011) The cain and Abl of epithelial-mesenchymal transition and transforming growth factor-β in mammary epithelial cells. Cells Tissues Organs *193:* 98–113.

Bamber, B., R.A. Reife, H.S. Haugen, C.H. Clegg (1998) Oncostatin M stimulates excessive extracellular matrix accumulation in a transgenic mouse model of connective tissue disease. J Mol Med *76:* 61–69.

Bates, R.C., A.M. Mercurio (2003) Tumor necrosis factor-alpha stimulates the epithelial-to-mesenchymal transition of human colonic organoids. Mol Biol Cell *14:* 1790–1800.

Birchmeier, C., W. Birchmeier, E. Gherardi, G.F. Vande Woude (2003) Met, metastasis, motility and more. Nat Rev Mol Cell Biol *4:* 915–925.

Bladt, F., D. Riethmacher, S. Isenmann, A. Aguzzi, C. Birchmeier (1995) Essential role for the c-met receptor in the migration of myogenic precursor cells into the limb bud. Nature *376:* 768–771.

Boing, I., C. Stross, S. Radtke, B.E. Lippok, P.C. Heinrich, H.M. Hermanns (2006) Oncostatin M-induced activation of stress-activated MAP kinases depends on tyrosine 861 in the OSM receptor and requires Jak1 but not Src kinases. Cel Signal *18:* 50–61.

Buck, E., A. Eyzaguirre, S. Barr, S. Thompson, R. Sennello, D. Young, K.K. Iwata, N.W. Gibson, P. Cagnoni, J.D. Haley (2007) Loss of homotypic cell adhesion by epithelial-mesenchymal transition or mutation limits sensitivity to epidermal growth factor receptor inhibition. Mol Cancer Ther *6:* 532–541.

Buck, E., A. Eyzaguirre, E. Brown, F. Petti, S. McCormack, J.D. Haley, K.K. Iwata, N.W. Gibson, G. Griffin (2006a) Rapamycin synergizes with the epidermal growth factor receptor inhibitor erlotinib in non-small-cell lung, pancreatic, colon, and breast tumors. Mol Cancer Ther *5:* 2676–2684.

Buck, E., A. Eyzaguirre, J.D. Haley, N.W. Gibson, P. Cagnoni, K.K. Iwata (2006b) Inactivation of Akt by the epidermal growth factor receptor inhibitor erlotinib is mediated by HER-3 in pancreatic and colorectal tumor cell lines and contributes to erlotinib sensitivity. Mol Cancer Ther *5:* 2051–2059.

Duband, J.L., F. Monier, M. Delannet, D. Newgreen (1995) Epithelium-mesenchyme transition during neural crest development. Acta Anat *154:* 63–78.

Fuchs, B.C., T. Fujii, J.D. Dorfman, J.M. Goodwin, A.X. Zhu, M. Lanuti, K.K. Tanabe (2008) Epithelial-to-mesenchymal transition and integrin-linked kinase mediate sensitivity to epidermal growth factor receptor inhibition in human hepatoma cells. Cancer Res *68:* 2391–2399.

Gal, A., T. Sjoblom, L. Fedorova, S. Imreh, H. Beug, A. Moustakas (2008) Sustained TGF beta exposure suppresses Smad and non-Smad signalling in mammary epithelial cells, leading to EMT and inhibition of growth arrest and apoptosis. Oncogene *27:* 1218–1230.

Gavert, N., A. Ben-Ze'ev (2008) Epithelial-mesenchymal transition and the invasive potential of tumors. Trends Mol Med *14:* 199–209.

Gomez-Lechon, M.J. (1999) Oncostatin M: signal transduction and biological activity. Life Sci *65:* 2019–2030.

Grande, M., A. Franzen, J.O. Karlsson, L.E. Ericson, N.E. Heldin, M. Nilsson (2002) Transforming growth factor-beta and epidermal growth factor synergistically stimulate epithelial to mesenchymal transition (EMT) through a MEK-dependent mechanism in primary cultured pig thyrocytes. J Cell Sci *115:* 4227–4236.

Gravdal, K., O.J. Halvorsen, S.A. Haukaas, L.A. Akslen (2007) A switch from E-cadherin to N-cadherin expression indicates epithelial to mesenchymal transition and is of strong and independent importance for the progress of prostate cancer. Clin Cancer Res *13:* 7003–7011.

Graveel, C.R., C.A. London, G.F. Vande Woude (2005) A mouse model of activating Met mutations. Cell Cycle *4:* 518–520.

Grotegut, S., D. von Schweinitz, G. Christofori, F. Lehembre (2006) Hepatocyte growth factor induces cell scattering through MAPK/Egr-1-mediated upregulation of Snail. EMBO J *25:* 3534–3545.

Huber, M.A., N. Kraut, H. Beug (2005) Molecular requirements for epithelial-mesenchymal transition during tumor progression. Curr Opin Cell Biol *17:* 548–558.

Illman, S.A., K. Lehti, J. Keski-Oja, J. Lohi (2006) Epilysin (MMP-28) induces TGF-beta mediated epithelial to mesenchymal transition in lung carcinoma cells. J Cell Sci *119:* 3856–3865.

Jechlinger, M., S. Grunert, I.H. Tamir, E. Janda, S. Ludemann, T. Waerner, P. Seither, A. Weith, H. Beug, N. Kraut (2003) Expression profiling of epithelial plasticity in tumor progression. Oncogene *22:* 7155–7169.

Kasai, H., J.T. Allen, R.M. Mason, T. Kamimura, Z. Zhang (2005) TGF-beta1 induces human alveolar epithelial to mesenchymal cell transition (EMT). Respir Res *6:* 56.

Kishimoto, T., S. Akira, M. Narazaki, T. Taga (1995) Interleukin-6 family of cytokines and gp130. Blood *86:* 1243–1254.

Kitase, Y., K. Yamashiro, K. Fu, J.M. Richman, C.F. Shuler (2011) Spatiotemporal localization of periostin and its potential role in epithelial-mesenchymal transition during palatal fusion. Cells Tissues Organs *193:* 53–63.

Kohn, E.A., Z. Du, M. Sato, C.M. Van Schyndle, M.A. Welsh, Y.A. Yang, C.H. Stuelten, B. Tang, W. Ju, E.P. Bottinger, L.M. Wakefield (2010) A novel approach for the generation of genetically modified mammary epithelial cell cultures yields new insights into TGF-beta signaling in the mammary gland. Breast Cancer Res 12: R83 PMID: 20942910.

LaGamba, D., A. Nawshad, E.D. Hay (2005) Microarray analysis of gene expression during epithelial-mesenchymal transformation. Dev Dyn *234:* 132–142.

Lamouille, S., R. Derynck (2011) Emergence of the phosphoinositide 3-kinase-akt-mammalian target of rapamycin axis in transforming growth factor-β-induced epithelial-mesenchymal transition. Cells Tissues Organs *193:* 8–22.

Lee, J.M., S. Dedhar, R. Kalluri, E.W. Thompson (2006) The epithelial-mesenchymal transition: new insights in signaling, development, and disease. J Cell Biol *172:* 973–981.

Mani, S.A., W. Guo, M.J. Liao, E.N. Eaton, A. Ayyanan, A.Y. Zhou, M. Brooks, F. Reinhard, C.C. Zhang, M. Shipitsin, L.L. Campbell, K. Polyak, C. Brisken, J. Yang, R.A. Weinberg (2008) The epithelial-mesenchymal transition generates cells with properties of stem cells. Cell *133:* 704–715.

Medici, D., E.D. Hay, D.A. Goodenough (2006) Cooperation between snail and LEF-1 transcription factors is essential for TGF-beta1-induced epithelial-mesenchymal transition. Mol Biol Cell *17:* 1871–1879.

Mosley, B., C. De Imus, D. Friend, N. Boiani, B. Thoma, L.S. Park, D. Cosman (1996) Dual oncostatin M (OSM) receptors. Cloning and characterization of an alternative signaling subunit conferring OSM-specific receptor activation. J Biol Chem *271:* 32635–32643.

Ng, G., D. Winder, B. Muralidhar, E. Gooding, I. Roberts, M. Pett, G. Mukherjee, J. Huang, N. Coleman (2007) Gain and overexpression of the oncostatin M receptor occur frequently in cervical squamous cell carcinoma and are associated with adverse clinical outcome. J Pathol *212:* 325–334.

Nieto, M.A. (2002) The snail superfamily of zinc-finger transcription factors. Nat Rev Mol Cell Biol *3:* 155–166.

Nightingale, J., S. Patel, N. Suzuki, R. Buxton, K.I. Takagi, J. Suzuki, Y. Sumi, A. Imaizumi, R.M. Mason, Z. Zhang (2004) Oncostatin M, a cytokine released by activated mononuclear cells, induces epithelial cell-myofibroblast transdifferentiation via Jak/Stat pathway activation. J Am Soc Nephrol *15:* 21–32.

Peinado, H., D. Olmeda, A. Cano (2007) Snail, Zeb and bHLH factors in tumour progression: an alliance against the epithelial phenotype? Nat Rev *7:* 415–428.

Pollack, V., R. Sarkozi, Z. Banki, E. Feifel, S. Wehn, G. Gstraunthaler, H. Stoiber, G. Mayer, R. Montesano, F. Strutz, H. Schramek (2007) Oncostatin M-induced effects on EMT in human proximal tubular cells: differential role of ERK signaling. Am J Physiol *293:* F1714–F1726.

Ponzo, M.G., R. Lesurf, S. Petkiewicz, F.P. O'Malley, D. Pinnaduwage, I.L. Andrulis, S.B. Bull, N. Chughtai, D. Zuo, M. Souleimanova, D. Germain, A. Omeroglu, R.D. Cardiff, M. Hallett, M. Park (2009) Met induces mammary tumors with diverse histologies and is associated with poor outcome and human basal breast cancer. Proc Natl Acad Sci USA *106:* 12903–12908.

Queen, M.M., R.E. Ryan, R.G. Holzer, C.R. Keller-Peck, C.L. Jorcyk (2005) Breast cancer cells stimulate neutrophils to produce oncostatin M: potential implications for tumor progression. Cancer Res *65:* 8896–8904.

Sanders, E.J., S. Prasad, N. Hu (1993) The involvement of TGF beta 1 in early avian development: gastrulation and chondrogenesis. Anat Embryol *187:* 573–581.

Schmidt, L., F.M. Duh, F. Chen, T. Kishida, G. Glenn, P. Choyke, S.W. Scherer, Z. Zhuang, I. Lubensky, M. Dean, R. Allikmets, A. Chidambaram, U.R. Bergerheim, J.T. Feltis, C. Casadevall, A. Zamarron, M. Bernues, S. Richard, C.J. Lips, M.M. Walther, L.C. Tsui, L. Geil, M.L. Orcutt, T. Stackhouse, J. Lipan, L. Slife, H. Brauch, J. Decker, G. Niehans, M.D. Hughson, H. Moch, S. Storkel, M.I. Lerman, W.M. Linehan, B. Zbar (1997) Germline and somatic mutations in the tyrosine kinase domain of the MET proto-oncogene in papillary renal carcinomas. Nat Genet *16:* 68–73.

Schramek, H., E. Feifel, I. Marschitz, N. Golochtchapova, G. Gstraunthaler, R. Montesano (2003) Loss of active MEK1-ERK1/2 restores epithelial phenotype and morphogenesis in transdifferentiated MDCK cells. Am J Physiol Cell Physiol *285:* C652–C661.

Shimao, Y., K. Nabeshima, T. Inoue, M. Koono (1999) Role of fibroblasts in HGF/SF-induced cohort migration of human colorectal carcinoma cells: fibroblasts stimulate migration associated with increased fibronectin production via upregulated TGF-beta1. Int J Cancer *82:* 449–458.

Shintani, Y., M. Maeda, N. Chaika, K.R. Johnson, M.J. Wheelock (2008) Collagen I promotes epithelial-to-mesenchymal transition in lung cancer cells via transforming growth factor-beta signaling. Am J Respir Cell Mol Biol *38:* 95–104.

Takayama, H., W.J. LaRochelle, R. Sharp, T. Otsuka, P. Kriebel, M. Anver, S.A. Aaronson, G. Merlino (1997) Diverse tumorigenesis associated with aberrant development in mice overexpressing hepatocyte growth factor/scatter factor. Proc Natl Acad Sci USA *94:* 701–706.

Tang, B., M. Vu, T. Booker, S.J. Santner, F.R. Miller, M.R. Anver, L.M. Wakefield (2003) TGF-beta switches from tumor suppressor to prometastatic factor in a model of breast cancer progression. J Clin Invest *112*: 1116–1124.

Thomson, S., E. Buck, F. Petti, G. Griffin, E. Brown, N. Ramnarine, K.K. Iwata, N. Gibson, J.D. Haley (2005) Epithelial to mesenchymal transition is a determinant of sensitivity of non-small-cell lung carcinoma cell lines and xenografts to epidermal growth factor receptor inhibition. Cancer Res *65:* 9455–9462.

Turley, E.A., M. Veiseh, D.C. Radisky, M.J. Bissell (2008) Mechanisms of disease: epithelial-mesenchymal transition – does cellular plasticity fuel neoplastic progression? Nat Clin Pract *5:* 280–290.

Valcourt, U., M. Kowanetz, H. Niimi, C.H. Heldin, A. Moustakas (2005) TGF-beta and the Smad signaling pathway support transcriptomic reprogramming during epithelial-mesenchymal cell transition. Mol Biol Cell *16:* 1987–2002.

Wellner, U., J. Schubert, U.C. Burk, O. Schmalhofer, F. Zhu, A. Sonntag, B. Waldvogel, C. Vannier, D. Darling, A. zur Hausen, V.G. Brunton, J. Morton, O. Sansom, J. Schuler, M.P. Stemmler, C. Herzberger, U. Hopt, T. Keck, S. Brabletz, T. Brabletz (2009) The EMT-activator ZEB1 promotes tumorigenicity by repressing stemness-inhibiting microRNAs. Nat Cell Biol *11:* 1487–1495.

Xie, L., B.K. Law, A.M. Chytil, K.A. Brown, M.E. Aakre, H.L. Moses (2004) Activation of the Erk pathway is required for TGF-beta1-induced EMT in vitro. Neoplasia *6:* 603–610.

Yauch, R.L., T. Januario, D.A. Eberhard, G. Cavet, W. Zhu, L. Fu, T.Q. Pham, R. Soriano, J. Stinson, S. Seshagiri, Z. Modrusan, C.Y. Lin, V. O'Neill, L.C. Amler (2005) Epithelial versus mesenchymal phenotype determines in vitro sensitivity and predicts clinical activity of erlotinib in lung cancer patients. Clin Cancer Res *11:* 8686–8698.

Author Index Vol. 193, No. 1–2, 2011

Cells
Tissues
Organs

KARGER
Fax +41 61 306 12 34
E-Mail karger@karger.ch
www.karger.com

Accessible online at:
www.karger.com/cto

Cells
Tissues
Organs

Subject Index Vol. 193, No. 1–2, 2011

KARGER

Fax +41 61 306 12 34
E-Mail karger@karger.ch
www.karger.com

Accessible online at:
www.karger.com/cto

F11317

Call for Abstracts
ASGCT 14th Annual Meeting
SEATTLE, WA
MAY 18-21, 2011
Deadline for Abstract Submissions January 11, 2011
Submit your abstracts online at www.asgct.org beginning November 1, 2010.
AMERICAN SOCIETY of GENE & CELL THERAPY
ASGCT Executive Office
555 East Wells Street, Suite 1100
Milwaukee, WI 53202 USA
414-278-1341
info@asgct.org

F11241

A meeting report of the first international Else Kröner-Fresenius-Symposium on Adult Stem Cell Aging

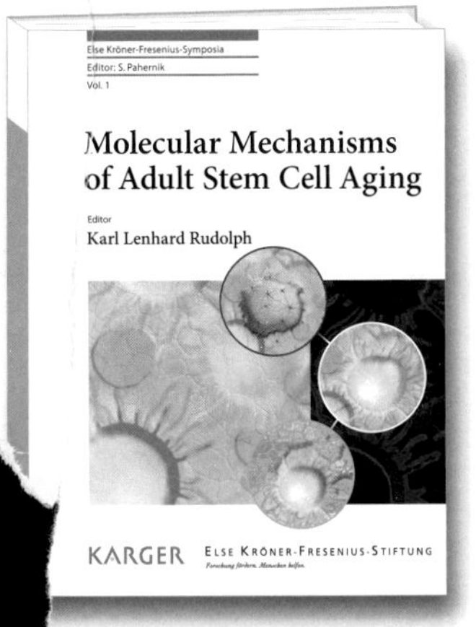

Molecular Mechanisms of Adult Stem Cell Aging

Else Kröner-Fresenius-Symposia

Editor
Karl Lenhard Rudolph

Cell Biology; Gerontology/Geriatrics; Molecular Biology, Biology of Physicians, Gastroenterology, Hematology

Contents

There is growing evidence that adult stem cells age. This process can result in alterations in the number and function of stem cells, leading to distinct phenotypic outcomes in different organ systems. This publication provides an outstanding overview of this emerging field.
The molecular causes of stem cell aging remain to be defined. Stem cell aging can involve cell-intrinsic as well as cell-extrinsic alterations affecting the stem cell niche or the macroenvironment. Stem cells have a longer life span than other cell populations and retain a capacity to proliferate and differentiate in adult organs. The aging of adult stem cells plays a key role in the decline of organ maintenance and regenerative potential during aging and during the end stage of chronic diseases. In addition, it can contribute to stem cell transformation and carcinogenesis.
Molecular Mechanisms of Adult Stem Cell Aging will appeal to scientists working in the fields such as stem cells, aging, regeneration and cancer. This subject matter should be of interest to physicians and scientists specializing in geriatric medicine, internal medicine, and surgery. It is also likely to be an invaluable resource for medical students and biologists who wish to enhance their understanding of molecular and stem cell biology.

KI 10220

www.karger.com/ekfsy

Else Kröner-Fresenius-Symposia, Vol. 1
Series Editor: Pahernik, S. (Heidelberg)
ISSN 1663–0114 / e-ISSN 1663–0122

Molecular Mechanisms of Adult Stem Cell Aging
Editor: Rudolph, K.L. (Ulm)
XII + 108 p., 21 fig., 19 in color, hard cover, 2010
CHF 79.– EUR 56.50 / USD 79.00
Prices subject to change
EUR price for Germany, USD price for USA only
ISBN 978–3–8055–9243–7
e-ISBN 978–3–8055–9244–4

KARGER

Order Form

Please send: ____ copy/ies

Postage and handling free with prepayment

Payment:
Please charge to my credit card
☐ American Express ☐ Diners ☐ Eurocard
☐ MasterCard ☐ Visa

Card No.: ____________

Exp. date: ____________

CVV/CVC ____________
(3 digits in the signature field on the back of Visa and MasterCard)

☐ Check enclosed ☐ Please bill me

Orders may be placed with any bookshop, subscription agency, directly with the publisher or through a Karger distributor.

Fax: +41 61 306 12 34

S. Karger AG, P.O. Box, CH–4009 Basel (Switzerland)
E-Mail orders@karger.ch, **www.karger.com**

Name/Address: ____________

Date: ____________

Signature: ____________

Summarizing the latest knowledge in the field

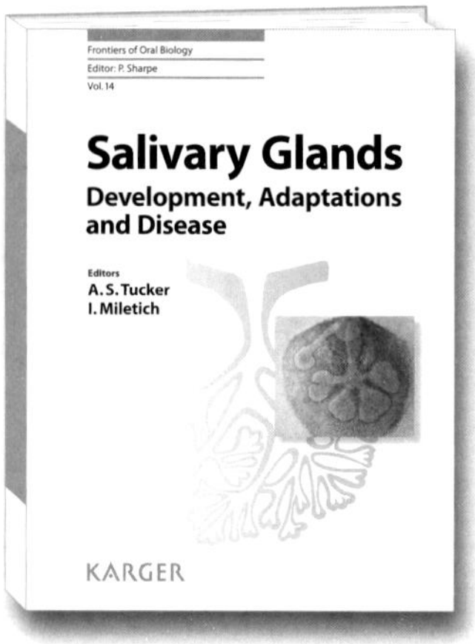

Salivary Glands

Development, Adaptations and Disease

Editors
Abigail S. Tucker
Isabelle Miletich

Salivary glands are of utmost importance for several physiological functions ranging from the protection of teeth and surrounding soft tissues to the lubrication of the oral cavity, which is crucial for speech and perception of food taste. This publication highlights specific aspects of salivary gland development, investigating the mechanisms involved in embryonic development, the current research in stem cells, the ability of adult glands to regenerate and the signalling pathways involved in this process. Key stages of salivary gland development, moving from initiation to differentiation of the glands, are discussed, as well as unusual adaptations, ranging from making silk to making venom. The book finally provides new data on surgical techniques and diagnostic tools for clinicians involved in salivary gland disorders.
Researchers and students with an interest in craniofacial sciences as well as clinicians dealing with salivary gland disorders will find this publication an excellent source of up-to-date information.

Contents

KI10419

www.karger.com/forbi

Frontiers of Oral Biology, Vol. 14
Series Editor: Sharpe, P. (London)
ISSN 1420–2433, e-ISSN 1662–3770

Salivary Glands
Development, Adaptations and Disease
Editors: Tucker, A.S.; Miletich, I. (London)
VIII + 150 p., 34 fig., 12 tab., hard cover, 2010
CHF 159.– / EUR 113.50 / USD 159.00
Prices subject to change
EUR price for Germany, USD price for USA only
ISBN 978–3–8055–9406–6
e-ISBN 978–3–8055–9407–3

KARGER

Order Form

Please send: ____ copy/ies

Postage and handling free with prepayment

Payment:
Please charge to my credit card
☐ American Express ☐ Diners ☐ Eurocard
☐ MasterCard ☐ Visa

Card No.: ____________________

Exp. date: ____________________

CVV/CVC ____________________
(3 digits in the signature field on the back of Visa and MasterCard)

☐ Check enclosed ☐ Please bill me

Orders may be placed with any bookshop, subscription agency, directly with the publisher or through a Karger distributor.

Fax: +41 61 306 12 34

S. Karger AG, P.O. Box, CH–4009 Basel (Switzerland)
E-Mail orders@karger.ch, **www.karger.com**

Name/Address: ____________________

Date: ____________________

Signature: ____________________